New Edition

advanced
expert
CAE

STUDENT'S RESOURCE BOOK
with key and audio CD

Jane Barnes • Drew Hyde • Nick Kenny • Jacky Newbrook

PEARSON
Longman

Contents

Module	Section	Reading/ Vocabulary	Listening	Use of English	Language development	Writing
7 Breaking the mould (pp. 72–82)	A **Against the odds**		**Paper 4 Part 1** Multiple choice: *Three extracts about life's challenges* (p. 76)	**Paper 3 Part 1** Multiple-choice cloze: *A family gap year* (p. 72) **Paper 3 Part 3** Word formation: *Iron men let off steam* (p. 74)	Spelling changes. Endings often misspelt. Commonly misspelt words. (p. 73)	Using synonyms. Using opposites. Changing the form. (p. 75)
	B **Kicking the habit**	**Vocabulary** Obsessions (p. 77) **Reading: Paper 1 Part 4** Multiple matching: *Don't just dream it ... do it!* (pp. 80–81)		**Paper 3 Part 5** Key word transformations (p. 79)	*wish/if only.* Other expressions. (p. 78)	**Paper 2 Part 1** Letter: complaint about smoking policy (p. 82)
8 Making life better? (pp. 83–93)	A **A changing society**		**Paper 4 Part 4** Multiple matching: Five people talk about current trends in society (p. 87)	**Paper 3 Part 3** Word formation: *What the world watches on TV* (p. 83) **Paper 3 Part 1** Multiple-choice cloze: *The eBay phenomenon* (p. 85)	Negative introductory expressions. Emphasis through fronting parts of the sentence. (p. 84) Attitude clauses and phrases. (p. 86)	
	B **Law and order**	**Vocabulary** Law and order (p. 88) **Reading: Paper 1 Part 3** Multiple-choice questions: *Facing facts* (pp. 92–93)		**Paper 3 Part 4** Gapped sentences (p. 90)	Comparatives and superlatives. *so/such. too/enough.* Double comparisons. *as/like.* (p. 89)	**Paper 2 Part 2** Essay: a sense of community (p. 91)
9 Communication (pp. 94–104)	A **Something to say**		**Paper 4 Part 3** Multiple-choice questions: A model's upbringing and career (p. 98)	**Paper 3 Part 1** Multiple-choice cloze: *The world's most talkative bird* (p. 94) **Paper 3 Part 5** Key word transformations (p. 97)	Review of reported speech. Patterns after reporting verbs. Impersonal report structures. (pp. 95–96)	
	B **Making a statement**	**Vocabulary** Clothing and fashion (p. 99) **Reading: Paper 1 Part 2** Gapped text: *In celebrities we trust* (pp. 102–103)		**Paper 3 Part 2** Open cloze: *Special offers you can't refuse* (p. 101)	Word formation. (p. 100)	**Paper 2 Part 1** Proposal: raising the profile of an Adventure Centre (p. 104)

A Learning experiences

Use of English
Multiple-choice cloze (Paper 3 Part 1)

▶ CB page 10, ER page 169

Exam strategy

For this task, you need a good knowledge of fixed expressions, phrasal verbs and collocations. Add any new expressions you come across to your vocabulary notebook. Remember to review them regularly, and try to use them in your speaking and writing.

1 a Read the title of the text. What do you think it is going to be about?

   b Read the whole text quickly for general understanding, ignoring the gaps for the moment.

2 a Read the text again carefully and think about the type of word which will fit in each gap. Try to predict what the answer will be.

   b Look at the options A–D and choose the option which you feel fits best in each gap. Use the Help clues if necessary.

3 Read through the text again when you've finished and check that the options you've chosen fit in with the overall meaning of the text.

HELP
➤ Question 1
   All of these words express the idea of *continue*, but only one of them collocates with *impression*.
➤ Question 2
   Each of these words is used to link two ideas. Read the whole sentence carefully to decide which one fits the meaning here.
➤ Question 11
   Only one of these words can follow the preposition *by*.

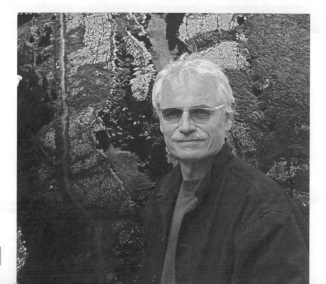

For questions **1–12**, read the text below and decide which answer (**A**, **B**, **C** or **D**) best fits each gap. There is an example at the beginning (**0**).

The Earth from the air

Around ten million people worldwide have been to see Yann Arthus-Bertrand's exhibition of aerial photos (**0**) A *The Earth from the Air*. The exhibition features shots taken in over 100 different countries and never fails to make a (**1**)...... impression on those who come to see it. (**2**)...... part of the fascination probably comes from the fact that Bertrand is (**3**)...... on record things that the public could not otherwise see, this alone cannot explain why people are so (**4**)...... affected by the photographs themselves. The exhibition (**5**)...... people feeling enriched, with a more positive outlook on life, and many return with their friends. It's almost as if the exhibition was communicating something of the spiritual and educational (**6**)...... of travel itself.

Bertrand was living in Kenya, studying lions, when he began taking the photographs. 'It's hard to get a clear idea of that sort of territory from the ground,' he explains, so when a friend offered to take him up in her plane, he (**7**)...... . 'Suddenly I could really see the beauty of the landscape in a new way,' he (**8**)...... . 'I was captivated.'

Since that day, Bertrand has been taking aerial photographs on a world-wide (**9**)...... . For some shots, he (**10**)...... with a specific place in mind, but around 80% of the destinations were found by (**11**)...... . What's more, he never (**12**)...... of searching for new places, always believing that he'll spot something tomorrow that will be even more impressive than what he has seen today.

	A	B	C	D
0	called	known	labelled	termed
1	persisting	keeping	lasting	remaining
2	Because	Since	Once	Although
3	giving	holding	catching	putting
4	widely	deeply	largely	wholly
5	leaves	sends	makes	lets
6	value	profit	gain	credit
7	complied	approved	accepted	consented
8	replies	recalls	repeats	retains
9	extent	spread	degree	scale
10	comes up	gets on	sets out	does away
11	luck	chance	fate	fortune
12	exhausts	weakens	tires	bores

Language development
Tense forms
▶ CB page 13, GR page 173

Past to present tenses

1 Complete each pair of sentences using one verb from the list. Put the verb into the present perfect simple or continuous.

cook   eat   hear   live   take   tell   steal   wear

1 a I .... you everything I know already.
  b Cal .... everyone about his promotion.
2 a Simon .... that jacket for years; it's the only one he's got.
  b I'm sure Keith .... that jacket before; it looks familiar.
3 a We .... in that restaurant before. It wasn't bad.
  b We .... in that restaurant for years. It's great.
4 a I've still got a headache and I .... aspirins all day.
  b I've still got a headache and I .... six aspirins today.
5 a I .... always .... in the same house.
  b I .... only .... in this house for two months.
6 a I .... this song everywhere I go recently. It's really annoying me.
  b I am sure I .... your name mentioned in a meeting.
7 a I .... dinner for 20 before, but it wasn't great.
  b I haven't had time to check the car because I .... dinner.
8 a Someone .... my CDs; they've all suddenly disappeared.
  b Someone .... my CDs; they keep disappearing.

2 a Complete the biography of the musician Norah Jones below by putting the verbs in brackets into the past simple or present perfect simple or continuous.

b In your notebook, write a short biography of someone you admire.

Past tenses

3 Correct the mistakes with past tenses. There are either one or two mistakes in each sentence.

1 I lived at home when I passed my driving test, but after that I moved out.
2 When the accident happened, John drove, but it wasn't his fault.
3 He said he was feeling sick and he was apologising for not coming.
4 My tooth was hurting again, so I was deciding to visit the dentist that afternoon.
5 I had already been hearing the news when the director told me.
6 When I arrived, I saw that 20 people waited; some were already waiting for over three hours.
7 When my exam results were coming, I got exactly the grades that I had hoped for.
8 I think my boss was sleeping badly the night before, as he was being very critical that day.

Norah Jones **(1)**.................. (be) born in March 1979 in New York, but her family **(2)**.................. (move) to Texas four years later. She **(3)**.................. (start) singing when she **(4)**.................. (be) five years old and **(5)**.................. (play) the piano since she was seven. She **(6)**.................. (study) music at North Texas University, where she **(7)**.................. (graduate) in jazz piano. Her mother and father, who are both in the music business, **(8)**.................. (influence) her greatly. She **(9)**.................. (learn) to mix diverse styles such as jazz, pop and country to develop her distinct style.

Five years ago, she **(10)**.................. (move) back to New York and **(11)**.................. (live) there ever since. In 2001, she **(12)**.................. (become) an overnight sensation when she **(13)**.................. (release) her first album *Come Away With Me*, which **(14)**.................. (sell) over 15 million copies and is still very popular. Since then, she **(15)**.................. (release) a second album, and continues to tour widely with her band.

4 Put the verbs in brackets into the correct past tense form.

Traditionally, it was students who took a 'gap year' (a year off to travel or gain experience), but last year 60% of 'gappers' **(1)**........................ (*be*) people taking a career break. Many of them **(2)**........................ (*give up*) their job before setting off around the world. Others **(3)**........................ (*work*) for companies that **(4)**........................ (*agree*) to give them unpaid leave in order to travel.

Why did they decide to take a gap year? Many **(5)**........................ (*work*) hard for years and simply **(6)**........................ (*feel*) they needed a break. Others **(7)**........................ (*want*) to 'give something back' by doing volunteer work abroad.

Fran Hodges is one of these people. Although she **(8)**........................ (*plan*) to be away for only six months, she **(9)**........................ (*end up*) staying away for a year. She **(10)**........................ (*celebrate*) her 40th birthday while she **(11)**........................ (*work*) at an elephant sanctuary in Sri Lanka.

Fran **(12)**........................ (*be*) a researcher, but she **(13)**........................ (*quit*) her job in order to go off travelling. She **(14)**........................ (*buy*) her ticket two days before she **(15)**........................ (*give in*) her notice so she couldn't be talked out of it. She **(16)**........................ (*never/travel*) alone before, but **(17)**........................ (*be*) surprised how easy it was and how much fun she had.

Referring to the future

5 Underline the most appropriate verb forms in italics.

By next month **(1)** we'll be living / we'll have been living in this house for 11 years! But **(2)** we're moving / we will move to a bigger place very soon. **(3)** We're buying / We will be buying a house just outside of town – the owners have accepted our offer.
It's a nice house, but it needs updating, so **(4)** we're going to plan / we plan to make quite a few changes. We estimate the work **(5)** is going to take / is taking two or three months, so we'll have to stay with friends until the builders **(6)** will finish / have finished. We'll move in as soon as the house **(7)** is / will be ready.
You must come and visit us.
On 12 September, **(8)** I'll start / I'll be starting a new job. I reckon it **(9)** takes / will take me a little longer to get to work in the mornings.

6 Complete each gap with a suitable word from the list.
about are bound due expect not unlikely verge

A: Hurry up! The train is just **(1)**........................ to leave.
B: Don't worry, it's **(2)**........................ to leave on time.
A: I am worried. They're on the **(3)**........................ of closing the platform barrier.
B: We have plenty of time. They **(4)**........................ people to be late.
A: The ticket says that passengers **(5)**........................ to board the train five minutes before departure.
B: But the doctor said you are **(6)**........................ to get stressed out on this trip. If we miss this train, there's **(7)**........................ to be another one soon.
A: No; the next one isn't **(8)**........................ to leave for another three hours.

7 Complete the sentences using an appropriate structure in the correct form: *be going to, be due to, be about to.*

1 I could tell from the expression on his face that he .... refuse the job.
2 We were sure the builders .... finished by now, but they say they need another two weeks.
3 We thought we .... moving house next week, but now it will be next month.
4 Petra .... graduated this year, but she's had a lot of illness, so now it won't be until next year.
5 Anna .... have the baby in May, but it was four weeks premature.
6 We were just .... leave when Peter arrived.

8 Complete the text, using an appropriate future form of the verbs in brackets.

By this time next week, I **(1)**........................ (*finish*) school. I'm looking forward to the holidays, as you can imagine. First, I **(2)**........................ (*spend*) some time just relaxing – I **(3)**........................ (*probably/stay*) at home. Then my boyfriend and I **(4)**........................ (*start*) work at a new hotel on the coast. It's not quite finished yet, but it's **(5)**........................ (*open*) in two weeks' time. George and I **(6)**........................ (*serve*) meals in the restaurant all day. It **(7)**........................ (*be*) quite a laugh. We **(8)**........................ (*work*) for my uncle, but had to cancel that as he **(9)**........................ (*plan*) to be away for the summer. After six weeks in the hotel, I think I **(10)**........................ (*need*) a holiday before my university course **(11)**........................ (*start*) in September!

Use of English
Open cloze (Paper 3 Part 2)
► ER page 169

1 Read the title of the text below to identify the topic. Why do you think carpentry might be 'a disappearing art'?

2 Read the whole text quickly for general understanding, ignoring the mistakes for the moment.
  1 How does the writer feel about the workshop he describes?
  2 What explanation does he give for what he describes there?

3 Read the text again carefully and complete the task. Use the Help clues if necessary. Remember that:
- most of the missing words are grammatical
- only one word goes in each gap.

4 When you've finished, read the whole text again to check it makes complete sense.

For questions **1–15**, read the text below and think of the word which best fits each gap. Use only one word in each gap. There is an example at the beginning (**0**).

The disappearing art of carpentry

In a little carpentry workshop deep (**0**)........in......... the English countryside, joiners have been making hand-crafted furniture for generations. Today, there is also a visitor centre, a gift shop and a viewing gallery (**1**)........................... you find yourself behind a glass panel, nose-to-nose with some joiners (**2**)........................... are busily working at their benches. They are cutting timber, making joints and carving wood – the sort of operations that carpenters have been carrying (**3**)........................... for centuries.

It may seem odd, therefore, that tourists (**4**)........................... be interested in observing them. But many clearly (**5**)........................... , probably because they will rarely, (**6**)........................... ever, have seen a chair or table in the process of (**7**)........................... made before. These simple tasks, which (**8**)........................... so long ago could be witnessed in workshops up and down the country, are now becoming (**9**)........................... unusual that skilled joiners are an endangered species, and watching them at work has been turned (**10**)........................... a spectator sport.

One reason for this (**11**)........................... the trend towards the mass-production of furniture, but there has also been a change in values. In the past, becoming a craftsperson (**12**)........................... to be a worthwhile ambition for a teenager. But sadly, now that education has become more widely available, people tend to regard skilled manual work (**13**)........................... suitable only for those youngsters not bright (**14**)........................... to get onto computer-studies courses. (**15**)........................... a shame that is.

HELP
➤ **Question 2**
Which relative pronoun is used to refer to a person?
➤ **Question 3**
Which preposition will complete the phrasal verb?
➤ **Question 4**
A modal verb is needed here – which one is best?
➤ **Question 12**
Which past form is needed here?

Language development
Look at all the verbs in the text, Which ones are in the present perfect? Underline them. Are any of them continuous tenses?

Listening
Multiple choice (Paper 4 Part 1)

▶ ER page 170

1 a Read the instructions for the task.
   1 How many extracts are you going to hear?
   2 What is each extract about?

   b Look at the questions for Extract One. How much
      do you find out the topics and speakers
      a) from the rubric?   b) from the questions?

   c Underline the most important ideas in each
      question stem and in the options (A, B or C). This
      has been done for you in Extract One.

2 ⌒ Listen to the recording and choose the correct
   option A, B or C. Follow the same procedure for
   Extracts 2 and 3.

TIP

*Each of the questions will focus on a different aspect of the
text. Some questions will ask about specific parts of the text
and others about the text as a whole. Make sure you know
which speaker you are listening for.*

HELP
➤ Question 1
   This is about the first part of the extract. Which of the
   three options summarises the information you hear?
➤ Question 2
   The second speaker's first words are 'The aim is to give …'
   Listen carefully to what she says after this.
➤ Question 3
   The interviewer asks Dora two questions. Her answer to
   the first question gives you the answer to question 3.
➤ Question 4
   The interviewer asks Dora about 'drawbacks'. This is
   another way of saying disadvantages.
➤ Question 5
   To answer this question you have to listen to both
   speakers – what do they both have the same opinion
   about?
➤ Question 6
   The student says: 'That's why I went for this course' and
   his reason follows.

You will hear three different extracts. For questions **1–6**,
choose the answer (**A**, **B** or **C**) which fits best according to
what you hear.

Extract One
You hear part of a radio programme about a course of
seminars.

1 What does the <u>first speaker</u> give us <u>information</u> about?
   A <u>reasons</u> for <u>choosing</u> the <u>name</u> of the seminars
   B <u>who</u> is providing <u>financial backing</u> for the seminars
   C the <u>type of student</u> who would <u>benefit</u> most from the
      seminars

2 What is the <u>aim</u> of the course of seminars?
   A giving <u>free business advice</u> to young people
   B <u>helping</u> young people <u>to start</u> their own businesses
   C showing young people <u>how to do business</u> on the
      <u>Internet</u>

Extract Two
You hear part of an interview with a student who is doing
some work experience as part of her course.

3 How does Dora feel about her choice of work
   experience placement?
   A She's pleased that she followed her tutors' advice.
   B She's grateful for the wide range of experience she's
      getting.
   C She appreciates the fact that her suggestions are
      valued.

4 What possible disadvantage of the work concerns her
   most?
   A becoming too focussed on what she does
   B losing interest in cooking as a hobby
   C having to work unsociable hours

Extract Three
You overhear two students talking about a lecture they've
just been to.

5 What do they agree about?
   A The lecturer wasn't very good.
   B It was difficult to follow.
   C It was on a boring topic.

6 Why did the male student choose this course?
   A the flexibility it offered
   B the reputation it enjoyed
   C the challenge it would provide

B A job for life?

Language development
Passive forms
▶ CB page 19, GR page 174

The passive in different tenses

1 a Rewrite the sentences using passive forms. Only include the agent where necessary.

1 The company requires a new training manager.

....

2 The Human Resources Department has advertised the post in all national newspapers.

....

3 The company is seeking a highly motivated individual.

....

4 We were training someone for the role, but she left.

....

5 The company has received 45 applications so far.

....

6 We will not contact unsuccessful candidates.

....

7 We are only going to interview the five best candidates.

....

8 The Director will have completed the interviews by the end of next week.

....

b Do the same with these sentences containing modal verbs.

1 Each candidate must complete an aptitude test.

....

2 You should have warned me that the interview room was unavailable.

....

3 We will have to rearrange the interviews.

....

4 People must tell me about any changes to the schedule.

....

5 The company has to do something about the lack of space.

....

6 The company could have improved its interview procedure.

....

2 Decide which of these sentences **can't** be rewritten in the passive. Then rewrite the rest. Only include the agent where necessary.

1 Jenny told the police officer a lie.

....

2 Louis hates people telling him what to do.

....

3 I hate you looking like that.

....

4 I don't like people checking up on me.

....

5 We encourage our customers to give us their opinions.

....

6 I walked into the restaurant and sat down at a table.

....

7 I think he has broken his arm.

....

8 The police are looking into the cause of the accident.

....

Passive -ing forms and infinitives

3 Decide whether the -ing or to-infinitive form fits the sentence. Underline the correct verb form.

1 The children remember *being / to be* taken to the museum.
2 Some people seem to enjoy *being / to be* frightened.
3 She wanted *being / to be* told the truth.
4 Harry deserves *being / to be* given a promotion.
5 Young children resent *being / to be* bossed around by older children.
6 Gary is hoping *being / to be* released from prison in a few weeks.
7 The manager insisted on *being / to be* kept informed of new developments.
8 I didn't expect *being / to be* invited to the party.

4 Rewrite the sentences using a passive -ing form or infinitive.

0 No one enjoys it when other people tell them what to do.
No one enjoys being told what to do.

1 I wanted someone to offer me the opportunity to travel.

....

2 She could remember someone carrying her out of the burning building.

....

3 He didn't expect the company to make him redundant.

....

4 She is hoping that voters will elect her as mayor.

....

5 My father insisted that we should call him 'Sir'.

....

6 I hate it when people let me down at the last minute.

....

have/get + object + past participle

5 **Complete the sentences using the correct form of the verbs in the list.**

alter   build   check   cut   enlarge   launder   redecorate   ~~replace~~

1 She has found a dress she likes, but she will need .... it .... before the wedding.
2 The price includes the cost of .... your hair washed, ... and dried.
3 I'd rather pay .... my shirts .... than spend the time doing it myself.
4 I took some great photos of the landscape and .... a couple of them .... and framed.
5 Look at the state of this room! Let's .... it .... before the holidays.
6 You should .... all electrical equipment .... regularly to make sure it is safe.

6 **Read the text and complete each gap with one suitable word. In some cases, there is more than one correct answer.**

```
⇧    ▾ ⇩    ▾ 📤    📥                          ▾

Ever since I first heard that I (1)...................... had
my paper accepted at the conference, I've
been worrying about everything that I need to
(2)...................... done.
First of all, I had to work out what to wear
when I give my talk. In the end, I've just
decided to (3)...................... my best suit cleaned
rather than have all the hassle of finding a new
one or (4)...................... one made.
Next, my hair (5)...................... cutting. I'm thinking
of (6)...................... it drastically restyled for a
smarter, more professional look. I'll get Tony
(7)...................... give me a few ideas on what will
look best.
As I (8)...................... my laptop stolen when my car
(9)...................... broken into, I've borrowed one and
I'll get one of the IT guys at the university
(10)...................... transfer my presentation onto it.
I'll (11)...................... a taxi to pick me up from
home, so I won't (12)...................... taking to the
airport, but thanks for asking!
```

Use of English
Gapped sentences (Paper 3 Part 4)
▶ ER page 170

1 a Look at the example in the gapped-sentence task on page 13 and read the task rubric.
   1 How many sentences are there?
   2 How many words are missing?
   3 What do the missing words have in common?

  b Look at the first sentence. What type of word is missing? Which two words in the list below fit in this sentence? Why do the other words not fit?

  | *kind   simple   problem   easy   nicely   hard* |

  c Look at the second sentence. Do the same two words fit in this sentence?

  d Now look at the third sentence. Only one of the two words fits in this sentence. Which is it? Why does the other not fit?

2 Now look at Question 1 in the task on page 13. What type of word is missing from all three sentences (e.g. noun, verb, adjective, etc.)?

3 a Look at the first sentence. Write a list of words that will fit in the gap in this sentence.

  b Make sure the words fit grammatically and also that they make sense in the context.

4 a Look at the second sentence. Which words from your list also fit in this sentence?

  b Are there other words that would fit this sentence? Would they also fit in the first sentence? You now have a list of words which fit in two of the sentences.

5 Look at the third sentence. Which of the words on your list fits here? There should only be one.

6 Write the one word in all three gaps and check carefully that it fits grammatically and makes sense in all three.

7 Now complete Questions 2–5 using the same technique.

For questions **1–5**, think of **one** word only which can be used appropriately in all three sentences. Here is an example **(0)**.

0 It is .... to see why the presenter is so popular – he's such a lively person.

Although the local people speak with an accent, it is .... enough for visitors to understand.

Tom's grandmother hadn't had an .... life, but she'd always had a very positive attitude.

1 Tom found that having to .... such a heavy bag everywhere was rather inconvenient.

Although we were getting poor results from our research, we were advised to .... on with the experiments.

The school is hoping to .... out an extensive programme of repairs during the summer break.

2 Although not professionally trained, Damian can produce a technical drawing with a .... degree of precision.

Cindy thought it really wasn't .... of her boss to blame her for all the mistakes in the document.

In common with most of her family, Glenda has very .... skin.

3 On her first day in the job, Keira was asked to .... through a long list of customer complaints and decide which needed an urgent response.

Graham couldn't .... out why he never seemed to get an interview when he applied for jobs.

Milly would get angry when she couldn't get the office photocopier to .... properly.

4 There has been a rather .... response to the job advertisement that the company placed in the local newspaper.

Although double-checking the customer database was a rather .... and time-consuming process, a number of serious mistakes were uncovered as a result.

Jamie was .... to realise that he was fundamentally unsuited to the job he was doing, and so hadn't been thinking of alternatives.

5 Although access to its website is free, there's a small .... if you want to receive the company's monthly newsletter.

Simon decided to take .... of his own financial affairs at the relatively early age of seventeen.

Derek is in .... of the office whilst his manager is on maternity leave.

HELP
➤ **Question 1**
In all three sentences the infinitive form of the verb is needed, but in the second and third sentences this is part of a phrasal verb. All of these verbs fit in the first gap: *bring, take, carry, drag*. Which of them fits in the other sentences?
➤ **Question 2**
An adjective is needed in the first sentence. All of these adjectives fit: *good, high, fair, reasonable*. Which two also fit in the second sentence? Which of these two can also be used to describe skin?
➤ **Question 3**
The verbs *go, look, work, hunt, sift* all fit in the first sentence
➤ **Question 4**
The adjectives *good, poor, quick, slow, disappointing, encouraging* all fit in the gap in the first sentence.

TIP

If you can't think of words that could go in the gap in the first sentence, try starting with one of the other sentences instead.

Language development

Look at all the verbs in the gapped sentences. Which of them are in the passive? What's the tense of the passive verb in each case?

Reading

Multiple matching (Paper 1 Part 4)

▶ ER page 168

1 Read the title of the text and the subheading. Make a list of jobs that you would describe as 'glamorous'.

2 a Read the instructions for the exam task. The text is about the three people in the options A, B and C.

 b Scan the article to find their names and write the letters A, B and C beside the paragraph relating to the person.

 c Now skim those paragraphs to find out what job each person does. Are any of their jobs on your list in Exercise 1?

3 a Read all the questions and highlight the key words in each question. The first four have been done for you.

 b Read the first section of the text about Kieran O'Rourke carefully. Look back at the questions and mark any parts of the text which mention similar information or ideas. For example:
   1 Look at question 1 and find the sentence in the paragraph which seems to have the same meaning. Mark the parts that mean *a team of colleagues* and *appreciates the value.*
   2 Look at question 4 and find the phrases in the paragraph that are similar in meaning to the highlighted key words.

 You have now found two questions which match option A. There are three more. Can you find them?

 c Look at question 9. Scan the whole text quickly to find the two places where stress is mentioned. These are marked for you. Which person *enjoys helping clients cope with stress*?

4 Now continue to match the rest of the questions to the text. Always read the section of text carefully, to check it has exactly the same meaning as the question. There may be several sections of text that are similar in meaning to the questions, but there is only one that matches exactly.

TIP

When you have found a match for the question in the text, write the question number in the margin next to the relevant piece of text – you will need to go back and check it later.

You are going to read a magazine article about three people with glamorous jobs. For questions **1–15**, choose from the people (**A–C**). The people may be chosen more than once.

A Kieran O'Rourke   **C** Sankha Guha
B Christina Booth

Which person

appreciates the value of working with a team of colleagues?	**1** ....
started training for the job as a teenager?	**2** ....
insists on working independently in the job?	**3** ....
accepts that immaturity can be a disadvantage in their job?	**4** ....
acquired experience for the job through their upbringing?	**5** ....
assists colleagues in the development of their career prospects?	**6** ....
has learnt to ignore other people's bad moods?	**7** ....
applied for a job about which there was little information?	**8** ....
enjoys helping clients cope with stress?	**9** ....
is able to achieve personal goals in the course of the job?	**10** ....
was keen to escape from a sheltered upbringing?	**11** ....
gained the experience for their present job through being assertive?	**12** ....
found a lack of experience in the job to be an advantage?	**13** ....
failed to achieve a childhood ambition?	**14** ....
feels that single-mindedness is necessary for success in the job?	**15** ....

'That's the kind of job I've always wanted.'

Katrina Bentley interviews three people who have very glamorous jobs.
How did they get these jobs and are they as good as they sound?

I was standing on a breezy mountainside in Scotland, watching the filming of a historical drama. I was waiting to interview the producer, **Kieran O'Rourke**, and I knew I'd have to be patient. As I watched him talking animatedly to two of the actors in the gateway to the ancient castle, I wondered how, at the surprisingly young age of 35, he came to be producing films for a leading film company. When an ill-timed rain shower stopped the filming, I asked him if this career had been his life-long dream. 'Not really,' he told me. 'I'd always wanted to act, but after years of playing really minor roles I realised I'd never make the big time. So I got a job working on the production side of films and found it fascinating. One evening at a party I was introduced to one of the top producers, and I plucked up the courage to ask him for a job.' **Kieran's** cheek paid off, and he began working amongst some of the best production teams in the film industry. He learned quickly, talking his way into key jobs by correctly assessing the techniques necessary to create a box-office success. Dealing with actresses who are notoriously temperamental was a new challenge for **Kieran**. 'My age does count against me at times, but I've learned to be diplomatic,' he says, with a rueful grin. 'I let their temper tantrums just bounce off me. After all, acting is very stressful. To make a successful film, a huge number of people are involved, and it's important that we're all pulling in the same direction.'

Another young person who has close contact with well-known celebrities in the course of her job is **Christina Booth** who, at only 26, works as the manager of the health spa in one of London's most luxurious hotels. 'I left school at 16 to begin my training as a beauty therapist at a salon in the town where I was brought up. My parents would've liked me to stay close to home where they could keep an eye on me, but I knew there was a far bigger world out there to explore. I soon realised that to achieve a lot in this business, you have to concentrate totally on your personal objectives. Now, I can hardly believe the kind of people I'm dealing with every day – I'll often see them on the front page of the newspapers!' **Christina** sees each day as a new challenge. 'But the most satisfying part of the job is helping my clients to relax,' she says. 'They come into the spa exhausted after living life in the spotlight and they literally leave as different people.' **Christina** loves having a team of therapists whom she is responsible for training. 'I enjoy the management side of the job and helping my team to develop skills that will help them when it comes to thinking about promotion.'

> **6** I soon realised that to achieve a lot in this business you have to concentrate totally on your personal objectives. **9**

As a child, **Sankha Guha** had no burning ambitions to work in TV. The fact that he was born in India, however, and travelled extensively with his family, equipped him very well to present one of TV's most successful travel programmes. After working in local radio, **Sankha** felt ready for new challenges, so when he came across a job advert for a researcher on a TV programme, he decided to go for it. 'There was no explanation for what the programme was,' he told me, 'but the next thing I knew, I was fronting a live show.' Being in front of a camera was a shock for **Sankha**. 'It was a totally new environment for me, and I was always searching for the right words,' he says. But he didn't have to worry, viewers perceived his chatty presentation as a fresh, irreverent style of journalism, and he was soon offered a range of travel and documentary programmes. A journalist by nature, he refuses to be told what to say and likes to do his own research. His most recent project is a documentary on the life of the Sherpa porters who provide the support for people on trekking expeditions in Nepal. **Sankha** was keen to film this, as he is full of admiration for the courage and stamina of the Sherpa guides in that mountainous country. Television, he says, has given him a lot. 'I've had fantastic opportunities to go places I've always wanted to see. My next programme is about polar bears in the north of Canada.'

Writing

Article (Paper 2, Part 2)

▶ CB pages 20–21, WR page 192

Exam strategy

For any piece of writing, you should use a style that is appropriate for the target reader. Read the task carefully to identify who that is, then decide on the appropriate style. Make sure you use that style consistently.

1 **Read the task below and answer these questions.**
  1 Who is the target reader?
  2 Will your answer be:
    a) formal or neutral? b) friendly and informal?
  3 What points should you include in your article? Mark them.

You have seen the following competition advertised in an international student travel magazine.

> **Win a holiday for you and your friend!**
> We are looking for the winner of this year's 'Best Friend' award and are offering a three-week all-inclusive holiday in the Caribbean. Write an article explaining why you are nominating your friend and saying how your friend would benefit from the holiday.

Write your **article** in 220–260 words.

2 a **Decide in what order you would deal with the following topics.**

Reason for nomination	Paragraph ....
Final recommendation	Paragraph ....
Name of nominee	Paragraph ....1.....
Benefits of winning	Paragraph ....
Specific example	Paragraph ....

  b **Read a student's answer opposite and compare your ideas.**

3 **Some of the student's writing is too formal. Find and replace the formal expressions in the answer with the informal expressions below:**
  1 turn to (paragraph 2)
  2 a bit down (paragraph 2)
  3 nothing is ever too much trouble for him (paragraph 2)
  4 let me (paragraph 3)
  5 with flying colours (paragraph 3)
  6 a real plus (paragraph 3)
  7 plus (paragraph 4)
  8 get so much out of (paragraph 5)

My best friend

① The moment I saw the advert for the 'Best friend' award I knew who I wanted to nominate – my oldest and best friend, Julio.

② I <u>know</u> Julio since we were four years old, when we   **T**
started school together. The teacher put us next to each other in class, and we've been inseparable ever since. I can always rely on him in a crisis, or when I'm feeling a little depressed. He is always willing to help.

③ Allow me to give you an example. Last summer I was working for an important exam, but it was very difficult. Julio gave up all his evenings to help me study, and never <u>complained to</u> the time he could have been   **Gr**
spending on something else. I managed to pass with an excellent mark – and it was <u>intirely</u> thanks to him.   **Sp**
Having his help was a valuable benefit.

④ This holiday would be perfect for Julio for two reasons. First, he has given up so much time for me, I wish I could find a way to repay him. Second, <u>he never has</u>   **Wo**
been abroad, but he would love to see new things and <u>experiment</u> different cultures at the same time. The   **Ww**
Caribbean would be the perfect destination for him to do this. Moreover, he is a fantastic photographer, so we could send in some pictures from our trip to the magazine.

⑤ So, for being the best friend anyone could ask for and a person who would benefit greatly from this holiday, I nominate Julio.

> **Key to correction symbols**
> P = punctuation
> Sp = spelling
> Gr = grammar
> T = verb tense
> Ww = wrong word
> Wo = word order
> St = style

4 **Correct the grammatical and spelling mistakes marked. Look at the key to see what the correction symbols mean.**

5 **Write your own answer to the task in your notebook.**

A The inexplicable

Use of English
Multiple-choice cloze (Paper 3 Part 1)

▶ CB page 26

1 a Read the title of the text and think about what you are going to read. What is hypnosis generally used for?

b Read the whole text quickly for general understanding, ignoring the gaps for the moment. What is it about?
   a) how to become a hypnotist
   b) making money out of hypnotism
   c) benefiting as a result of being hypnotised

2 a Read the text again carefully and think about the type of word which will fit in each gap. Try to predict what the answer will be.

b Look at the options A–D and choose the option which you feel fits best in each gap. Use the Help clues if necessary.

TIP
Remember to answer all the questions, even if you have to guess. But if you have no idea about one item, leave it until the end. Once you've worked through and fully understood the whole text, it might be easier to guess the right answer.

3 Read through the text again when you've finished and check that the options you've chosen fit in with the overall meaning of the text.

HELP
➤ Question 1
Which of these phrasal verbs means *found by chance*?
➤ Question 3
Two of the verbs can be followed by *up*. Which one fits the context?
➤ Question 7
Only one of these words makes sense after *but*. Which is it?
➤ Question 8
Only one of these words is typically followed by a *to*-infinitive. Which is it?

For questions **1–12**, read the text below and decide which answer (**A**, **B**, **C** or **D**) best fits each gap. There is an example at the beginning (**0**).

Can hypnosis make you prosperous?

I was **(0)** A some research into the use of hypnosis in business training when I **(1)**....... the website of a hypnotist who **(2)**....... courses in something called 'abundance training' or 'learning to accumulate wealth through hypnosis'. I was, to say the least, intrigued and so I **(3)**....... up for a workshop that was **(4)**....... to be held in a city-centre hotel.

The hypnotist began by explaining that people could be surprisingly slow to take advantage of money-making opportunities. To illustrate her **(5)**....... , she revealed the first page of her flipchart. Attached were a number of banknotes below the heading: 'Free money'. The room fell silent. Then one participant **(6)**....... from his seat. I assumed he was going to leave the room, but **(7)**....... he stopped at the flipchart and pocketed a note. For a moment, nobody **(8)**....... to copy him; then there was a stampede.

Next came the actual hypnosis. I had always imagined it would be a vivid, dreamlike experience. In the event, it felt more like **(9)**....... breathing for relaxation, or listening attentively with your eyes shut. Once under hypnosis, I heard a voice telling me to **(10)**....... the obstacles that prevented me achieving abundance, and I climbed over the wall that appeared before me. It was a terrific feeling. Released from my trance, I left the hotel on a **(11)**....... of optimism. A stern letter from the bank awaited me at home, however, reminding me that once again I'd reached my credit-card **(12)**....... . I realised that 'achieving abundance' might take me a while.

	A	B	C	D
0	**A** doing	**B** getting	**C** making	**D** seeking
1	**A** dropped into	**B** tripped over	**C** came across	**D** checked up
2	**A** sets	**B** deals	**C** guides	**D** runs
3	**A** enlisted	**B** signed	**C** enrolled	**D** joined
4	**A** shortly	**B** currently	**C** briskly	**D** eventually
5	**A** point	**B** issue	**C** matter	**D** topic
6	**A** stood	**B** rose	**C** spun	**D** left
7	**A** instead	**B** although	**C** however	**D** therefore
8	**A** risked	**B** chanced	**C** feared	**D** dared
9	**A** strong	**B** soft	**C** deep	**D** heavy
10	**A** triumph	**B** overcome	**C** outdo	**D** defeat
11	**A** wave	**B** stream	**C** flood	**D** drift
12	**A** deadline	**B** boundary	**C** limit	**D** extent

Language development

Relative clauses ▶ CB page 29, GR page 175

Relative pronouns

1 a Use each of the pronouns in the list once to complete the following sentences.

who   whose   whom   why   which
where   when   that

1 My friend got to meet Brad Pitt, ... was very exciting for her.

2 Is that the magician .... often appears on TV?

3 I'm interested in an area of the brain .... images are processed.

4 The dogs, ... trainer has supplied animals for a number of films, could do some incredible tricks.

5 These days, there are few occasions .... I need to wear a tie.

6 The director from .... we received the information shall remain anonymous.

7 My past is not something .... I'd like people to know much about.

8 I'd like to know the reason .... you didn't act sooner.

b In which sentence above can the pronoun be omitted?

2 Complete the text by putting one word in each gap.

Borley Rectory – 'The most haunted house in Britain'

Borley Rectory was built in 1863 on a site with a long history. All **(1)**..................... who lived there reported strange occurrences, as a result of **(2)**..................... it was named 'the most haunted house in Britain'. The house was first occupied by Henry Bull and his son Harry, **(3)**..................... of whom died in the 'Blue Room' there.

Later residents, several of **(4)**..................... wrote down their experiences, claim to have seen the figure of Henry Bull. The strange incidents, most of **(5)**..................... have never been explained, include objects being thrown, objects appearing and disappearing, sightings of people, writing appearing on walls. A nun, believed to have died there in the 15th century, is often seen walking along a path in the garden, which is **(6)**..................... it is known as 'The Nun's Walk'.

The house was destroyed by fire in 1939, **(7)**..................... which point the number of incidents in the area dropped sharply. The site, **(8)**..................... which a number of modern houses have now been built, is still a source of interest to many visitors.

3 Mark the option(s) that can fit in each space. There may be more than one.

1 Please show your ID card .... you visit the club.
   A every time   B all times   C whenever
   D each time that

2 You can use this phone .... you go.
   A where   B wherever   C anywhere
   D in which place

3 .... I do seems to go wrong.
   A All what   B Which   C Everything that
   D Whatever

4 I'd like to speak to .... is in charge.
   A whoever   B who   C the person who
   D whom

5 I explained .... I wanted him to do.
   A what   B whatever   C the things what
   D the things that

6 They both love sports; that's .... they get on so well.
   A why   B the reason that   C for why
   D because

7 I've been thinking about .... we did yesterday.
   A what   B the things that   C which   D it's what

8 I recommend all these books – you can borrow .... you want.
   A them   B any one   C whichever one   D one

Reduced relative clauses

4 In each text, make <u>one</u> sentence shorter by using a reduced relative clause: a present or past participle or *to*-infinitive.

1

Janine is very superstitious. She always wears a necklace with a locket that contains a lucky clover leaf. I don't know where she got it from or why she believes in it.

2

People who wish to learn more about the paranormal would be well advised to contact a local paranormal society. A number of such groups exist, especially in places where there are high numbers of incidents.

3

A number of people here can help you. However, Jeremy is the person who you should talk to if you want information about local customs. He has lived in the area all his life and is an expert.

4

There are many numbers that have huge significance. People who are asked to choose a lucky number most frequently pick three or seven. Thirteen is the least popular number.

Use of English
Key word transformations (Paper 3 Part 5)

▶ CB page 28, ER page 170

1 a Look at the example (0) below. There are two sentences and a key word. Read the two sentences carefully and think about what they mean.

b What part of the meaning of the first sentence has not been included in the second sentence?

c Look at the key word. How can you use this word to express the idea missing in the second sentence? Remember the key word cannot be changed.

d Write between three and six words in the gap including the key word. The words must complete the sentence logically and grammatically.

e Read both sentences again to check that they mean the same thing.

2 Repeat the procedure for questions 1–8. Use the HELP clues if necessary.

HELP
➤ Question 1
 Be careful: an indefinite article is needed before 'more'.
➤ Question 2
 The verb needs to be in the past tense.
➤ Question 5
 A passive form is needed here.
➤ Question 8
 Be careful: the form of the adjective has changed, so you need to add a new verb.

For questions **1–8**, complete the second sentence so that it has a similar meaning to the first sentence, using the word given. **Do not change the word given.** You must use between **three** and **six** words, including the word given. Here is an example **(0)**.

0 There hasn't been quite so much snow as there was last year.
 SLIGHTLY
 This year, it ....HAS SNOWED SLIGHTLY LESS THAN...... it did last year.

1 My grandmother was the most hardworking person I've ever known.
 MORE
 I've .... than my grandmother.

2 Robin has not been back to his birthplace for over twenty years.
 LAST
 It is over twenty years .... to his birthplace.

3 A strike by check-staff led to all flights being delayed.
 BECAUSE
 There were .... of a strike by check-in staff.

4 Everyone assumed that Dennis would sell the haunted house he inherited from his uncle.
 GRANTED
 People .... Dennis would sell the haunted house he inherited from his uncle.

5 You have to pierce the plastic film first and then you can put the tray in the microwave oven.
 BEFORE
 The plastic film .... the tray is placed in the microwave oven.

6 Everyone expects Maura to resign at the end of the month.
 HAND
 Maura is widely .... at the end of the month.

7 We missed the start of the concert because we arrived at the venue late.
 BY
 The concert .... we arrived at the venue.

8 When she was at school, Sandra was fascinated by the idea of hypnotism.
 USED
 Sandra .... of hypnotism fascinating when she was at school.

Vocabulary

Film reviews

▶ CB page 30

1 a Think of a word that matches the following definitions. If you are stuck, choose from the nouns in this list.

adaptation   background   close-up   epic
location   plot   scene   score   screenplay
soundtrack

   1 a film that tells a long story about brave actions and exciting events ....
   2 a single piece of action that happens in one place ....
   3 a place away from a film studio where scenes are filmed ....
   4 the events that form the main story of a film ....
   5 music written specially for the film ....
   6 the recorded music from a film ....
   7 the words that are written down for actors to say in a film, and the instructions that tell them what they should do ....
   8 a film that is based on a book or play ....
   9 the situation or events that explain why something happens in the way that it does ....
   10 a shot in which the camera seems to be very near ....

  b Complete the following extract from a film review with words from Exercise 1a.

2 Rewrite the following extract from a review in your notebook, replacing the parts in italics with expressions from the list, making any changes necessary. There are more expressions than you need.

box-office hit/smash   be a runaway success   sequel to
remake   action packed   on the edge of one's seat
a dramatic finale   lavish production   on a shoestring
thrilling   blockbuster   cult classic

The Mexican film 'El Mariachi' is a great example of how good movies can be produced (1) *with a very small budget*. Made in 1992 by Robert Rodriguez for $7,000, it (2) *quickly became successful* at the box office and has become a (3) *very popular film with some enthusiasts*. The story, about an innocent musician who is mistaken for a killer who carries his gun in his guitar case, will keep you (4) *feeling excited* from start to finish. With some twists along the way, it leads to (5) *an exciting ending*. Rodriguez went on to make 'Desperado', starring Antonio Banderas, in a (6) *big, expensive film* that was meant to be a (7) *continuation of the story of* 'El Mariachi'. However, the film was not the (8) *popular and successful film* that everyone had expected and was criticised for being more of a (9) *different version of the same film*, as the stories were so similar.

3 Find and read some other film reviews in English, both positive and negative, and note down more useful expressions in your vocabulary notebook.

Doctor Zhivago, made in 1965, remains a classic of the period. This (1).................. film, which spans many years in the lives of the central characters, is a simple love story. The basic (2).................. of the poet doctor in love with two women is set against the (3).................. of the Russian Revolution.

   The director, David Lean, makes good use of the (4).................. , and the vast snow-covered fields are beautifully shot. The dialogue is superb, and the (5).................. , which is an (6).................. of the book by Boris Pasternak, won one of five Oscars for the film. Another was for the music, composed by Maurice Jarre, which has been described as 'the greatest (7).................. in movie history'.

   Classic (8).................. include one where Lean is able to show the horror of fighting just by using a (9).................. of Yuri's face as he witnesses the destruction.

Listening

Multiple matching (Paper 4 Part 4)

▶ ER pages 170–171

1 a Read the instructions for the task.
   1 How many speakers will you hear?
   2 What will they all be talking about?
   3 How many tasks do you have to do?
   4 How many times will you hear the texts?

 b Read Task One carefully. Think about the vocabulary and expressions you would expect to hear connected with each sport and note them down.

 c Read Task Two carefully and highlight key words in the options A–H. This has been done for you in the first two options.

2 a ⌒ Listen to the recording once. The first time you listen, try to do Task One. Use the Help clues if necessary.

 b Listen again. This time try to do Task Two. Use the Help clues if necessary.

TIP

Don't worry if you don't understand every word in the recording – in Part 4, you are listening to identify the speakers and understand their main points, attitudes and opinions.

You will hear **five** short extracts in which various sportspeople are talking about superstitions that they have.

TASK ONE
For questions **1–5**, choose from the list **A–H** the sport which each speaker competes in.

TASK TWO
For questions **6–10**, choose from the list **A–H** the reason each person gives for carrying on with their superstition.

You will hear the recording twice. While you listen you must complete both tasks.

A skiing

B motor racing

C swimming

D sailing

E canoeing

F wind-surfing

G cycling

H running

Speaker 1	1
Speaker 2	2
Speaker 3	3
Speaker 4	4
Speaker 5	5

A It takes my mind off the risks involved.

B It helps me to prepare mentally.

C It's just a joke really.

D It helps me cope with nerves.

E I don't know why I bother with it.

F It reminds me of my objectives.

G It is a family tradition.

H It helps me when I'm feeling low.

Speaker 1	6
Speaker 2	7
Speaker 3	8
Speaker 4	9
Speaker 5	10

HELP
➤ Question 1
   At the beginning, the speaker tells us that she doesn't use *valuable gear* in her sport. Which of the sports A–H doesn't require equipment? Listen to the rest of the text to hear confirmation of which is her sport.
➤ Question 2
   At the beginning, the speaker tells us that he does his training *on the roads*. Which of the sports could this refer to? Listen to the rest of the text for confirmation of which is his sport.

HELP
➤ Question 6
   Listen for why the speaker takes a coin to competitions. How does she feel before a race?
➤ Question 7
   The speaker says *I can't think what makes me do it*. Which option does this match?

B It's only logical!

Language development
Speaking skills

▶ CB pages 32–33, ER pages 171–172

Giving full answers to questions

1 **For each question, choose an appropriate response for Part 1 of the Speaking test.**

1 Have you travelled far today?
A Not really.
B It depends, what do you call far?
C No. I'm quite lucky in that I only live about 15 minutes from here.

2 Can you tell me a little about your family?
A Let me see, I have a mother, a father, one sister, one brother, seven uncles and aunts and 14 cousins.
B We have our own business. We run a hotel and restaurant that together employ about 14 people. It's hard work, particularly in the summer when the hotel is full. We have many tourists and that's why I need to study English.
C I don't see that much of my family since I moved into my own flat a couple of years ago. I tend to spend more time with friends and just see my family a few times a year.

3 What do you like about your town?
A My town is famous for its traditional industries. Tiles have been made here for over 200 years and are vital to the region's economy.
B There are a lot of shops, cinemas, museums and art galleries and other places to visit.
C The town itself is not so exciting, but it's where all my friends and family are. That's why I'm happy there.

4 How important is sport and exercise in your life?
A I hate it.
B I think it's important to take some exercise on a regular basis. I enjoy playing football with my friends, but I'm not a very good player, I'm afraid. So I think it's a fairly important part of my life.
C I like football, basketball, volleyball and I watch sport on TV too. In the winter I go skiing and also ice-skating and tobogganing. I can swim too, but not in the sea. I prefer the pool.

5 How might you use your English in the future?
A I don't know really. It depends, but I know it's important if you want to get a job.
B I think English is the most important language in the world because so many people can speak it. Spanish is important too and I'm also learning that, but I don't know anything about Chinese, which might become even more important in the future.
C I'm hoping to be able to use English in my work. I'm training to be a lawyer and I hope I'll get the chance to work on international cases or for an international firm. But if I don't, English will still be useful because I love to travel and most places you can find someone who can speak at least a bit of English, so it's always useful.

> **TIP**
>
> *In the test, you will be examined with a partner, but in Part One you will each be asked different questions in turn. Give full answers, but don't speak for too long. Look for signs from the examiner to see whether you've said enough or not.*

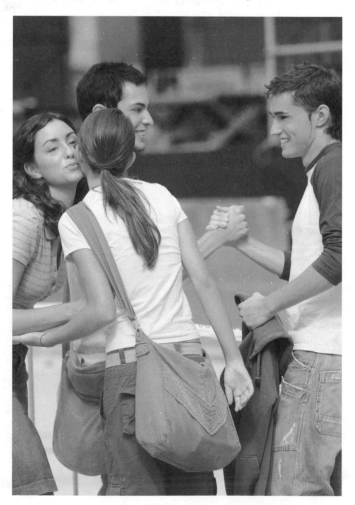

Language development

Articles

▶ CB page 35, GR page 176

Use of articles

1 Complete the sentences with *a/an, the* or ø (no article).

1 Graham is .... biologist and for .... last three years, he's been studying .... lifecycle of .... ant.

2 After .... accident, ... injured were quickly taken to .... hospital.

3 As .... MP (Member of Parliament), he does .... lot of work to help .... disabled people and .... elderly.

4 On .... Sunday we are going to .... coast for .... day. We'll probably have .... dinner in .... local restaurant.

5 Generally speaking, ... Spanish love .... fish and Madrid has .... second-largest fish market in .... world.

6 Before I go to .... sleep, I like to watch .... TV or listen to .... radio.

7 I'd like two coffees, please; .... large black one and .... one with .... cream.

Singular or plural verb?

2 Correct the mistakes in these sentences.

1 Some of the girl's clothing were torn.

2 He gave us some very useful advices.

3 None of the information he gave me were correct.

4 A number of students has complained about the poor quality of food in the canteen.

5 A lot of people enjoys watching sport.

6 The number of people interested in the job have surprised us.

Quantifiers

3 Mark the correct quantifier in these sentences.

1 I've got very *few / little* money left.

2 Please could you send me *some / any* information about your training courses?

3 We haven't had *much / many* success with our search so far.

4 Not *much / many* people would choose to live in such a remote place.

5 I'm afraid we haven't got *some / any* of these shoes in your size.

6 He's a child who needs *a lot of / enough* encouragement.

7 Could you try to make *little / less* noise, please?

8 We haven't got *enough / much* players for a team.

4 Complete each gap in this text with a word from the list. You will have to use some of the words more than once.

each
both
either
neither

Jane and Emily are twin sisters, separated at birth and reunited after 40 years. Since meeting again after such a long time, **(1)**............... Jane and Emily have been struck by the number of things they have in common. For example, they **(2)**............... work in the media, Jane as a television producer and Emily as a radio sound assistant. **(3)**............... of them is married, but **(4)**............... have steady partners. They **(5)**............... own their own house, but **(6)**............... has a car.

As I interviewed them, I noticed time and time again that, as I put a question to **(7)**............... sister in turn, the other seemed to know the answer before it had been given, as if they knew what the other was thinking. I asked if **(8)**............... of them felt threatened by meeting the other after all this time. 'Definitely not,' says Jane. 'It's great. **(9)**............... of us feels threatened at all.'

And why are they so similar? For once, they don't agree. Jane believes it's all in the genes, whereas Emily is convinced that the time they spent together in the womb accounts for their many similarities. Maybe they are **(10)**............... right!

Making uncountable nouns countable

5 Fill each gap with a word from the list to complete the common phrase.

bit   drop   heap   hint   piece   pinch
shred   slice

1 There isn't a .... of evidence against this man!

2 Before serving, add a .... of salt to taste.

3 Oh dear, I think I just felt a .... of rain.

4 I came across a very interesting .... of information.

5 I don't have much for breakfast; usually just a cup of tea and a .... of toast.

6 Maria's quite upset, and could do with a .... of support at the moment.

7 There was a .... of anger in his voice.

8 There was a .... of clothes in the middle of the floor.

Use of English
Open cloze (Paper 3 Part 2)

▶ ER page 169

1 a Read the title of the text and think about the topic.

 b Read the whole text quickly for general understanding, ignoring the gaps for the moment.

  1 Why was the story of Frane Selak reported in the news?

  2 How many lucky escapes are mentioned in the text?

2 a Read through the text again and think about the type of word which will fit in each gap. For example, is it an article, a preposition, a pronoun, etc.?

 b Look at the words before and after the gap and decide which word is missing. Use the Help clues if necessary.

TIP

If you aren't sure about an answer, try reading the sentence in the text using different words in the gap. If you're still not sure, leave this gap until the end.

3 Read the whole text again to check that the words you've chosen fit in with the overall meaning of the text.

HELP

➤ Question 1
 Look at the second part of the sentence after the comma.

➤ Question 3
 Which preposition goes here to give the idea of *entering water*?

➤ Question 5
 Which preposition do we use after the verb *to suffer*?

➤ Question 12
 Is it the definite or indefinite article that is needed in this phrase?

4 Look back at questions 1–15. How many of them tested:
 • use of articles?
 • use of pronouns?
 • a fixed phrase?
 • a phrasal verb?
 • prepositions which follow a particular noun or verb?

For questions **1–15**, read the text below and think of the word that best fits each gap. Use only **one** word in each gap. There is an example at the beginning (**0**).

World's luckiest man wins the lottery

Frane Selak, a 74-year-old from Croatia, has been dubbed the world's luckiest man by his friends (**0**) ...after... hitting the jackpot with his first lottery ticket in 40 years. Frane's story was picked up by the world's media (**1**)................ so much because of this particular stroke of luck, but because it comes after (**2**)................ life characterised by lucky escapes.

The first came in 1962 when a train Frane was travelling on jumped the rails and plunged (**3**)................ an icy river. Frane made (**4**)................ to the riverbank suffering (**5**)................ hypothermia, shock and a broken arm. A year later, he was thrown out of a DC-8 airliner when a door flew open. This time, Frane was lucky enough to land in a haystack and escaped (**6**)................ cuts, bruises and shock. In 1970, he lost control of his car, (**7**)................ plunged 300 feet down a precipice (**8**)................ exploding. Frane, of course, managed to jump out just in (**9**)................ , landing unhurt in a tree. It was after this accident that his friends gave him the nickname 'Lucky', but (**10**)................ Frane says, 'There are two ways of looking at it – I am (**11**)................ the world's unluckiest man or the luckiest. I prefer to believe (**12**)................ latter.'

In all, Frane has survived seven major disasters, including accidents on most forms of transport. So is Frane (**13**)................ forward to a quiet retirement on his £600,000 jackpot? It (**14**)................ seem not. First, he'll be marrying his girlfriend, who is 20 years (**15**)................ junior, then he'll be investing in a speedboat!

Language development

Look at all the uncountable nouns in the text. Can you find a phrase that is used to make an uncountable noun countable?

Writing
Information sheet (Paper 2 Part 2)

▶ CB pages 36–37, WR page 190

Exam strategy

For any piece of writing, you should make a plan so that you don't include irrelevant information. Read the task carefully, then make your plan, using notes which you can expand when you write your answer. When writing an information leaflet, make sure that the information is clearly organised. You can use headings and bullet points to help you do this.

1 **Read the task below and answer these questions.**
   1 What is the purpose of the information sheet?
   2 What information do you have to include? Mark the relevant parts of the task.
   3 Should the style be formal or informal?

> You have been asked to write an information sheet to promote a new leisure complex which is opening in your town. You should give a brief description of the complex, outlining why it is important to the town, describe its main facilities and plans for the future and mention any other points that you think are important.
>
> Write **the text for the information sheet** in 220–260 words.

2 **Read part of a student's answer to the task on the right. Match four of the topics in the student's plan to each section (1–4) of the answer.**

   a Describe facilities in the centre. ....

   b Inform readers about the opening. ....

   c Introduce the centre in an eye-catching way. ....

   d Outline future plans for the centre. ....

   e Explain the importance of the centre to the town. ....

   f Give further information about the centre or opening-day activities. ....

3 **The student has not added any headings. Decide which of these headings would be suitable for each section of the information sheet.**
   A When will the New Metro Complex open?
   B What can you expect to find in the New Metro Complex?
   C THE NEW METRO COMPLEX
   D Why is the New Metro Complex important for this town?

① It's here at last! Are you bored? Are your evenings dull and uninteresting? Help is at hand!

Whether you are 14, 40 or 80, the New Metro Complex has something for you.

② Opening Day is September 15th, and for the first week there's a spectacular offer of BUY ONE GET ONE FREE on all available facilities. Don't miss out! Come to the old converted Cattle Market on September 15th!

③ The Complex offers a ONE-STOP SHOP for everyone in the town, a place where you can meet friends, relax and socialise, get fit or go shopping – all under one roof! As well as this, it will attract more people from the outlying towns and villages. This can only be good for local businesses!

④ In the welcoming atmosphere of the complex, you will find lots of different things. You will find three restaurants catering for a wide variety of tastes, and five cafés for a quick bite to eat. There is also an indoor sports arena which will host tournaments and provide facilities for local clubs. A five-screen cinema will show the latest films, and there will also be specialist boutiques. Finally, a multi-storey car park will ensure easy access to the complex.

4 In section 4, bullet points would help to make the information easier to read. Rewrite this paragraph, organising the information with bullet points.

5 Complete the sample answer, using the remaining topics from Exercise 2. Make some notes before you write so that your answer is clear and relevant.

B

Reading

Gapped text (Paper 1 Part 2)

▶ ER page 168

1 Read the title and subtitle of the text. What does *faking* mean?

2 Read the main text quickly, ignoring the gaps for the moment. Answer these questions to check your comprehension.

   1 What does Richard Wiseman want to find out?
   2 What research has his team already carried out?
   3 Why did the results surprise them?
   4 What does Richard Wiseman think really causes people's 'spooky' experiences?
   5 How is he planning to test this out?

3 a Look at question 1.
   • Read the text above the gap. It contains information about Wiseman's strange idea and what he plans to do.
   • Now read the text below the gap. It contains the phrase *evidence to support this explanation*.
   • Read extract E. It contains both a reference to a strange idea and an explanation.

  b Now look at questions 2–6 and repeat the procedure. In questions 2 and 3, words and phrases in the main text and extracts have been highlighted to help you.

TIP

Write in the letter of any answers you are sure about. If you're not sure which option fits a gap, then put a question mark (?) and return to it later.

4 When you have finished the task, read the whole text through to check it makes sense.

You are going to read an extract from a magazine article. Six paragraphs have been removed from the article. Choose from the paragraphs **A–G** the one which fits each gap (**1–6**). There is one extra paragraph you do not need to use.

FAKING A GHOSTLY FEELING

Scientists want to put people in a scary situation, just to test their reactions. Nathan Booth finds out about a strange experiment in a purpose-built 'haunted' house.

The image of a haunted house inhabited by the ghosts of its former occupants is a familiar one from literature and horror movies. But do such places really exist? A team of scientists aims to find out. Richard Wiseman, a
5 psychologist, is building his own 'haunted' house for the purposes of scientific research. He wants to be able to terrify visitors with spooky special effects that he's designed himself. By controlling where and when these effects appear, he hopes to find out much more about
10 how and why people have spooky experiences. 'We want to build our own haunted house, so that we're in total control,' says Wiseman. 'Then we might get significant scientific results.'

> **1**

Earlier this year, Wiseman and his team produced some
15 well-documented scientific evidence to support this explanation. They recorded the experiences of hundreds of volunteers, visiting some of the best-known haunted spots in the UK.

> **2**

Beforehand, Wiseman's team surveyed these sites,
20 recording things such as air temperatures, magnetic fields and lighting levels. Then they asked visitors to report exactly where they felt or saw anything strange. To their astonishment, they found that people's scariest experiences were often in the precise spots reputed to
25 be haunted. And these same spots were often those where subtle variations in temperature and magnetic fields had already been recorded.

> **3**

As a result, Wiseman thinks he can discover even more through experiments in which he dictates exactly when
30 people are exposed to subtle environmental effects.

'The only way you know if something is causal is if you control the signal,' he says. In addition, he wishes to prepare people psychologically before they visit a site.

4 [   ]

35 He also intends to create the perfect environment for his research, where he would direct the lighting effects and other features within the rooms. And as spook-master general, he could play with the effects; introducing minor changes in temperature and

40 perhaps wisps of a draught here and there. 'It's the subtle things that count,' says Wiseman. 'Less is more.' In earlier research, he discovered that people found the special effects less believable as they became more obvious.

5 [   ]

45 What's more, such feelings become even stronger where they match instinctive reactions to natural hazards that date back to the days of the first humans. Poisonous insects can lurk in cramped, shadowy corners, for example. That's why Wiseman

50 considers control over lighting and room size to be crucial. 'I think many experiences are visually driven,' he says. In a castle in Scotland, people often reported the strangest feelings when entering the darkest, tiniest rooms. Objects such as old furniture

55 are also important for reinforcing expectations about where ghosts hide, and he expects his house to have an 'Old World' feel.

6 [   ]

So, at present, he is searching for disused buildings in the grounds of large aristocratic houses, which

60 could be converted for the purpose, perhaps an old hunting lodge. Wiseman is contacting organisations that manage historic properties open to the public to see if they're interested, reminding them that his previous experiments at Hampton Court attracted a

65 record number of visitors.

A Wiseman seems to have all the details worked out, but how likely is any of this to happen? He is optimistic because his house could pay for itself by becoming a tourist attraction in its own right, especially if it was associated with historic venues already full of ghostly folklore.

B An equally practical way of controlling the temperature in the house would be with air-conditioning units hidden behind the walls. 'People are very sensitive, so the temperature wouldn't have to drop much,' says Wiseman. 'You can feel a quarter of a degree change.'

C This provided Wiseman with a more earthly explanation for what some people feel. 'We showed that people had odd experiences in the same places, and now we know that these are based on environmental factors,' says Wiseman. He also found that it didn't matter whether volunteers knew beforehand where the most haunted spots were located. So, the idea that the experiences relied solely on prior knowledge was disproved.

D Yet surprisingly, for a man with such an unusual idea, Wiseman doesn't believe in ghosts. But he is sure that the sensations felt by people who have ghostly encounters, like fear and even nausea, result from a mixture of psychology and a spooky environment.

E It's the same in everyday life, we are sensitive to very slight alterations in our environment especially in situations where we feel nervous. As Wiseman explains, whenever we have preconceptions about ghostly goings-on, our sense of unease is heightened.

F One was Hampton Court, the former royal palace near London which is said to be haunted by the screaming ghost of Catherine Howard, fifth wife of Henry VIII, the notorious 16th-century English king. Another was the South Bridge Vaults, a series of underground rooms and corridors in Edinburgh, Scotland.

G Wiseman insists that he should be able to tell the volunteers beforehand whatever he wants: which spots may be haunted and so on. In other words, he's in total control. He is convinced this would make the results of the experiment more wide-reaching.

A The burden of fame

Use of English
Word formation (Paper 3 Part 3)

▶ CB page 42, ER page 169

Exam strategy

For this task, you need a good knowledge of prefixes, suffixes and spelling rules. When learning new vocabulary, make a note of other words that can be formed from the word you are learning, for example a noun formed from a verb or a negative form of an adjective. Also make a note of the spelling rules that apply when the form of a word changes.

1 a **Read the title of the text to identify the topic and think about what you are going to read.**
   - Do famous people experience problems with friendships?
   - Are the friendships of famous people different from those of other people?

b Read the text through quickly for general understanding, ignoring the gaps for the moment. Who do famous people usually choose as their friends?

2 a Read the text again carefully and think about the type of word which will fit in each gap. Try to predict what the answer will be.

b Now fill in the gaps.

3 Read through the text again when you've finished and check that the words you've written fit in with the overall meaning of the text and are spelled correctly.

For questions **1–10**, read the text below. Use the word given in capitals at the end of some of the lines to form a word that fits in the gap in the same line. There is an example at the beginning **(0)**.

Famous friends

The lives of celebrities are coming **(0)** _increasingly_ under the close scrutiny of the public at large. One consequence of this trend is that it can sometimes be difficult for people in the spotlight to forge genuine and lasting **(1)**........................... with others. When it comes to making friends, celebrities have a **(2)**........................... to pick other celebrities, for example. This is not **(3)**..........................., of course, given the nature of the social circles in which such people move, and given the fact that one of the **(4)**........................... of the celebrity lifestyle is **(5)**........................... the opportunity it offers to rub shoulders with the rich and famous.

Very often, however, an air of **(6)**........................... can hang around a high-profile friendship, where an outward show of affection actually masks an underlying **(7)**........................... . In the celebrity world, friends clearly have to be chosen with **(8)**........................... care. There needs to be a degree of mutual **(9)**........................... combined with equal standing in the eyes of the outside world, so that there is no question of one friend appearing to be in the shadow of another. How else can we explain the **(10)**........................... of close friendships between stars who, in any other situation, would have very little in common?

	INCREASE
	RELATION
	TEND
	EXPECT
	ATTRACT
	SUPPOSE
	TENSE
	RIVAL
	CONSIDER
	ADMIRE
	EXIST

Language development

Punctuation

▶ CB page 44, WR page 201

Capitals

1 Correct the following sentences by adding capitals where necessary.

1 the planet venus is warmer than mars because it is closer to the sun.

2 this winter, I'll be working every saturday in december in the run-up to christmas and new year.

3 my friend fabio's father has a house near lake como in the north of italy.

4 i'd like to study spanish in south america, in either argentina or chile.

5 she's the new doctor; she's taken over from doctor digby.

6 for more information, please contact barclays bank at 42 high street, biggleswade.

7 the sacred river ganges starts high in the himalayan mountains and eventually flows through bangladesh into the bay of bengal.

8 are you fascinated by fame? do you seek out celebrities? if so, read *stalkers weekly*, the new magazine for star spotters.

Apostrophes

2 Rewrite the following messages using contractions where appropriate and adding apostrophes as necessary.

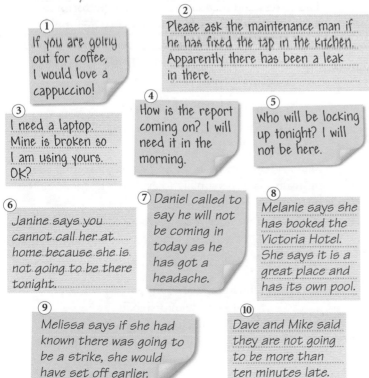

① If you are going out for coffee, I would love a cappuccino!

② Please ask the maintenance man if he has fixed the tap in the kitchen. Apparently there has been a leak in there.

③ I need a laptop. Mine is broken so I am using yours. OK?

④ How is the report coming on? I will need it in the morning.

⑤ Who will be locking up tonight? I will not be here.

⑥ Janine says you cannot call her at home because she is not going to be there tonight.

⑦ Daniel called to say he will not be coming in today as he has got a headache.

⑧ Melanie says she has booked the Victoria Hotel. She says it is a great place and has its own pool.

⑨ Melissa says if she had known there was going to be a strike, she would have set off earlier.

⑩ Dave and Mike said they are not going to be more than ten minutes late.

Speech marks

3 Add speech marks and other punctuation where necessary to the following quotes.

1 It was the American journalist Henry Louis Mencken who said a celebrity is one who is known to many persons he is glad he does not know.

2 Fame and tranquility can never be bedfellows said Michel de Montaigne, the 16th-century French writer.

3 I may be a living legend said singer Roy Orbison but that doesn't help when I've got to change a flat tyre.

4 The actor Alan Alda once joked it isn't necessary to be rich and famous to be happy. It's only necessary to be rich.

5 It was the actor and film director Woody Allen who remarked I don't want to achieve immortality through my work. I want to achieve it through not dying.

4 Punctuate the text about Robert Garside.

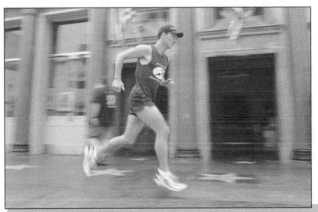

robert garside is nothing if not dedicated for the last six years the 36-year-old briton has had just one goal to be the first person to run around the world since starting out in new delhi in october 1997 robert has dodged bullets in russia outrun thieves in mexico and found true love in venezuela garside who often feels homesick says i miss a really good pot of tea

in june 2004 he plans to set off on his next venture to become the first person to swim around the world covering a distance of approximately 25000 miles he says that as with the run the greatest problems will be isolation politics and the weather

Use of English
Gapped sentences (Paper 3 Part 4)

▶ ER page 170

1 Look at the example in the gapped-sentence task and read the task rubric.

   1 How many sentences are there?
   2 How many words are missing?
   3 What do the missing words have in common?

2 a Read all three sentences in the example carefully. What type of word is missing from all three (noun, verb, adjective, etc.)?

   b Make a list of words that will fit in the gap in the first sentence. Think about both the grammar and the context. Which of these words would you include in your list?

> *take tour lead show demonstrate*
> *guide escort prove*

   c How many of the words on your list also fit the gap in the second sentence? Think about both the grammar and the context. Cross any words off your list which don't fit here.

   d Look at the third sentence. Will one of the words left on your list fit here?

   e Write your answer in all three gaps. Read the sentences again to check that it fits well in all three.

3 Now look at Questions 1–5 and repeat the procedure, using the HELP clues if necessary.

TIP

If you can't think of words that could go in the gap in the first sentence, try starting with one of the other sentences instead.

HELP

➤ **Question 1**
In all three sentences the past form of the verb is needed. All of these verbs fit in the first gap: *earned, won, gained.* Which of them fits in the other sentences?

➤ **Question 2**
A verb is needed in the first sentence. All of these verbs fit: *spot, choose, pick, select, find.* Which one also fits in the second sentence? Be careful, the word you choose needs to make a phrasal verb in the third sentence.

➤ **Question 3**
The verbs *determine, affect, influence* all fit in the first sentence

For questions **1–5**, think of **one** word only which can be used appropriately in all three sentences. Here is an example (**0**).

0 When groups of visitors come to the television studios, guides .... them round the set of the popular soap opera.
Any inaccuracies in the data will .... up when the graphs are produced on screen.
The success of perfumes bearing the name of top models really does .... how influential celebrities can be.

1 Although initially regarded only as a soap star, Emily has .... the respect of the critics for her recent film roles.
For young singers, there is nothing to be .... from over-exposure in the media at an early stage in their career.
The former model is reported to have .... a lot of weight since her retirement.

2 The casting director has an excellent eye for talent and generally manages to .... young actors who go on to perform very well in the show.
Brian was in a really bad mood, ready to .... a fight with anyone who disagreed with him.
In the darkness, it was just possible to .... out the outline of a building in the distance.

3 A person's age and background will always .... their choice of friends.
The actress said that she was happiest performing in front of a large group of people, so first-night nerves didn't .... her greatly.
This disease is often difficult to identify as it doesn't .... everyone in the same way.

4 Erin was on the .... of resigning from the club, when she was unexpectedly offered the role of Treasurer.
Michael had made a .... of contacting all of his team mates personally to explain why he would be missing the important match.
As they had numbered seats, Diane couldn't see the .... of getting to the concert hall an hour before the performance was due to start.

5 If it is not tended regularly, any garden will soon .... into a state of disrepair.
Successful television personalities generally .... into one of two categories – either they are very lucky or they are very determined.
Sonia had to miss a lecture, but asked to borrow a friend's notes so that she didn't .... too far behind with the work.

Writing

Coherence

▶ CB page 46, WR page 200

1 **Read the following paragraphs. For each paragraph:**
   1 underline the topic sentence
   2 underline any linking devices used to organise the details
   3 cross out any sentences that are not relevant to the main idea.

① It is hard to say why the marriages of well-known actors seldom last. Some have said it is because of the pressure of being in the public eye. Others have suggested it is because actors spend a lot of time away from their partners as they are touring or filming. Many films take months to shoot, and there are often delays. Another possible reason is that the opportunities for being unfaithful are so much greater, especially if you are in constant contact with adoring fans. Some actors are gorgeous and have huge fan clubs. The final reason could be that actors are people who crave constant attention and need to be loved, and it is hard to maintain that level of devotion in a long-term relationship.

② I'm not that interested in fame. Some famous people have far more money than they need. For me, the most important thing in life is to know that I have used my time and energy well. So I'd rather have a lower-paid job where I was helping others than earn a fortune making money from those around me. Some people judge their success by how much they have gained for themselves, whereas I'd like to be judged on what I have given back, not on what I have taken from life. My mother has always gone out of her way to help people. The more people give, the more everyone has. When I'm old, I'd like to be able to look back on my life with a clear conscience.

2 **Read the following paragraphs and choose the most appropriate topic sentence from the options A–C.**

1 _____
Glossy magazines have always carried features on celebrities. *Hello* was the first successful magazine that was based solely on celebrity gossip and PR. It was quickly followed by a stream of similar publications. Initially, they tended to be very supportive of the celebrities and were happy to promote whatever image the people featured wanted to project. These were followed by others that were keener to get beneath the mask and find out what the individuals were really like. Finally, came the rise of Internet-based gossip sites that, less restricted by libel laws, find it easier to say what they like about people.

A The last few years have seen the rise of celebrity magazines.
B Interest in celebrities is constantly growing and changing.
C There is a lot more to read than there used to be.

2 _____
Years ago, young people dreamt of such things as having their own successful business, being a top athlete or an accomplished musician. Fame was secondary, and came as a result of getting to the top of their profession. Nowadays, however, it seems as if the aim of many young people is simply to 'be famous'. How they achieve fame is not important. Fame itself is the goal. Hence the rise of 'reality' TV shows such as *Big Brother* and growing numbers of people wanting to work in the media. Being on TV is enough; what you do when you are on is less important. One direct result is that there is seldom anything worth watching.

A People's attitude to fame is changing.
B Young people have lost touch with reality.
C TV is not as good as it was.

3 **Look at the plan for a composition describing the job of a paparazzo.**

a **Select a topic sentence for each paragraph.**
   1 Other paparazzi are friends as well as rivals.
   2 To be successful, a paparazzo needs as many contacts as possible.
   3 A paparazzo's days are long and often boring.
   4 A paparazzo is nothing without his camera.

b **Write the notes into a coherent composition. Link the ideas in each paragraph using linking devices.**

The job of a paparazzo

Paragraph 1: _____
• typical day, start early in the morning, finish late at night
• spend a lot of time standing around and waiting
• depressing at times, no picture, no pay
• always hoping for the one special piece of good luck

Paragraph 2: _____
• other paparazzi are in the same situation
• chat, compare work, share ideas, experiences
• makes the job more enjoyable, less lonely

Paragraph 3: _____
• take your camera everywhere – something important could happen at any time
• have to practise – must be able to use it quickly and accurately
• keep it in good working order, update for new technology – can't afford to be let down by it

Paragraph 4: _____
• rely on contacts to give information and tip-offs
• must get on well with people, hotel porters, barmen, taxi drivers, hairdressers
• they are in contact with rich and famous – might phone one day with the big story

Listening

Sentence completion (Paper 4 Part 2)

▶ ER pages 170–171

1 a Read the instructions for the task below.
  1 Who are you going to hear?
  2 What will she be talking about?

  b Read the sentences. Think about the topic and what you expect to hear.
  • How much do you find out about the television programme from the sentences?
  • What do you find out about the order of information in the talk?

  c Try to predict the type of information you will be listening for. For example:
  1 In which question are you looking for someone's occupation?
  2 Which answer is likely to be an adjective?
  3 Which answers are likely to be abstract nouns?

2 ◠ Listen to the recording once and complete the sentences. Use the Help clues if necessary. Remember that:
  • although you won't hear exactly the same sentences, the information comes in the same order as the sentences on the page
  • your answers need to fit into the sentence grammatically.

HELP
➤ Question 1
You are listening for the actual words the speaker uses. Listen for the phrase *what I call* … The answer comes directly afterwards.
➤ Question 4
What were the bags full of? Be careful, because two possible things are mentioned, but only one is correct.
➤ Question 5
The word *and* is already in the box. This is there to help you. Add two more words which, together with *and,* will give you the answer.
➤ Question 6
Do you know any other words or expressions for *old-age pensioner*? Three are mentioned in the recording. Listen for the other one that Anita thinks is patronising.

3 Listen again to check and complete your answers.

4 Look at these wrong answers that students gave to some of the questions. Listen again and decide why these answers are not correct.
  2 costume designer   6 such as senior
  5 anger   8 emplymant

You will hear the well-known businesswoman Anita Roddick talking about a TV programme in which she pretended to be an old person. For questions **1–8**, complete the sentences.

HOW DOES IT FEEL TO BE OLD?

Anita uses the words [___ 1] to describe what she did to find out about old age for the programme.

Anita feels that the programme's [___ 2] made her look older than necessary.

Anita says that she felt as if she was [___ 3] when disguised as an old person.

Anita carried shopping bags full of [___ 4] to see if anyone would offer to help her.

Anita's impression was that people had feelings of [and ___ 5] when she crossed the road slowly.

Anita feels that it is no longer appropriate to use terms like '[___ 6]' and 'old-age pensioner'.

Anita prefers the term 'elder' because it suggests both [___ 7] and respect.

Anita gives the example of Sweden as a country where older people stay in [___ 8] longer.

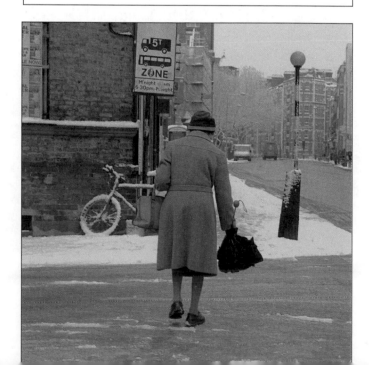

Language development
Modal verbs
▶ CB page 50, GR page 177

Expressing necessity

1 Complete the sentences using a suitable form of *must, have (got) to* or *need to.*
  1 All students .... register with the faculty before 15 September.
  2 When he gets home from work, he .... just sit and chill out for half an hour.
  3 Food .... be consumed in the library.
  4 I should be free that day, but I .... check in my diary to make sure.
  5 The report isn't urgent and .... be completed until next week.
  6 I can't find my key. I .... left it at home.
  7 I won't be ready for another half hour, but you .... wait for me. I can catch you up later.
  8 It was very kind of you to clean the flat for me, but you .... done it because we have a cleaning lady.

Expressing advice

2 Complete the sentences using a suitable form of *should, ought to* or *must.*
  1 It's a lovely little town. You really .... go there!
  2 .... I tell the police what I saw?
  3 You really .... drink so much. It's bad for you.
  4 You were very silly to leave the car unlocked. You .... locked it.
  5 You .... tell your tutor if you're falling behind with your work.
  6 Do you think we .... take some drinks with us?

Expressing ability

3 Complete these sentences using a suitable form of *can, could* or *be able to.*
  1 I looked for your book, but I .... find it.
  2 After a lot of effort, we .... hook the bag out of the water.
  3 If I had known that you needed some extra bags, I .... lent you one.

4 Next week, I'll have more time, so I .... get started on this work.
5 I've been trying to phone Jim all morning, but I .... get hold of him.
6 I'm afraid I .... come to the party this evening.
7 When I was younger, I .... run around for hours without getting tired.
8 I've been practising like mad, and I .... juggle now!

Expressing possibility/probability

4 Complete the sentences by choosing the correct modal.
  1 The temperature *can / could* reach 40 degrees tomorrow.
  2 We *might / should* go to Italy this summer, but it's not definite yet.
  3 He's not answering his phone. I suppose he *might have / can have* popped out of the office.
  4 These animals *must / can* grow to over two metres long.
  5 We're leaving at ten o'clock, so as long as the traffic isn't too bad, we *should / would* be there by 12.
  6 It looks fairly straightforward, so there *can't / shouldn't* be any problems.

Expressing deduction

5 Rewrite the two sentences as one sentence, using a modal to express the meaning in the second sentence.
  0 Although it seems unlikely, he is telling the truth. There is no other explanation.
    Although it seems unlikely, he must be telling the truth.
  1 This is not the building we're looking for. It's not possible.
    ....
  2 I suppose that maybe he phoned while I was out. It's possible.
    ....
  3 Someone broke into the house while we were out. That is the only explanation.
    ....
  4 Michael was in New York all last week, so it wasn't him that you saw. It's not possible.
    ....
  5 He didn't crash the car. It's impossible.
    ....

Same verb, different meanings

6 For each set of sentences, decide which modal verb fits all five sentences.

1 a 'No one is answering.' 'There .... be a problem with the phone.'
   b I'm so full, I .... n't eat another thing!
   c In my last job, I .... start work any time I wanted.
   d .... you do me a favour? .... you feed my cat while I'm away?
   e 'I really need to lose some weight.' 'You .... join a gym.'

2 a .... you let me know when Mr Burns arrives?
   b I think it .... be better to keep that opinion to yourself.
   c I can't remember what time I got home, but it .... have been around ten.
   d I .... love to go to Peru.
   e Ruth was very reliable. She .... always be the first to arrive in the morning.

3 a We are hoping our petition .... make the councillors change their minds.
   b Mr Jenkins .... see you now, if you .... come this way.
   c .... you please be quiet. This is a library!
   d 'What's that noise?' 'That .... be Peter practising the violin.'
   e How much water .... the swimming pool hold?

4 a The jury .... rise.
   b I .... attempt to explain the differences between the two systems.
   c What .... I wear for the party?
   d .... I keep an eye on your house while you're away?
   e Let's agree to differ on that topic, ... we?

7 Read the letter and then decide which word or phrase (A, B or C) fits each gap. Only one answer is possible.

Dear fellow traveller

Welcome to everyone who has signed up for our Jungle Safari Adventure Tour. Please read the following carefully as it contains important information about your holiday.

Passports / visas

I **(1)**....... like to remind you that **(2)**....... to make sure that your travel documents are in order. Your passport **(3)**....... valid for at least six months beyond your return date or you will not be **(4)**....... entry to the country. In addition, you will require a visa. Please note that, in light of recent events, the visa regulations have changed and many people who previously **(5)**....... a visa now do so.

   You are **(6)**....... obtain the visa in person at the embassy. It **(7)**....... be done by post. If applying by post, you must allow two weeks, and it is **(8)**....... use registered post. If applying in person, you **(9)**....... submit your details before 11 a.m. All applications **(10)**....... two recent photos.

Health

If you received a note about yellow fever, please ignore it. Our representatives **(11)**....... given it to you, as it does not apply to this trip. If you have not had a hepatitis vaccination because you thought that you **(12)**....... one, then please think again. We recommend that all travellers have it.

   There **(13)**....... be a lot of mosquitoes around, so we recommend that you take malaria tablets. For them to be fully effective, you **(14)**....... start taking them a week before departure.

   If you are taking any prescription medicines, you must inform the guide. Please ensure that you have enough for the whole trip. Also, it's **(15)**....... to take a spare pair of glasses.

Wildlife

You can, of course, take as many photos as you wish of all the amazing plants and animals that you will see. However, you **(16)**....... take enough film for your entire trip, as it is unavailable once we arrive. You are, however, **(17)**....... bring any plant samples back with you. Be warned that some plants are very poisonous, and children in particular **(18)**....... be allowed to touch them. The guides will explain which they are.

If you have any further questions, please contact me at the address above.

	A	B	C
1	would	will	could
2	you require	you must	it's up to you
3	could be	must be	needs be
4	obliged	required	allowed
5	did not need	need not	must not have
6	not supposed to	not obliged to	need not
7	can	ought to	is allowed to
8	required to	advisable to	forbidden to
9	are obliged to	had better	require
10	are allowed	require	are obliged
11	must not have	need not have	should not have
12	didn't need	needn't have had	must have
13	should	will	are to
14	are allowed to	can	must
15	required	forbidden	advisable
16	will need to	must not	are allowed to
17	mustn't	not allowed to	can't
18	needn't	should not	may not

Use of English
Key word transformations (Paper 3 Part 5)

▶ ER page 170

1 a Look at question 1. There are two sentences and a key word. Read the two sentences carefully and think about what they mean.

  b What part of the meaning of the first sentence has not been included in the second sentence?

  c Look at the key word. How can you use this word to express the idea missing in the second sentence? Remember the key word cannot be changed.

  d Write between three and six words in the gap including the key word. The words must complete the sentence logically and grammatically.

  e Read both sentences again to check that they mean the same thing.

2 Repeat the procedure for questions 2–8. Use the HELP clues if necessary.

HELP
➤ Question 1
  You need to include the words 'is it' in your answer.
➤ Question 2
  A phrasal verb replaces the verb 'organised' here.
➤ Question 4
  Be careful: this sentence is already in the past tense and you can only write up to six words.
➤ Question 8
  Be careful: is a positive or a negative idea needed here?

For questions **1–8**, complete the second sentence so that it has a similar meaning to the first sentence, using the word given. **Do not change the word given.** You must use between **three** and **six** words, including the word given.

1 What are the chances of the film becoming a box-office success?
  LIKELY
  How .... will become a box-office success?

2 You could have organised your report in a more logical way.
  SET
  Your report could ....
  in a more logical way.

3 It's possible that some supporters got into the stadium without paying by climbing over a fence.
  GAINED
  Some supporters may ....
  to the stadium by climbing over a fence.

4 As Silin wasn't answering his emails, Roger assumed she was away.
  MUST
  Roger thought that ....
  she wasn't answering his emails.

5 Only fully-qualified teachers should apply for this post.
  WORTH
  It's .... unless you are a fully-qualified teacher.

6 Although it sounds unlikely, Peter has got a job as a celebrity's bodyguard.
  SEEM
  Strange ...., Peter has got a job as a celebrity's bodyguard.

7 Look at all this water – I can't have turned the tap off in the bathroom.
  LEFT
  Look at all this water – I ....
  the tap in the bathroom on.

8 There has been very little research into what constitutes luckiness.
  DEAL
  There has .... research into what constitutes luckiness.

Reading

Multiple-choice questions (Paper 1 Part 3)

▶ ER page 168

1 Read the title of the text and the subheading.
   1 What do you think is meant by the phrase *ethical employer*?
   2 Who do you think the article is aimed at?

2 Read the text quickly to check whether your predictions about the text and topic were correct. A number of organisations and people are mentioned in the text. As you read, make a note of why each of these is mentioned.

London University	Axiom Software
Rachel Hare	Tom Chance
Ethical Consumer Magazine	*People and Planet*
Lauren Steadman	Reading University
the Industrial Society	Helen Wallis

3 Read all the questions and highlight the key words in each one. The first two have been done for you. The questions follow the same order as the text, and there is one piece of text for each question.

4 a Read question 1. This relates to the first paragraph of the text.

   b Read this piece of text carefully, then look back at the question. It asks what the research has shown us about companies which claim to be socially responsible. The paragraph tells us that:
   1 we should not necessarily believe their claims
   2 employees expect companies to live up to their claims
   3 good graduates want to work for ethical companies.

   c Now look at the options. Which one is closest to one of these three things?

   d Now look at the other three options – look carefully at the text to see why they are wrong.

5 Follow the same procedure for question 2, which relates to the second paragraph of the text. Again, the key information has been highlighted for you.

6 Now continue to answer the rest of the questions. Always read the section of text carefully, to find your own answer to the question, then find the option which is closest in meaning to your own answer.

You are going to read a magazine article. For questions **1–6**, choose the answer (**A**, **B**, **C** or **D**) which you think fits best according to the text.

How to choose an ethical employer

Students and graduates shouldn't underestimate their power to bring about change by choosing an ethical employer.

According to some research findings published this week, we should be slightly sceptical when large companies say that they are committed to 'socially responsible behaviour'. Such companies could actually be chiefly interested in their public-
5 relations image. They make these claims as a way of attracting customers and shareholders who want to be involved in a business that is 'ethical'. The research does highlight one positive trend, however. It seems that companies which claim to be socially responsible are facing
10 increasing pressure from their employees to put these principles into practice. What's more, the researchers say there is even evidence to suggest that those companies which continue to have a negative impact on the environment and on the communities in which they work may fail to attract
15 the most able candidates in the job market. Could this be an incentive for them to change their ways, and an opportunity for young people to have some influence?

'I think most people who are concerned about society or development as a whole want to work for a company whose
20 policies are not hurting parts of society or stopping their development,' says Rachel Hare, a student at London University. Another survey, this time by graduate careers publisher Axiom Software, bears out these sentiments. It found that 79% of UK graduates would prefer not to work for
25 a company with a poor ethical record. What's more, over half of UK graduates said they would choose a job which fitted their ethical principles rather than one with a more lucrative salary or prospects – despite having student debts to pay off. But establishing which companies are truly socially
30 responsible, as opposed to those simply hiding behind their public-relations image, is no easy task.

Some companies involved in oil, tobacco and timber have been publicly criticised for their behaviour, but many apparently harmless companies maybe equally irresponsible.
35 It depends where they invest, where their raw materials come from and to whom they sub-contract work. Some companies have what's known as a Company Social Responsibility (CSR) policy; others go as far as to engage the services of highly qualified consultants to advise them on human rights
40 and environmental policies. 'It's a potential minefield for students,' says Lauren Steadman, co-editor of *Ethical Consumer Magazine*. 'We get lots of calls asking for help in assessing whether or not a company is ethical. There's a lot of 'greenwash' where companies have sophisticated PR and
45 produce reports without much substance to try to look good. Students need to be sceptical.'

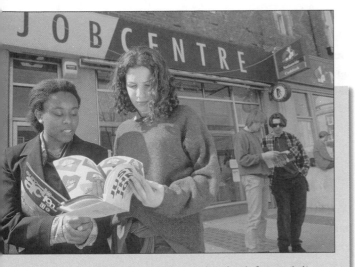

But to be sceptical, students need to be informed. It was in response to a growing demand for advice on such issues that the first ethical careers service in the
50 UK, *People and Planet*, was set up. Manager Helen Wallis tours universities giving workshops for students on how they can find a job that fits with their beliefs. Everyone has their own idea of what is ethical, and what one person will question, another will accept. For
55 example, Tom Chance from Reading University has his own boundaries: 'I wouldn't work for an oil company full stop. I don't think I'd ever be that desperate for a job. I wouldn't work with anything to do with logging, genetically modified food or child labour.' Other
60 students appreciate the chance to talk through the issues in order to arrive at their own particular priorities.

Once an individual has sorted out in their own mind what they consider to be acceptable working practices,
65 Helen helps them investigate whether the company they are interested in is living up to those standards. 'You can find out what social and environmental policies the organisation has by looking at its reports and mission statements,' she says. 'Then look at its
70 website or annual review for proof that those things have been achieved. You can also look for facts it's not going to be publicising by doing your own web search. Has there been anything in the media criticising their practices, or are there independent reports from
75 campaigning groups and charities?' says Helen. 'Finally, when candidates are asked at interview if they have any questions, they should take advantage of the opportunity, and not be fobbed off. Companies should be able to justify what they say they are doing.'

80 So, students and graduates shouldn't underestimate their power to bring about change; after all, most of them will spend more than 70,000 hours of their lives in the workplace. Research by the Industrial Society a couple of years ago claimed 65% of businesses would
85 change their policies if pushed by employees. To quote Helen Wallis: 'Choosing a socially and environmentally responsible career and persuading your employer to respect your values has enormous potential to benefit both the community and environment.'

1 What does recent research say about companies which claim to be socially responsible?
   A Their claims may not always be very sincere.
   B Their shareholders may not support their principles.
   C Their customers may not really believe their claims.
   D Their employees may not always be aware of their policies.

2 What did Axiom Software discover about graduates in the job market?
   A Most have unrealistic expectations of ethical employers.
   B Most see financial necessity dictating their choice of employer.
   C Most would avoid working for companies believed to be unethical.
   D Most do not know which companies claim to have ethical principles.

3 In the third paragraph, the writer is suggesting that some companies
   A may be less ethical than they appear.
   B have tended to be rather unfairly criticised.
   C have misused the services of experts in the field.
   D may not respond well to enquiries about their policies.

4 Through its workshops, the careers service *People and Planet* aims to
   A promote a general awareness of the idea of ethical employment.
   B help students to establish their own criteria for judging employers.
   C reach a standard definition of what represents an ethical employer.
   D discourage students from working in certain sectors of the economy.

5 Helen Wallis encourages individual students to
   A share any information they uncover about a company's activities.
   B find independent confirmation of information obtained from the media.
   C look for evidence that a company's ethical policies are actually effective.
   D make their views known to companies in advance of attending an interview.

6 In the article as a whole, the writer is
   A critical of employers who have no ethical policy.
   B sceptical about the findings of various research projects.
   C sympathetic towards companies failing to meet ethical targets.
   D supportive of students who wish to work for ethical employers.

Writing
Report (Paper 2 Part 1)
▶ CB pages 52–53, WR page 191

Exam strategy

Read all parts of the Part 1 task carefully. When writing a report, remember to include topic sentences, as these will help you to present your information clearly. Make sure you use linking words so that your points are clearly connected. Remember to use an impersonal style.

1 Look at the task on page 52 of the Coursebook again. Read the first part of a student's answer below.

2 The student has not used topic sentences. Choose the best topic sentence to begin each paragraph from this list.
   a) On the whole, the day was a great success.
   b) Some events were more successful than others.
   c) The purpose of this report is to describe the fundraising day held on June 16th.

3 Choose and add appropriate linking words and phrases from the list below where indicated by numbers 1–4 in the text. There is one word which you do not need.
   Apparently   *On the other hand*   *Finally*
   This was in spite of the fact that   *In addition*

4 Change the underlined sentences into the passive to make them less personal.

5 Write the 'Recommendations' and 'Conclusions' paragraphs, using the information given. Remember to include a topic sentence. Use linking words and the passive where appropriate.

Report

Introduction
It was an extremely enjoyable day. I will evaluate its success and make recommendations for future events.

Overview
Events organised included house-to-house collection and a jumble sale. <u>They raised more money than on the same day last year</u>, and more people attended. <u>About 50 people organised the event</u>, mostly students from the university.

Evaluation of events
It was clear that one event raised a lot more money than the others, and this was the house-to-house collection. This raised 40% of the overall total. This may be because <u>people felt obliged to give money when collectors approached them directly</u>. **(1)** The street collection was very successful financially, probably for the same reason. **(2)** <u>Everyone attending the jumble sale enjoyed it</u>, but it only raised 20% of the money. **(3)** The sale was very popular, being the only interactive event of the day. **(4)** The last 10% came from various activities including an appeal in the local newspaper.

Recommendations
Events with a personal touch were very successful, so suggest:
• provide greater range of interactive activities, e.g. ...
• give all officials a badge so that ...
• advertise the event well in advance so that ...

Conclusions
• very successful day
• with some careful thought and planning – could raise even more money next year

A Making choices

Use of English
Multiple-choice cloze (Paper 3 Part 1)

▶ CB page 58, ER page 169

1 Read the title of the text, then read the whole text quickly for general understanding, ignoring the gaps for the moment.
1 What is David Adjaye's profession?
2 Which building has made him well known internationally?
3 What job does Karen Wong do?

2 Read the text again carefully and try to predict what each answer will be. Then look at the options **A–D** and complete the task. Use the Help clues if necessary.

TIP

Remember that each of the items will be testing a slightly different area of language knowledge. So sometimes you are looking for collocations, sometimes for fixed phrases and sometimes for other grammatical relationships between words. Some items, however, simply test whether you know the correct word in the given context – so always think about the meaning of the text as a whole.

3 Read through the text again when you've finished and check that the options you've chosen fit in with the overall meaning of the text

HELP
➤ Question 2
Which of these words can be followed by the preposition *for*?
➤ Question 6
All of these words are used to describe something extra. Only one completes this fixed phrase, however. Which is it?
➤ Question 9
Only one of these words collocates with *great*. Which is it?

David Adjaye

For questions **1–12**, read the text below and decide which answer (**A**, **B**, **C** or **D**) best fits each gap. There is an example at the beginning (**0**).

A successful working relationship

For centuries, the typical architectural practice has had at its (**0**) ..A.. the skill and reputation of one extremely gifted individual. This creative genius has generally been supported by a (**1**)........ of talented juniors, (**2**)........ for bringing the master's designs to life. Normally it is impossible to (**3**)........ out one especially important underling, but in the office of one of London's fastest-rising architectural stars, David Adjaye, identifying that pivotal (**4**)........ is simple. It is Karen Wong, managing director of his ever-expanding business.

In his (**5**)........ thirties, David Adjaye, is one of the city's most fashionable architects, designing, amongst other things, the private homes of celebrities such as the actor Ewan McGregor. In (**6**)........ to this, Adjaye's impressive design for the building that will (**7**)........ the Nobel Peace Centre in Oslo is also (**8**)........ him a lot of international recognition.

Karen Wong is an arts graduate from Boston, Massachusetts, who possesses one of the sharpest minds and most efficient personalities working in architecture today. David is in great (**9**)........ , not only for his architectural skills, but also for public (**10**)........ and media interviews. Meanwhile, Karen is the backbone of the office, taking the (**11**)........ off David's shoulders by dealing with clients, contractors and others. Every creative genius needs a firm base to work from, and David is lucky to have Karen. She not only understands creativity, but is also (**12**)........ of realising a project. It's a combination that is quite rare in the artistic world these days.

0	**A** heart	**B** middle	**C** essence	**D** focus
1	**A** cast	**B** side	**C** team	**D** crew
2	**A** responsible	**B** agreeable	**C** liable	**D** dependable
3	**A** separate	**B** select	**C** stand	**D** single
4	**A** issue	**B** figure	**C** factor	**D** aspect
5	**A** last	**B** end	**C** late	**D** final
6	**A** addition	**B** supplement	**C** attachment	**D** extension
7	**A** home	**B** reside	**C** lodge	**D** house
8	**A** lending	**B** gaining	**C** bearing	**D** drawing
9	**A** demand	**B** claim	**C** request	**D** call
10	**A** invitations	**B** encounters	**C** audiences	**D** appearances
11	**A** bother	**B** load	**C** matter	**D** bulk
12	**A** capable	**B** practised	**C** skilful	**D** experienced

Language development

Word formation

▶ CB page 60

Spelling

1 Add *a* or *e* to complete these nouns. Use your dictionary to check your answers if necessary.
   1 differ__nce
   2 persist__nce
   3 confid__nce
   4 appear__nce
   5 perform__nce
   6 correspond__nce
   7 depend__nce
   8 assist__nce
   9 exist__nce
   10 prefer__nce

2 Add *a* or *i* to complete these adjectives.
   1 respons__ble
   2 believ__ble
   3 collaps__ble
   4 defens__ble
   5 adapt__ble
   6 suit__ble
   7 revers__ble
   8 break__ble
   9 flex__ble
   10 adjust__ble

Negative prefixes

3 Make these words negative and underline the odd word out in each case in terms of its negative prefix.
   1 safe   secure   predictable   well
   2 able   capable   formal   adequate
   3 responsible   relevant   realistic   rational
   4 patient   pleasant   probable   mature
   5 legal   logical   literate   lucky

Word families

4 Complete each sentence with the correct form of the word in capitals. Decide if you need to make the word negative or plural.

1 GENERAL
   a It's dangerous to .... from a limited number of examples.
   b It's impossible to make .... about what men and women are like.
   c I find my colleagues are .... very pleasant and helpful.
   d The discussion got no further than .... ; another meeting will be needed to decide on action.

2 INTEND
   a The plane had to divert from its .... destination due to bad weather.
   b He's full of good .... , but he never actually does anything.
   c He said his rudeness was .... and that he regretted it.
   d His speech was .... vague and lacking in concrete promises.

3 DEPEND
   a His friends knew that he was utterly reliable and ....
   b The company plans to split into two separate .... companies.
   c Western countries need to reduce their .... on oil.
   d This small state has been fighting for .... for nearly 20 years.

4 POWER
   a The new Mercedes has an even more .... engine.
   b He was .... to stop the children from drowning.
   c The course aims to .... young people by giving them confidence.
   d Her uncle was a tall man, and .... built.

5 ORIGIN
   a The old house still has a lot of its .... features.
   b No one knows the .... of this custom.
   c She is a young artist with a lot of talent and ....
   d I'm .... from Canada, but I've lived in London for 20 years now.
   e A lot of their ideas are rather dull and ....

6 PLEASE
   a It was a .... to meet you.
   b What a .... surprise! It's lovely to see you.
   c Shareholders who are .... with this decision should write to the chairman to complain.
   d His landscape paintings are .... to the eye, if not very exciting.
   e One way to make reading .... is to find books that your children will love to read.

7 VARY
   a The music is played on .... kinds of instruments.
   b The students on the course come from very .... backgrounds.
   c The quality of her work is rather ....
   d Several government ministers hold opinions which are at .... with the official government view.
   e We tried several different methods, with .... degrees of success.
   f They sell a very wide .... of cheeses.
   g He has been .... described as courageous and foolhardy.

Use of English

Word formation (Paper 3 Part 3)

▶ CB page 60, ER page 169

1 Read the title of the text to identify the topic. Then read the whole text quickly for general understanding, ignoring the gaps for the moment.
  1 Why have team-building courses become popular recently?
  2 According to the text, what are the benefits of sending employees on a team-building course?

2 Read the text again carefully and think about the type of word that could fit in each gap. Then complete the task by filling in the gaps. Remember to check if the word:
  • is singular or plural
  • has a positive or negative meaning.

3 Read through the text again when you've finished and check your answers.

For questions **1–10**, read the text below. Use the word given in capitals at the end of some of the lines to form a word that fits in the gap in the same line. There is an example at the beginning (**0**).

Working as a team

In many jobs the (**0**).....ability...... to work as a member of a team is of great | ABLE
importance. But when it comes to developing a good working relationship with
colleagues, life is not always a bed of roses. These days, most employers
(**1**).................... the fact that that disputes between staff are not only | KNOWLEDGE
(**2**).................... in the short term, but can have a negative effect on a | DISRUPT
company's long-term performance if not tackled (**3**).................... . | EFFECT

For this reason, team-building courses have become very (**4**).................... in | FASHION
recent years. Courses can be held in the workplace, but most companies find
that it is better if employees are sent on (**5**).................... courses lasting two or | RESIDE
three days. Away from the office environment, and faced with different tasks
and challenges, they often gain a better understanding of each other's
(**6**).................... and weaknesses. | STRONG

Some courses appeal to the more (**7**).................... side of people's character | ADVENTURE
and include activities such as skydiving, whilst others are more (**8**).................... , | CREATE
like art and musical workshops. These may allow people to demonstrate
(**9**).................... talents not always obvious from their normal duties. However, | HIDE
the organisers are keen to stress that such courses are only (**10**).................... | BENEFIT
to the employees if they are followed up by meaningful discussions afterwards.

Language development

When you have checked your answers to the task, add any new words to your vocabulary notebook and use your dictionary to help you complete a word family for each item. Remember to review these words regularly and try to use them in your writing and speaking.

Listening
Multiple matching (Paper 4 Part 4)
▶ ER pages 170–171

1 a Read the instructions for the task.
   1 How many speakers will you hear?
   2 What are they talking about?
   3 How many tasks do you have to do?
   4 How many times will you hear the texts?

   b Read Task One carefully. Think about the vocabulary and expressions you would expect to hear connected with people's lifestyles and note them down.

   c Read Task Two carefully and highlight key words in the options A–H. Think about the words and expressions you might use to express the feelings in this task and make a note of them.

2 a 🎧 Listen to the recording once. Try to answer as many questions from the two tasks as you can on one listening. Use the Help clues if necessary.

   b Listen again. This time try to answer the questions you couldn't do the first time. Use the Help clues if necessary.

TIP

There are different ways of approaching this task. Some people like to do the two tasks one by one (see page 21) and some people prefer to do both at the same time. Practise doing these tasks both ways and decide which is best for you.

HELP
➤ Question 1
The speaker says it 'happened overnight' and 'I'd hardly any savings'. Which option does this match best?
➤ Question 6
The speaker says: 'Looking back, I can't believe I ever had the nerve.'
Which option does this match?
➤ Question 5
The speaker uses the words 'retirement' and 'generous pension' – which of the options would best match somebody in this position?
➤ Question 10
The speaker talks about something 'really exciting' in her new life. Which of the options describes a similar feeling?

You will hear **five** short extracts in which people are talking about how they completely changed their lifestyle.

TASK ONE

For questions **1–5**, choose from the list **A–H** what made each speaker decide to change their lifestyle.

TASK TWO

For questions **6–10**, choose from the list **A–H** what each speaker says about their new lifestyle.

While you listen you must complete both tasks.

A a wish to develop a hobby

B encouragement from the children   Speaker 1 [1]

C a desire for independence   Speaker 2 [2]

D an unsatisfying career   Speaker 3 [3]

E respect for a partner's wishes   Speaker 4 [4]

F an unexpected loss of income   Speaker 5 [5]

G increased leisure time

H a need for a more settled routine

A I'm annoyed by some people's reactions

B I'm more aware of my limitations   Speaker 1 [6]

C I'm thrilled to find I have certain skills   Speaker 2 [7]

D I'm pleased with a new qualification   Speaker 3 [8]

E I'm surprised at my own courage   Speaker 4 [9]

F I'm grateful for the support of friends   Speaker 5 [10]

G I'm worried about my financial position

H I'm relaxed about possible difficulties

B Human nature

Vocabulary
Relationships
▶ CB page 64–65

1 Match the sentence halves and underline the correct particle in each phrasal verb.
1 I'm very lucky because I get *on / off* with
2 She fell *for / to*
3 In most respects, Danny takes *over / after*
4 My brother and I fell *off / out* over
5 We should all look up *on / to*
6 Laura relies *on / with*
7 In the past, he's been badly let *down / off,*

a Peter for his courage and determination.
b a girl we both liked.
c my in-laws very well.
d her mother to look after the two children.
e so he finds it hard to trust people.
f Harry the moment she saw him.
g his paternal grandfather.

2 Complete the sentences using an appropriate idiomatic expression from the list in the correct form.
*get your own way   hit it off   lose touch
run in the family   see eye to eye
the black sheep (of the family)*

1 Patrick is treated as the odd man out, the misfit, ...
2 A: Do you and your mother-in-law get on?
   B: Not really. We've never ....
   about anything.
3 It's not good parenting to spoil children and let them .... all the time.
4 A: So they're going out together?
   B: Yes, they met at my party and obviously .... immediately.
5 A: She's very attractive, just like her mother.
   B: Yes, good looks must ....
6 A: Do you see much of Ian these days?
   B: No, I'm afraid I .... with him.

3 Complete the text below with words and phrases from the list.
*acquaintances   associate   circle of friends
close family   colleagues   companion   confidant
ex   extended family   flatmate   friend of a friend
mate   partners   siblings*

For many couples, deciding when and where to get married is the easy part. The trouble starts when they have to decide who to invite to the wedding. Some like to keep it small and stick to just their (1)........................... such as parents and (2)... . However, for a bigger wedding how much further do you go into the (3)... ? Uncles, aunts, first or second cousins?

Most people will invite friends, and there is often a special role for their best friend or a special (4)... that they have turned to over the years – but how widely into your (5)... do you go? However large your wedding, you have to distinguish between those who are friends and those who are just (6)... . And do you have to invite the (7)... who you've never met but was the one that made the cake?

Many people have friends at work, but if you invite one or two, you could upset other (8)... who are not invited. And the numbers double if you include their (9)... – that's before you even start with the children.

The list goes on. What about the travelling (10)... you spent months with a few years ago or the (11)... you used to live with? You may have a close business (12)... who is important to you and who you see a lot of – but do you really want to mix business and pleasure?

Something that is generally agreed is that the one person you don't usually invite is your (13)... !

Language development
Noun clauses
▶ CB page 66, GR page 179

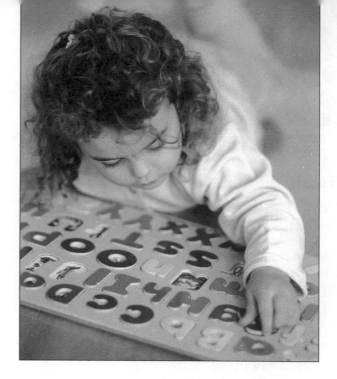

that-clauses

1 Rewrite each sentence using a *that*-clause, starting with the words given.

1 My brother passed his exam with flying colours, which came as no surprise to me.
It ....

2 How could you accuse me of such a thing? It horrifies me.
I'm ....

3 The deal is likely to be finalised tomorrow.
It ....

4 I'm delighted to be able to bring you this good news.
I'm ....

5 Funding for the project has been cut, which is ridiculous.
It ....

6 There is no proof of his involvement in the fraud.
There ....

7 I really regret not going to university when I was young.
I ....

8 Her guilt was obvious to the jury.
It ....

2 Read the following text then choose the best phrase from the list A–I to fill each of the spaces. The first is given as an example (0).

Clauses beginning with a question word

3 Complete the sentences with a suitable word from the list.

who   what   where   when   which   why   how

1 I can't decide .... to use the money I won.

2 I know he's off work at the moment, and I'm not sure .... he'll be back.

3 Scientists don't understand .... some people are more likely to suffer from the disease than others.

4 Can you remember .... you left your bag?

5 We haven't decided yet .... film we're going to see.

6 I think you should tell the police .... you know.

7 I know I've got to phone someone, but I've forgotten .... it is.

The genius in every child.

The idea **(0)** .D. is not new. It doesn't mean **(1)**......... or write music like Beethoven but that every child has the capacity for greatness. Babies are born with wonder, curiosity and a vast capacity for learning. Young children have vivid imaginations, creative minds and sensitive personalities. It is important **(2)**......... as the children grow and mature.

It is sad **(3)**......... by following a curriculum that is too rigid and restricted. Added to this is the problem **(4)**......... with its violence, mediocrity and poor role models.

The good news is **(5)**......... to help children develop their natural genius. To do this, adults have to set an example, so it is essential **(6)**......... . When children are surrounded by creative adults, they too will become more creative.

Secondly, adults need to provide simple toys and activities to stimulate a child. Einstein said **(7)**......... to awaken his love of learning. Then create an atmosphere that is free from criticism, comparison and pressure. Finally, understand **(8)**......... . Forget IQ tests and let kids succeed in their own ways.

A that schools restrict genius
B (that) a simple compass was all it took
C that educators (parents and teachers) help preserve these characteristics
D that every child is a genius
E that they find within themselves their own creativity and sense of wonder
F that the mass media suppresses creativity
G that every child can think like Einstein
H that each child will be a genius in a different way
I that there is much a teacher or parent can do

4 Complete the sentences with a suitable question word.

1 .... she said was very interesting.

2 .... these animals behave in the way they do is still a mystery.

3 .... I choose to spend my evenings with is my own business!

4 .... you treat your children when they are young will affect the way they develop into adults.

5 .... you know is more important than .... you know.

5 Underline one or both of the options in these sentences.

1 *If / Whether* I go to the party or not depends on what time I get back from work.

2 I'm in such a rush I don't know *if / whether* I'm coming or going.

3 The question is not *if / whether* he did it but **when** he did it.

4 We can't agree on *if / whether* to move house or not.

5 I'm not sure *if / whether* I want to go to France on holiday.

6 I've seen a great car. I have to decide today *if / whether* to buy it.

7 I can't make out *if / whether* she is trustworthy or not.

8 I'm going out *if / whether* you like it or not.

to-infinitive and -*ing* clauses

6 Complete the text by putting the verbs into the correct form.

(1)..................... (*grow up*) in a big family can be tough. The most difficult thing is **(2)**..................... (*keep*) your independence. Sometimes it's impossible **(3)**..................... (*assert*) yourself when you have so many brothers and sisters. But for me, **(4)**..................... (*criticise*) my family would be unfair. I am pleased **(5)**..................... (*say*) they have always been great. **(6)**..................... (*go*) away to university was a big thing for me. I was proud **(7)**..................... (*be*) independent, but also proud of **(8)**..................... (*have*) my supportive family behind me.

7 Rewrite these sentences using a *to*-infinitive clause, starting with the words given.

1 Discussing problems with a friend can be helpful.
It ....

2 He aims to become a top chef by the age of 30.
His aim ....

3 Tom wants us to meet Mary. He's really keen.
Tom's really keen ....

4 We have to cut costs. It's the only way the company can survive.
The only way ....

5 Human beings can solve problems. This is one of the definitions of intelligence.
The ability ....

6 The oldest child in a family tends to be the most ambitious.
The tendency is ....

7 Younger siblings want to establish their own identity. That is their main priority.
The main priority of ....
....

8 Therapists can help people recognise patterns of behaviour they need to change. That is the most valuable contribution they can make.
The most valuable contribution ....
....

8 Starting a sentence with a *to*-infinitive clause is more common in formal, written English. In everyday language, starting with introductory *It* or an -*ing* clause is preferred. Rewrite these sentences in two ways.

1 To meet the Dalai Lama would be a great honour.
a It ....
....
b Meeting ....
....

2 To spend time on your own is very important.
a It ....
....
b Spending ....
....

3 To find out his true identity would be very hard.
a It ....
....
b Finding ....
....

4 To say that the company is not interested in making money is ridiculous.
a It ....
....
b Saying ....
....

Use of English

Open cloze (Paper 3 Part 2)

▶ ER page 169

1 Read the title of the text, then read the whole text quickly for general understanding, ignoring the gaps for the moment.
  1 Why do the children in this school do special physical exercises?
  2 What effect have teachers noticed on the children's behaviour?

2 Read through the text again and think about the type of word which will fit in each gap. Look at the words before and after the gap and decide which word is missing. Use the Help clues if necessary.

3 Read through the whole text again when you've finished and check that the words you've chosen fit in with the overall meaning of the text.

HELP
➤ Question 1
  An auxiliary verb is needed here, but it's not a modal verb.
➤ Question 3
  In this question, a word is missing from a fixed phrase.
➤ Question 6
  Read the whole sentence carefully. Is a relative pronoun or a conjunction needed here?
➤ Question 12
  Which preposition completes the idea of *incorporate*?

Language development

Read the text again. Can you find one sentence that begins with an *-ing* clause, and one that begins with *It* and contains a *to*-infinitive clause?

For questions **1–15**, read the text below and think of the word that best fits each gap. Use only **one** word in each gap. There is an example at the beginning (**0**).

Give the brain a breather

If you didn't know what was going (**0**)......*on*......, you might think the children at Westfields Primary School were demonstrating a bizarre dance routine. They are swinging their arms above their heads – to the right and the left – and as they (**1**)................... so, they are also reciting the alphabet.

What they are actually doing (**2**)................... having what the school calls a 'brain break' – in (**3**)................... words, using a specially designed physical exercise to help them concentrate and learn. The exercises (**4**)................... supposed to help different parts of the brain to work in harmony, and many of them involve (**5**)................... are called 'cross-lateral' movements, (**6**)................... , it is thought, help the left and right sides of the brain to work together. An example of this is marching on the spot whilst at the (**7**)................... time touching your left knee with your right hand, (**8**)................... vice versa. Another exercise, known (**9**)................... 'Nose and Ears', involves putting your right forefinger on your nose, crossing over your left hand to touch your right earlobe, then swapping. It is actually quite difficult to make (**10**)................... that your arms always end up crossed over.

Westfields is (**11**)................... of a growing number of schools to incorporate such exercises (**12**)................... the school day. Doing the exercises helps the children settle down quickly after break time, and can help when concentration begins to flag, halfway (**13**)................... a lesson. In (**14**)................... to their beneficial effects, the exercises are also fun – so they (**15**)................... down extremely well with the children.

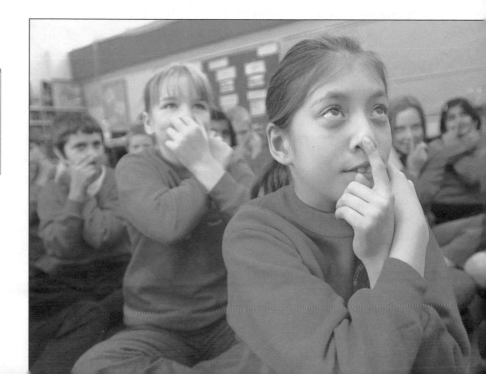

Writing

Competition entry (Paper 2 Part 2)

▶ CB pages 68–69, WR page 192

Exam strategy

A competition entry should engage its readers, so it is very important to keep their attention. Make your writing interesting by using colourful vocabulary and varying the type of sentence you use. Think of a good title if the entry is an article.

1 **Read the task below and answer these questions.**
   1 What type of text is the competition entry?
   2 What must you write about? Underline the part that tells you.
   3 What style will be appropriate?
      a) formal   b) informal   c) neutral

> **Want to become a writer? Enter the competition below!**
> An international magazine wants to run a series of articles on the importance of family, and has invited readers to submit articles about why they think the family is still the most influential part of a young person's life. The best entries will be published as part of the series.
> This is your chance to see your name in print!
> Write your **competition entry** in 220–260 words.

2 **Read a student's answer on the right. Which plan, A or B, has the student followed?**

A	B
• introduction establishing topic	• introduction establishing topic
• advantages and disadvantages of friends	• what young people need
• advantages and disadvantages of family	• reasons why only family can give support
• conclusion	• conclusion

3 **Substitute the words and phrases from the list below for the underlined parts of the answer to make it more interesting.**
   a vast array   incredible demands   blood is thicker than water
   through thick and thin   bombarded on all sides
   the going gets tough   play a part   bedrock

4 a **Look at the highlighted sentences at the end of the second paragraph. Look at the different ways of writing these sentences below, and match them to the sentence types a–d.**

1	I don't think this is what friends do.	a rhetorical question and exclamation
2	This is not what friends do!	b rhetorical question
3	Is this what friends do?	c statement
4	Is this what friends do? I don't think so!	d exclamation

It is often said that the role of the family is less important nowadays than in the past. I'm not convinced that this is actually the case. **(1)** <u>Relatives are closer than friends.</u>

It's perfectly true that young people today have **(2)** <u>a lot of pressures</u> put on them – they are expected to do well at school, to get good jobs, to look good, to keep up with the latest fashion – they are **(3)** <u>hit everywhere</u> by **(4)** <u>lots</u> of stresses. What they need is someone to talk things through with – someone they can trust to give independent yet caring advice, who won't make them feel small or imply that they are getting it wrong. Is this what friends do? I don't think so! It's the family.

It is the family, too, who rally round when **(5)** <u>things become difficult</u>, not friends – friends have their own problems. No one understands a young person better than the family who brought them up. Where do young people get their role models from? Is it the exotic media stars admired by so many? Of course, these stars do **(6)** <u>contribute something</u>, but ultimately they are removed from real life and probably have problems of their own! No, it's the family, the people who can be relied on to be there **(7)** <u>always</u>.

In the past, the family was the **(8)** <u>basis</u> of society, and in spite of rising divorce rates, this remains the case today. There certainly is 'no place like home', and no one is a better friend than a parent!

---

b **Which of the sentence types in Exercise 4a**
   1 states an opinion?
   2 states an opinion strongly?
   3 involves the reader?
   4 involves the reader and states an opinion strongly?

c **Find two more exclamations and two more rhetorical questions in the student's answer.**

5 **Choose the best title for the article.**
   a) Blood is thicker than water
   b) A family united
   c) The pressures of being young today

6 **Plan and write your own answer to the task.**

Reading
Multiple matching (Paper 1 Part 4)

▶ ER pages 168

1 Read the title and the subtitle of the text. Answer these questions before you read on.
   1 What do the people in the text have in common?
   2 What does *high-flying* mean?
   3 What is *sibling rivalry*?

2 Read the text quickly to find out:
   1 in which field each pair of twins is a high-flier
   2 how the twins feel about each other.

3 a Read the instructions for the exam task, then read all the questions and highlight the key words. The first four have been done for you.

   b Read section A (about Bryony and Kathryn Frost) carefully and mark any sections of text that contain similar ideas or information to the questions 1–16. For example:
   1 Look at question 2. Find the sentence in section A of the text that seems to have the same meaning. Mark the parts that match *a family member has suffered as a result of their relationship*. Find the phrasal verb that means *someone felt excluded*.

2 Look at question 3. Find the phrases in section A of the text that are similar to *fall out over unimportant matters*.

You have now found two questions which match option A. There are two more. Can you find them?

c Now read section B (about Neil and Adrian Rayment) carefully. Look at question 11 and find the phrases in the text that match *people assume them to be identical in every respect* and *resents the fact that*. When you scan the whole text, there are several places where the attitude of people to identical twins is mentioned, but only one pair of twins resents the attitude.

4 Now continue to find the rest of the questions in the text.

You are going to read an article about twins. For questions **1–15**, choose from the sets of twins (**A–D**). The sets of twins may be chosen more than once.

Which pair of twins

recognises that their natural similarities are a bonus professionally?	1 ....
feels that a family member has suffered as a result of their relationship?	2 ....
only tends to fall out over unimportant matters?	3 ....
recognises that they might each be more cautious on their own?	4 ....
feels that some people have taken unfair advantage of their relationship?	5 ....
has recently realised a long-held career ambition?	6 ....
experienced contrasting reactions to being parted from each other?	7 ....
is convinced that their working partnership will be temporary?	8 ....
recognises that their professional talent is inherited?	9 ....
has a laid-back attitude to their professional rivalry?	10 ....
resents the fact that people assume them to be identical in every respect?	11 ....
enjoys a stronger bond than may at first be apparent to others?	12 ....
realises they may be influenced by false impressions of their personalities?	13 ....
feels their relationship enables them to avoid serious professional disagreements?	14 ....
admits to being apprehensive at the prospect of a life apart?	15 ....

MIRROR IMAGES

What is it about the relationship between twins that can produce such a creative bond? We asked four pairs of high-flying twins to tell us about how they cope with a situation that must be the ultimate in sibling rivalry.

A Bryony and Kathryn Frost: Athletes

The Frost twins are professional athletes – middle-distance runners, who have been racing for as long as they can remember. The 18-year-olds have eyes the colour of swimming pools and long, white-blonde hair. Kathryn wears hers up, otherwise it would be impossible to tell them apart. They train, compete and live together in a house with their parents and brother, Richard (21) who's in computers. The longest they have spent apart was when Kathryn went to Italy for a week. Although they compete in the same races, they don't seem to be competitive. 'We have a love-hate relationship,' says Kathryn, 'Bryony and I spend a lot of time together. She's not really my friend, more a part of me. Sometimes she's faster than me, then suddenly, I'm better than her. It's not something we get worked up about.' Bryony agrees: 'At the moment, she'd beat me, but so what?'

Bryony tells me they have quite a close relationship with their brother. 'He did feel left out because there was Mum and Dad, me and Kathryn. I feel sorry for him.'

'I love him, but I'll never know him like I know Kathryn,' adds Bryony. Asked what they do row about, Kathryn says it's invariably over petty things, such as who gets in the shower first, 'We haven't developed separately, so we've got the same strengths and weaknesses, but our mood swings can be identical, too! We have to learn to give each other some space.' The Frost twins will inevitably have to face up to building separate lives, but neither relishes the prospect. 'I'd be more likely to make an effort on my own,' admits Kathryn, 'but it's scary.'

B Neil and Adrian Rayment: Actors

When the Rayment twins are asked who's the better actor of the two, Neil laughs. 'Don't wind us up! We don't even like to think about it.' But it's a reasonable question, considering they appear as identical bad guys in their latest sci-fi film. What's more, they are soon to be seen as the leads in *Team One*, an all-action martial-arts feature. These two films represent the Rayment twins' big break. Although the pair previously ran their own separate businesses, they have been avid film fanatics for years; ready to grab any acting part that turned up since the age of 19.

As their twin careers seem to be taking off big time, how will they develop – together or apart? Adrian says that he doesn't see them following the same path. 'We're both trying to tie down this new craft, acting. I'm sure we'll head in different directions because we have different styles, but maybe not for a while.' As Neil explains: 'Our lifestyles and goals are the same, but we have different outlooks. Adrian's a bit more calculated, he thinks before he steps in, whereas I'm impulsive.'

Indeed they don't always see eye to eye, but despite the occasional heated discussion (usually about acting techniques), they enjoy working together. 'It's being with someone you know inside out,' says Neil. 'There's this unexplained synchronicity on screen which looks really cool and the producers appreciate it. When we move together, the timing's already there, both physically and mentally.'

'We've been pushed together since we were born, forced to accept people's indifference to our distinct personalities,' says Adrian. 'We tolerate it. But after 24 hours with us, someone we've just met is able to tell us apart.'

C Louise and Jane Wilson: Artists

The first time Louise and Jane were apart for any length of time was when they were studying at different universities. The former found the separation 'a bit traumatic'; the latter viewed it as 'a terrific challenge'. Although in different cities, they found themselves working on similar ideas and experimenting with photography. They ended up producing all but identical photographic displays on completion of their courses. 'We produced two of everything,' says Jane, who has dark hair and wears black, unlike her sister who favours lighter colours. They are not identical; in fact, you might not even think they were sisters. 'The colleges had to confer to make sure we got the same marks,' says Louise. They haven't stopped working together since. 'We did paintings together in our first year in business,' says Jane. 'They were fakes, poor copies. Then in the second year, we returned to photography.'

So it was that they began to photograph 'different environments and spaces'. They now live in separate areas of London, but come together most days in their studio. Asked if they argue like all good business partners, they say they do, but have never had any irreconcilable differences. 'Obviously, working with Jane there's an enormous element of trust within a familial bond, so there's no need to define who's responsible for what,' says Louise. Jane agrees: 'A lot of producing art is collaborative, but it's only now becoming more acceptable to art galleries.

Until recently, they wanted to give us just one fee for our exhibitions!'

'That's taking sisterly love a bit far!' laughs Louise.

D Anita and Carole Pitman: Musicians

The Pitman twins – Anita on piano, Carole on violin – are a renowned classical musical duo. They have a brother, 16 months their senior, a mechanical engineer. 'We miss him because he's living in France,' says Carole. 'But we still feel close. As kids, being similar in age and all looking alike, people used to take us for triplets. But he's quite different to us now – we take after our mother, who's very musical. Although we always had a three-way dynamic – it wasn't always us against him.'

The twins had a five-year period when Anita was at university and Carole worked in a bank, which they now feel was advantageous to them both intellectually and socially. When it was over, they were ready to come back together. They made music together as a hobby, until their talent was discovered and they were unexpectedly offered a recording contract. Now they have the best of both worlds, recognising they need each other, but quite able to stand on their own two feet.

'I'm not worried that we can only ever work as twins,' Carole says. 'But at the moment it's something we can capitalise on, and that's great. We're not yet in a situation to be choosy!'

'We feel we take more risks precisely because there's two of us. We spur each other on,' Anita says candidly. 'Deep down, we're very similar, but people often label Carole as more confident, and me as less so, and there's a danger of living up to that label after a while.'

A In the slow lane

Use of English

Word formation
(Paper 3 Part 3)

▶ CB page 74, ER page 169

1   Read the title of the text to identify the topic. Then read it through quickly for general understanding, ignoring the gaps for the moment.

2   Read the text again carefully and try to decide what type of word will fit in each gap. Then fill in the gaps, using the Help clues if necessary. Remember to check if the word:
    • is singular or plural
    • requires a suffix or prefix
    • has a positive or negative meaning.

3   Read through the text again when you've finished and check that the words you've written fit in with the overall meaning of the text and are spelled correctly.

HELP

➤ **Question 1**
You are looking for an adverb that means 'without doubt'. You need to add both a prefix and a suffix to the base word.

➤ **Question 8**
How do you form the adjective from this noun?

➤ **Question 9**
You need to make an adverb from this adjective.

➤ **Questions 10**
Notice that the word collocates with 'source of' to form a common expression.

For questions **1–10**, read the text below. Use the word given in capitals at the end of some of the lines to form a word that fits in the gap in the same line. There is an example at the beginning **(0)**.

BOOK REVIEW

The pleasures of slow food

The **(0)** _growth_ of what has become known as fast-food culture, with its standardised restaurants and meals in identical takeaway boxes, shows no sign of slowing down. Indeed, ready-meals that can be popped into the microwave are	GROW
(1)............................ convenient and the market for such food continues to expand. At the same time, another trend is developing, perhaps in	DENIABLE
(2)............................ to the fast food itself, and this involves a rediscovery of the joys of traditional food	RESPOND
and methods of **(3)**............................ . This book is at the centre of that rediscovery.	PREPARE
The Pleasures of Slow Food is a **(4)**............................ of heritage recipes, artisan skills and the	CELEBRATE
(5)............................ of a philosophy which aims to make good food a part everyday life. 'Slow Food' is the name of a 65,000-strong international	EMERGE
(6)............................ which numbers amongst its	MOVE
members some of the most **(7)**............................ names in the world of food.	INFLUENCE
The book showcases over sixty recipes from the world's most **(8)**............................ chefs. In these	PRESTIGE
dishes, local handmade ingredients feature **(9)**............................ alongside traditional cooking	PROMINENT
methods. There are also profiles of some of Slow Food's leading exponents, such as Italian cheese-maker Roberto Rubino. This engaging collection of fantastic recipes and personal stories makes for an enjoyable read. It will also be a source of	
(10)............................ for anyone wishing to bring the best of the world's food to their table.	INSPIRE

Language development

When you have checked your answers to the task, add any new words to your vocabulary notebook and use your dictionary to help you complete a word family for each item. Remember to review these words regularly and try to use them in your writing and speaking.

Language development
Modifying gradable and ungradable adjectives
▶ CB page 77, GR page 180

Gradable and ungradable adjectives

1 a Complete the table below with pairs of adjectives from the list which are related in meaning.

amazed angry bad delighted disastrous fascinating huge hungry identical interesting irate large minute pleased priceless rare ravenous similar small surprised unique valuable

	Gradable (+ *very*)	Ungradable (+ *absolutely*)
0	surprised	amazed
1		
2		
3		
4		
5		
6		
7		
8		
9		
10		

b Complete these sentences with an appropriate adverb from the list. Then write '+' if it makes the adjective stronger, and '−' if it makes it weaker. Use each word once only. In some sentences, more than one adverb is possible.

slightly quite fairly utterly completely absolutely a bit rather

1 I was .... surprised to see my name on the shortlist of candidates.
2 A .... large crowd had turned out to welcome the team home.
3 The wildlife of this region is .... unique – these creatures are found nowhere else.
4 If the project lost its funding now, it would be .... disastrous for all the people involved.
5 The two pictures are .... identical.
6 She looked puzzled and .... angry.
7 I was .... amazed to discover that he had served in the army.
8 Shall we have some lunch? I'm starting to feel .... hungry.

2 Use the following adverbs to change the register of the sentences below as indicated in brackets.

a bit dead somewhat incredibly rather most

1 The article on climate change was ~~very~~ .... informative. (*formal*)
2 I thought the lecture on greenhouse gases would be ~~very~~ .... boring, but it turned out to be quite interesting. (*informal*)
3 The results of the initial tests were ~~slightly~~ .... surprising. (*formal*)
4 I'm ~~slightly~~ .... worried about what's in this food. (*informal*)
5 I found the first exam ~~very~~ .... difficult. (*informal*)
6 You look ~~slightly~~ .... confused. Can I help you? (*polite*)

3 a One of the adjectives on the right does not collocate with the adverb on the left. Cross it out.
1 **bitterly** cold / disappointed / opposed / sensitive
2 **deeply** ashamed / critical / hurt (emotionally) / moving
3 **heavily** dependent / armed / criticised / useless
4 **highly** controversial / respected / unacceptable / valued
5 **painfully** slow / aware / useless / shy
6 **perfectly** educated / satisfactory / genuine / understandable
7 **totally** disturbed / harmless / incompetent / unacceptable
8 **utterly** alone / appalled / healthy / miserable

b Write down which of the adverbs in Exercise 3a could be used with the words you crossed out.
1 *highly sensitive*
2 ....
3 ....
4 ....
5 ....
6 ....
7 ....
8 ....

c Complete the sentences with an appropriate adverb/adjective collocation from Exercise 3a or b. Use each collocation once only.
1 The convoy was attacked by a small group of .... soldiers.
2 Your concerns are .... However, there is little that the company can do.
3 The independent report was .... of the government's policy towards road building.
4 All Western economies are .... on oil.

5 I should take a warm coat with you as there's a .... wind blowing today.

6 The deliberate polluting of the sea is .... and ship owners will be prosecuted in all cases.

7 The government is .... of the need to change policies, but is concerned about the cost.

8 It is a beautiful and .... film.

9 The author of the report is a .... university lecturer and leader in his field.

10 People were confident that the minister would make great changes, but he turned out to be ....

Confusing adjectives/adverbs

- Some adverbs have the same form as adjectives e.g. *He works **hard*** (adv.). *He's a **hard*** (adj.) *worker*.
- Some adverbs have two forms, with different meanings, e.g. *I had to stay **late** at the office.* (after the usual time) *What have you been doing **lately**?* (recently)

4 **Underline the correct word in the contexts below. In some cases, both are possible.**

1 Remember to hold on *tight / tightly* when we go round the corners.

2 You shouldn't have been driving so fast; it serves you *right / rightly*.

3 The group's supporters are *most / mostly* students.

4 He is so unreliable you can guarantee he'll arrive *late / lately*.

5 When he heard the news, he didn't say much but I could tell he took it *hard / hardly*.

6 They worked for three days, *hard / hardly* stopping to eat or rest.

7 As I left the house, it was raining *hard / hardly*.

8 Do you like these shoes? I got them *cheap / cheaply* in the market.

9 Be careful; there are lots of snakes in the forest, some of them are *dead / deadly*.

10 He was *dead / deadly* tired that night and that's probably what led to the crash.

11 Open the window as *wide / widely* as you can so we can get rid of the smell in here.

12 Organic food is now much more *wide / widely* produced than it was a few years ago.

13 The cost of public transport puts people off. They should be able to travel *free / freely* within the city.

14 The information is *free / freely* available in the public library.

Use of English
Gapped sentences (Paper 3 Part 4)
▶ ER page 170

1 **Look at the example in the gapped-sentence task on page 53 and read the task rubric.**

1 How many sentences are there?

2 How many words are missing?

3 What do the missing words have in common?

2 a Read all three sentences in the example carefully. What type of word is missing from all three (noun, verb, adjective, etc.)?

b Make a list of words that will fit in the gap in the first sentence. Think about both the grammar and the context. Which of these words would you include in your list?

| *sure good firm close best loyal near old* |

c How many of the words on your list also fit the gap in the second sentence? Think about both the grammar and the context. Cross any words off your list which don't fit here.

d Look at the third sentence. Will one of the words left on your list fit here?

e Write your answer in all three gaps. Read the sentences again to check that it fits well in all three.

3 **Now look at Questions 1–5 and repeat the procedure, using the HELP clues if necessary.**

TIP

Look carefully at the words before and after the gap. Does your answer fit with all articles, prepositions and verb forms that surround the gap?

HELP
➤ **Question 1**
In all three sentences the infinitive form of a verb is needed. All of these verbs fit in the first gap: *lay, set, prepare.* Which of them fits in the other sentences? Be careful, in each sentence the word has a slightly different meaning.

➤ **Question 2**
An adjective is needed in each of these sentences. It means 'very uncommon'.

➤ **Question 3**
An adverb is needed in each of these sentences. These adverbs fit in the first sentence: *extensively, widely.* Which of them can also be used in the other two sentences?

For questions **1–5**, think of **one** word only which can be used appropriately in all three sentences. Here is an example **(0)**.

0   Even though they don't work together any more, Michelle and Peter are still very .... friends.

The scientists are .... to reaching a breakthrough in their research programme.

Don't get too .... to Anthea, she's got a really bad cold.

1   Paula's job each day was to .... the table before each meal.

The dog ran across the new path before the concrete had had the chance to .... properly.

If you want people to respect local traditions, you have to .... an example.

2   This bird is so .... that it appears on the endangered list in many countries.

Sadly, restaurants that source only local products are all too .... these days.

Pam took advantage of a .... opportunity to meet the elusive leader of the political movement.

3   Students on that course are expected to read really ...., even beyond the immediate subject matter.

Supporters of slow food aim to promote the idea as .... as possible.

It is .... believed that tourism has a positive effect on small island communities.

4   Eating good food should be a natural .... of everyday life.

Sally was delighted to be offered a .... in a new television drama.

William was keen to acknowledge the .... played by his parents in establishing his successful business.

5   The idea that we shouldn't be eating food that has been flown half-way across the world has really .... off in recent years.

Although he's not a professional musician, Clive has always .... his singing very seriously.

An international charity has .... over the running of the second-hand shop in the village.

Listening
Multiple-choice questions (Paper 4 Part 3)
▶ ER pages 170–171

1 Read the instructions for the exam task. Then read the multiple-choice questions and highlight the most important ideas in the questions and options. This has been done for you in questions 1 and 2.

2 🎧 Listen to the whole recording once, and try to answer the questions. Use the Help clues if necessary.

3 Listen again to check and complete your answers.

TIP

Listen to the interviewer's questions – they'll help you to keep your place – but the answers will come from the main speaker.

HELP
➤ Question 1
Christopher's answer comes after he mentions the 'business potential' of walking tours. There is a gap in the market, but who will go on the tours?
➤ Question 2
There are two parts to each of the options – how Christopher feels, and what he has those feelings about. Listen to his whole answer to this question before choosing the correct option.
➤ Question 3
Listen to the whole of Christopher's answer to the interviewer's question. What point is he making about the people both at the beginning and the end of his answer?

You will hear an interview with a man called Christopher Winney, whose holiday company organises environmentally friendly walking tours. For questions **1–6**, choose the answer (**A**, **B**, **C**, or **D**) which fits best according to what you hear.

1 Christopher explains that he started the ATG Oxford holiday company because
   A he had little hope of getting further work as a writer.
   B he saw a gap in the market for holidays aimed at older people.
   C he believed organised walking holidays would have a wide appeal.
   D he had always wanted to set up an environmentally friendly company.

2 When discussing the company's finances, Christopher says he is
   A worried that his holidays may be overpriced.
   B determined to spend the company's profits wisely.
   C fortunate in being free of personal money worries.
   D restricted by his agreement with charity organisations.

3 What does Christopher say about the sort of people who go on ATG holidays?
   A They tend to expect a high standard of service.
   B They need to build up their level of fitness.
   C They have to have a good sense of humour.
   D They often have similar views about things.

4 When asked about the decision to stop advertising the company's holidays, Christopher says he is
   A worried that the level of business may still decrease as a result.
   B convinced that the previous style of advertising was ineffective.
   C pleased that clients have generally responded well to his motives.
   D concerned that the environmental message may have been weakened.

5 In Christopher's opinion, responsible tourism is best achieved through
   A the support given to carefully selected staff.
   B the monitoring of activities offered to clients.
   C the insistence on using only organic produce.
   D the simple nature of the accommodation provided.

6 How does Christopher feel about the current state of environmentally friendly tourism?
   A concerned at the attitude of some sections of the media
   B alarmed at the prospect of larger companies moving in
   C unsure what can be done to win more tourists over
   D satisfied to see the growing acceptance of the idea

B A fight for survival

Vocabulary
The environment
▶ CB pages 80–81

1 Match these words to their definitions.

1 sustainable
2 biodiversity
3 renewable energy
4 hydroelectric
5 environmentally friendly
6 tidal
7 biosphere
8 solar

a a form of energy that replaces itself naturally, or is easily replaced because there is a large supply of it
b the part of the world in which animals, plants, etc. can live
c the variety of plants and animals in a particular place
d able to continue without causing damage to the environment
e relating to the sun
f using water power to produce energy
g relating to the regular rising and falling of the sea level on the shore
h used about products and methods that do not damage the environment

2 Complete the text with expressions from Exercise 1.

A **(1)**.. is any naturally occurring energy source that we can tap into without depleting the world's finite resources, without contributing to the greenhouse effect, and often without causing any pollution. Renewable energies are therefore **(2)**.. , and the effect they have on the **(3)**.. is considerably less than with fossil fuels.
    Some forms of renewable energy, such as **(4)**.. power in countries with high rainfall, are already well established. **(5)**.. power is cost efficient in dry, sunny countries, as is wind power in exposed places. **(6)**.. energy has not yet been effectively harnessed, as it requires huge off-shore construction. All these energy forms are **(7)**.. , as they have low emissions and result in very little damage to a region's **(8)**.. .

3 Read the text below and complete it with words from the list. Change the form where necessary.

consume   contribute   destroy   exhaust   fuels   increase inefficiency   means   renewable   rise   tackle

Transport fuels

In the last 50 years, the number of cars on British roads has **(1)**.................. from two million to over 20 million, and this figure continues to **(2)**.................. . Even after a century of engineering, the conventional car is incredibly **(3)**.................. . Almost 80% of the fuel energy a normal car **(4)**.................. is lost as engine heat and **(5)**.................. fumes, so that only 20% is actually used to move the car.
Cars and lorries cause noise, pollution, harm to health, and the **(6)**.................. of habitats. They also **(7)**.................. to global warming.

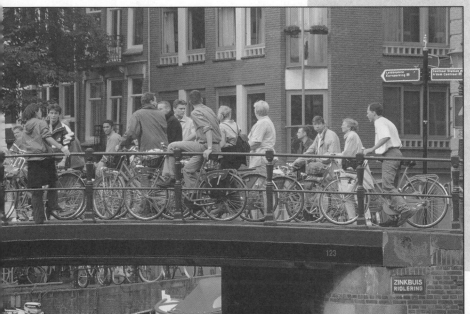

These problems can really only be **(8)**.................. in two ways. Firstly, by using cars and lorries less and looking at alternative **(9)**.................. of transport such as trains, buses, trams, bicycles and of course our feet! Secondly, by moving towards alternative **(10)**.................. . Amongst possible solutions are biodiesel, made from plant or animal oils, as well as using electricity from **(11)**.................. sources to power electric motors.

Language development
Conditionals
▶ CB page 83, GR page 180

Review of conditionals

1 **Put the verbs into the most suitable tense.**
1 Imagine you .... (*walk*) in the mountains and there .... (*be*) suddenly a thunderstorm – .... (*you know*) what to do and how to avoid being struck by lightning?
2 As long as you .... (*can see*) lightning and hear thunder, you .... (*be*) at risk.
3 Lightning strikes are rare, but you .... (*have*) a much better chance of survival if you .... (*crouch*) down.
4 The last person to be killed by lightning was standing under a tree. It's possible that if he .... (*not stand*) under the tree, he .... (*survive*).
5 Another recent victim probably .... (*not injure*) if he .... (*not carry*) an umbrella.

Mixed conditionals

2 **Rewrite the sentences using a mixed conditional.**
0 I'm lost and I can't find my way home.
If I <u>wasn't lost, I would be able to find</u> my way home
1 I didn't light a fire because I don't know how to.
If I .... one.
2 I understand how the economy works because I studied economics at university.
If ....
the economy works.
3 We don't know where to look for her because she didn't tell us where she was going.
If she .... look for her.
4 We're in danger now because we didn't take sensible safety precautions.
If we .... in danger now.
5 I was bitten by a snake because I work in a zoo.
If .... by a snake.
6 I can't show you my essay because I handed it in this morning.
If .... show it to you.
7 It didn't snow last night, so it's not freezing on the mountain today.
If it ....
freezing on the mountain today.
8 I don't think he's got his phone with him because he hasn't called me to say he was going to be late.
If he .... going to be late.

Alternatives to *if*

3 **Underline the correct alternative.**
1 Please do not hesitate to contact me .... you require further information.
A should   B whether   C as long as   D providing
2 .... we got there earlier, we would have got tickets.
A Provided   B Had   C Imagine   D Should
3 I don't mind babysitting, ... the children are in bed and asleep.
A unless   B but for   C providing   D otherwise
4 I'm going to this conference .... the company pays for me or not.
A whether   B unless   C as long as
D provided that
5 .... you hold a snake by its head, it can't bite you.
A Unless   B As long as   C Were   D Supposing
6 I'm sure the woman would have died .... the help of a man who was passing and knew what to do.
A but for   B whether   C providing   D otherwise
7 .... the electricity supply to fail, the machines would automatically switch off.
A Should   B Provided   C As long as   D Were

4 **Decide which of the following sentences are correct, and correct those that aren't.**
1 If you want to avoid pesticides, you would eat organic food.
2 If the company didn't dump chemical waste in the river, the fish won't have been killed off.
3 Unless we don't stop burning oil, we'll destroy the ozone layer.
4 If you won't help us, I'll find someone who will!
5 If the government will change the law, companies would have to stop dumping waste.
6 If it will make you happy, I'll recycle all these magazines.
7 I'd be grateful if you will investigate the issue of water quality soon.

Use of English
Multiple-choice cloze (Paper 3 Part 1)
▶ ER page 169

1 a Read the title of the text and think about what it is going to be about. Do you use an umbrella? Why (not)? In your opinion, are umbrellas useful things?

   b Read the text quickly for general understanding, ignoring the gaps for the moment. What is the writer's main point?
   1 not everybody likes using umbrellas
   2 umbrellas are not always very practical
   3 new technology will soon make umbrellas redundant

2 a Read the text again and think about the type of word which will fit in each gap. Try to predict what the answer will be.

   b Look at the options A–D and choose the one which best fits in each gap. Use the help clues if necessary.

3 Read the text again when you've finished and check that the options you've chosen fit in with the overall meaning of the text.

HELP
➤ Question 6
Which of the options means *disadvantage*?
➤ Question 7
Which word completes a three-word phrase that means *more than*?
➤ Questions 11
Which of the words is used to add something with emphasis?
➤ Questions 12
Which of the prepositions completes the phrasal verb meaning *to invent*?.

For questions **1–12**, read the text below and decide which answer (**A**, **B**, **C** or **D**) best fits each gap. There is an example at the beginning (**0**).

Useless things, umbrellas

If there's one thing I dislike about living in London, it's when weather forecasters, after predicting showers, (**0**)..A.. with a smile: 'So don't forget your umbrellas.' But they haven't said anything of the (**1**)......... this week for the very good reason that it's been both wet and windy, and umbrellas are useless in a (**2**)......... wind. Today, you can see people all over the city who look as if they are being pulled along by their umbrellas. You see them twisting and (**3**)......... as if struggling to control some large ill-behaved bird. Then suddenly, the umbrella blows inside out, after which it is (**4**)......... useless, either because the material is torn or because the metal (**5**)......... is broken.

Another (**6**)......... of umbrellas is that no object is so frequently left in public places. In (**7**)......... of twelve thousand a year are abandoned on the London Underground alone, according to a radio report broadcast this week. 'You used to get a lot of very nice golfing umbrellas,' an employee told the reporter. 'But now they tend (**8**)......... to be dumpy, folding ones.' One of these is, of course, more (**9**)......... , because it will fit into your bag or briefcase, thereby (**10**)........ its chances of being left somewhere. But unfortunately, a folding umbrella performs no better in the wind, (**11**)......... may even be less robust. I can't help but think that if we can invent ingenious things like the mobile phone and the MP3 player, then someone should have (**12**)......... up with a gadget to replace the umbrella by now.

0	**A** add	**B** remind	**C** claim	**D** warn
1	**A** genre	**B** type	**C** sort	**D** category
2	**A** large	**B** tough	**C** heavy	**D** high
3	**A** winding	**B** trailing	**C** turning	**D** curling
4	**A** rendered	**B** remained	**C** resulted	**D** regarded
5	**A** frame	**B** net	**C** grid	**D** stand
6	**A** outcome	**B** upshot	**C** drawback	**D** letdown
7	**A** quantity	**B** advance	**C** excess	**D** amount
8	**A** widely	**B** mostly	**C** greatly	**D** hugely
9	**A** amenable	**B** comfortable	**C** convenient	**D** accommodating
10	**A** removing	**B** receding	**C** reducing	**D** replacing
11	**A** indeed	**B** whereas	**C** instead	**D** however
12	**A** earn	**B** come	**C** get	**D** gain

Language development

Can you find an example of a mixed conditional in the text?

Reading

Multiple-choice questions (Paper 1 Part 3)

► ER pages 168

1 Read the title of the text and the subheading.

1 What is meant by the phrase *throwaway society*?

2 What attitude do you think the artist will have towards the *throwaway society*?

3 What type of art do you think the artist will be working in?

   a) portraits   b) abstract sculpture

   c) modern art installations

2 Read the text quickly to check whether your predictions about the artist were correct.

3 Read all the questions and highlight the key words in each question. The first two have been done for you. The questions follow the same order as the text, and there is one piece of text for each question.

4 a Read question 1. How do you know how to locate the relevant piece of text?

   b Read this piece of text carefully. Look back at the question and think of your own answer. Now read the options – which one is closest to your own answer?

   c Read the paragraph again carefully to check that your answer is right and that the other options are definitely wrong.

5 Now continue to answer the rest of the questions. Always read the section of text carefully, to find your own answer to the question, then find the option which is closest in meaning to your own answer.

You are going to read a magazine article about an artist. For questions **1–7**, choose the answer (**A**, **B**, **C** or **D**) which you think fits best according to the text.

GARBAGE GURU

We live in an increasingly throwaway society. I meet an artist who's making a material difference.

Steve Bradley freely admits his work is garbage. 'It's true,' he says. 'My work is rubbish.' As an environmental artist, Steve's spent most of his working life picking up the things that other people have thrown
5 away, and devising new ways to use art and humour to get us thinking about the environment. His work has been concerned with what our attitudes to rubbish and the environment say about our society. But these aren't abstract gallery pieces for people in smart suits to
10 spend a fortune on. Steve believes in taking art to the people: a market stall in the city of Hull; a window on a street in downtown Tallahassee, Florida; and now, the Visitors' Centre in an English National Park where we meet.

15 I'd read about Steve in a tabloid newspaper. He explains the project that had earned this notoriety: 'In Hull, I picked up used lottery scratchcards off the streets and sold them on a market stall, three for 50p. Of course, they were worthless, and that was the whole
20 point. Kids wanted to know what I was doing, and I'd explain the disappearing act to them, how something could be worth a pound (the cost of a scratchcard), then worth nothing. It was a ploy, you know, to get them thinking about the value of things. You look at any
25 drinks can, or a bottle; the material you throw away is often worth more than the product you have paid for and consumed!'

'When I called the National Park authorities for permission to pick up rubbish in a famous beauty spot
30 and do something unspecified but vaguely arty next to the Visitors' Centre, they were understandably wary that I might give people the impression that our National Parks are filthy. But the truth is, the problem of litter isn't confined to the National Parks. Litter costs
35 taxpayers £410 million a year, or at least that's what it costs local government authorities to clean up across the UK. However, on private land – such as farmland – the cost of clearing litter is met by the landowner, so the real cost is even higher. The National Park has now

40 removed all bins from car parks and laybys, because it
encourages people to take their litter home rather than
leave it for overstretched local authorities to deal with.

But there's still plenty to be found – Steve and I are
filling large black bin-liners with the stuff. He notices
45 that most crisp packets have been obsessively folded
into tiny origami-like structures, or tied into a knot: 'I've
seen this in a few places; I call it pre-litter anxiety.
There's obviously a time lapse between consuming the
contents and discarding the waste ... it's really rather
50 creative behaviour.'

In the grounds of the Visitors' Centre, Steve sets up the
canvas where he'll display the litter we've just
collected. A garden net is strung up between three
trees and pegged to the ground by one corner. After
55 about an hour, a coachload of would-be art critics
arrive, invited over for the occasion from a local
school. They're intrigued and eager to join in. They tie
rubbish to the net and surround Steve with cheeky
questions until they're chivvied back onto the coaches
60 by their long-suffering teachers. Steve's in his element
as he adopts the role of lively, gesticulating artiste. 'So,
Steve,' I say, surveying the scraps of debris, drinks
bottles and sweet wrappers which have been retrieved
and recruited into a new existence as art, rather than
65 litter: 'What does it all mean?' Refreshingly, he's more
interested in what the kids made of it than what he, as
the artist, wants the work to say: 'I'm not looking for
people to see anything specific in my work. If pressed,
I'd want the audience to be surprised, then laugh; but
70 any emotion or reaction is good. It's about raising their
awareness of the environment they live, work and play
in.'

After spending the day with Steve, I've succumbed ever
so slightly to garbage fever. As we untie the net, I feel
75 a tinge of regret at destroying our original piece; this is
my first venture into the world of modern art. From
rubbish to litter to art, then back to rubbish, our
installation, entitled 'Net Deposit', is rolled into a bin-
liner to be thrown away (again) when we get home.
80 Everyone's got their own reasons for hating litter, but
until now I've always kept my dislike of detritus quiet.
Who cares about a few crisp packets? Well, in his
classic book *My First Summer in the Sierra*, published
in 1911, the Scottish nature lover John Muir came to
85 the conclusion that: 'when we try to pick out anything
by itself, we find it hitched to everything else in the
universe.' In a nutshell, and about 70 years before a
single Greenpeace calendar was sold, he'd summed up
the essence of ecology; that everything matters, even
90 if some things matter more than others. I'm guessing,
but I suspect John Muir would never have dropped his
crisp packet at a beauty spot.

1 In the first paragraph, we learn that Steve Bradley's art
 A has not been well received in some circles.
 B is not based on an entirely original concept.
 C is intended to raise awareness of certain issues.
 D has been taken quite seriously by some buyers.

2 What was the main aim of Steve's project in Hull?
 A He wanted to get press coverage for his activities.
 B He was trying to raise money for environmental causes.
 C He wanted to encourage young people to clean up their area.
 D He was trying to draw attention to the way resources are wasted.

3 When Steve approached a National Park for permission to create a work of art there, the authorities
 A assumed he would be critical of their litter policy.
 B were concerned that he might attract negative publicity.
 C felt that his activities would be more appropriate elsewhere.
 D were worried that people would see this as a waste of public money.

4 To Steve, what does the example of the folded crisp packets suggest?
 A People feel guilty about the places where they drop litter.
 B Some people may actually discard litter accidentally.
 C He's not the only person to be artistic with litter.
 D Litter is not only dropped by thoughtless people.

5 When the schoolchildren arrive at the Visitors' Centre, the writer observes that Steve
 A clearly enjoys the performance aspect of his work.
 B doesn't really have the approval of their teachers.
 C is surprised by the children's reaction to his work.
 D gets pleasure from explaining the meaning of his art.

6 After her day with Steve, the writer
 A has begun to realise how frustrating his work is.
 B feels angry that their work will not be preserved.
 C realises that she has begun to understand modern art.
 D no longer feels so negative about the problem of litter.

7 At the end of the article, the writer quotes John Muir in order to
 A illustrate how her own views have changed through meeting Steve.
 B question some of the assumptions that we may have about ecology.
 C demonstrate that there has long been a link between art and ecology.
 D underline her view that the work Steve does is actually of great value.

Writing Informal letter (Paper 2 Part 1)

▶ CB pages 84–85, WR pages 195–197

Exam strategy

In Paper 2 Part 1 you should read the information from all the input texts carefully before you start to plan your answer. Make sure that you include all the relevant points from the notes you are given, and that you organise your points logically.

1 Look at the Part 1 task below and answer these questions.

1 Who wrote the article?
2 Who must you write a letter to?

> Your friend Chiara was involved in a clean-up campaign at her college, organised by the Student Union. You want to organise a similar campaign at your college. Chiara has sent you a copy of their advertising poster, notes from their planning meeting, and an extract from an article she wrote for her college newspaper after their clean-up event. Read the poster, the meeting notes and extract from her article. Using the information, write a letter to your own Student Union President, explaining what happened at Chiara's college, why it would be a good thing to do at your college and what work it would involve.
>
> Write your **letter** in 220–260 words.

2 Read all the notes and underline the points that you should include in the letter.

3 Read the letter written by a student in answer to the task. Some information is missing. Underline the parts of the task that have been left out.

> Dear Cris,
>
> I am writing to tell you about a special event that was organised at East College and was extremely successful.
>
> It was a clean-up day, aimed at solving problems of litter in the college. The day started with volunteers meeting up outside the Union building – they picked up litter around the grounds and gave out leaflets to other students encouraging them to be tidier. They all had a free meal afterwards, and what was so good about the day was the impact it seems to have had on the college afterwards. Students have become a lot more aware of the importance of keeping the campus clean. They also tried imposing fines for dropping litter, which was not very successful.
>
> I think we should do the same thing here. We would need to organise some publicity (posters and leaflets) and some sort of reward for volunteers. At East College they provided a free meal, but I think that would be really difficult to organise. We could give volunteers a free ticket to the next disco instead.
>
> Can we meet to talk about it? What about next Saturday?
>
> Best wishes
>
> Sam

4 Decide where the missing information should go in the letter and write sentences that you can insert.

Clean-up-the-campus day!

Saturday June 14th
Come and join us.
We need volunteers to:
- pick up litter
- give out leaflets
- make a difference to our environment

Free supper in the evening for all volunteers. Email Chiara for more info.

- Must provide cleaning materials
- Give volunteers reward
- Need lots of advertising (leaflets?)
- Students need to feel proud of campus
- Someone to design a poster

On the positive side, we were inundated with volunteers only too keen to clean up the college grounds, although they were relieved that we gave them rubber gloves. The high spot was the free buffet supper in the evening, but since then we have seen a radical change in the attitude of students. They are more aware of the need to keep our campus clean, and although the imposition of fines for dropping litter turned out to be unpopular, the policy of no-smoking on the campus has been a roaring success.

A Health and fitness

Use of English
Word formation (Paper 3 Part 3)
▶ CB page 90, ER page 169

1 Read the title of the text to identify the topic. Then read the text through quickly for general understanding, ignoring the gaps for the moment.

2 Read the text again carefully and try to decide what type of word will fit in each gap. Then fill in the gaps, using the Help clues if necessary.

3 Read through the text again when you've finished and check that the words you've written fit in with the overall meaning of the text and are spelled correctly.

HELP
➤ **Question 1–4**
One of these questions requires a negative prefix and another one requires a positive prefix. You have to read the surrounding text very carefully to be sure.

➤ **Question 5**
Add a suffix to this verb to make the noun. Two nouns are possible; this one is used to talk about people rather than events. Check if it needs to be singular or plural in this context.

➤ **Questions 6**
Which suffix will you add to form the adjective?

➤ **Question 7–8**
Both of these words need two suffixes to make them into adverbs.

For questions **1–10**, read the text below. Use the word given in capitals at the end of some of the lines to form a word that fits in the gap in the same line. There is an example at the beginning **(0)**.

Science matters

The scene is the Olympic Games in around fifteen years' time. All eyes are on an **(0)** ..exceptionally.. gifted twenty-year-old athlete who runs like the wind. What makes this athlete so special is that he was born with an **(1)**.............................. genetic advantage: enormous muscles. The body contains a natural mechanism that normally acts as a brake on muscle **(2)**.......................... . In the case of this athlete, however, for some reason that mechanism simply didn't work. **(3)**........................... who have studied the rules can find no reason to **(4)**.............................. him. He has taken no drugs; his is a natural advantage. Officials are faced with a dilemma. Should the rules against doping be relaxed to give his less genetically endowed **(5)**........................... more of a fair chance?

The Olympic scenario is **(6)**............................ , but the person is not. He's a real five-year-old German boy who is **(7)**........................ able to hold two 6.6lb weights with his arms extended **(8)**........................... , a feat beyond many adults. He is the human equivalent of the so-called mighty mice, whose muscle power was genetically enhanced by scientists searching for a new form of **(9)**........................... for muscular diseases. It hasn't taken people long to see the sporting potential of such genetic **(10)**........................... , however.

EXCEPTION

ORDINARY

DEVELOP

LAW

QUALIFY

COMPETE

HYPOTHESIS

REPORT
HORIZON

TREAT

MODIFY

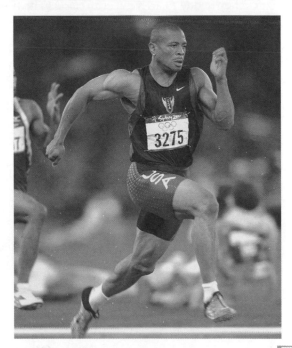

Language development
Emphasis
▶ CB page 93, GR page 181

Emphasis with *what, the thing that,* etc.

1 Complete the sentences with the words or phrases from the box.

What   The reason   The person who
The place where   The thing that

1 .... deals with all the accounts is Mr Johnson.
2 .... I enjoy is just sitting relaxing by the pool.
3 .... we're late is that all the trains were delayed because of a bomb scare.
4 .... you should do now is write to the school asking for an apology.
5 .... the accident happened is just behind the sports centre.

2 Rewrite each sentence to emphasise the words in italics, using the words given.

1 All the teenagers usually hang out in *the park*. (The place …)

....

2 I was so angry with her because *she had promised to be home by nine o'clock*. (The reason …)

....

3 *His ability to score goals from outside the penalty area* is so impressive. (The thing …)

....

4 *Her habit of leaving her things all over the house* drives me mad! (What …)

....

5 They're due to arrive at *six o'clock*. (The time …)

....

6 You need to talk to *your tutor* about this. (The person …)

....

3 Rewrite each sentence to emphasise the words in italics, using *What, The person, The reason,* etc.

1 She dialled 999 because *she panicked*.

....

2 We usually meet in *the café on the High Street*.

....

3 The aid agencies are trying to help *the refugees*.

....

4 *France* has the best health service in Europe.

....

5 I would really like *to train as a doctor*.

....

6 Our sales are highest in *August*.

....

Emphasis with *It* and *be*

4 Read the following text, then correct the sentences below.

> Louis Pasteur, the French chemist and founder of the science of microbiology, discovered that the process of fermentation is caused by micro-organisms and that heating can prevent it. The heat treatment became known as pasteurisation, and it is now routinely used to treat milk for domestic consumption. Later, he developed the 'germ theory of disease', which was probably the most important medical discovery of all time, as it provided both an understanding of the cause of disease as well as the means to prevent it. In 1885, he created the first vaccine for rabies.

1 Fleming discovered the process of fermentation.
No, it was ....
2 Pasteur founded the science of molecular biology.
No, it was ....
3 Fermentation is now routinely used to treat milk for domestic consumption.
No, it is ....
4 Pasteurisation was Pasteur's most important medical discovery.
No, it was ....
5 He created a vaccine for rabies in 1865.
No, it was ....

5 Rewrite the sentences using an *it*-clause to emphasise the words in italics.

1 I developed a bad allergic reaction *last Wednesday*.

....

2 I first felt ill *on the way home*.

....

3 The following morning I went back to bed *because I felt so lousy*.

....

4 The cough was bad but *the headache* was the real problem.

....

5 I *only* discovered the cause *when I saw the doctor*.

....

6 I felt well enough to go back to work *on Monday*.

....

7 *Someone at work* suggested what might have caused the problem.

....

8 The problem was caused by *breathing in paint fumes*.

....

Use of English

Key word transformations (Paper 3 Part 5)

▶ ER page 170

1 a Look at question 1 below. There are two sentences and a key word. Read the two sentences carefully and think about what they mean.

b What part of the meaning of the first sentence has not been included in the second sentence?

c Look at the key word. How can you use this word to express the idea missing in the second sentence? Remember the key word cannot be changed.

d Write between three and six words in the gap including the key word. The words must complete the sentence logically and grammatically.

e Read both sentences again to check that they mean the same thing.

2 Repeat the procedure for questions 2–8. Use the HELP clues if necessary.

HELP

➤ Question 1
You need to use a phrasal verb which means 'suggest/propose an idea'.

➤ Question 2
A superlative adjective is needed before 'ambition'.

➤ Question 3
What verb usually collocates with 'care' to form a phrase meaning 'look after'?

➤ Question 6
Be careful: 'hardly' already expresses a negative idea.

For questions **1–8**, complete the second sentence so that it has a similar meaning to the first sentence, using the word given. **Do not change the word given.** You must use between **three** and **six** words, including the word given.

1 The idea of going to the new health centre was Pat's suggestion.
FORWARD
It was Pat .... idea of going to the new health centre.

2 More than anything else Grace wanted to start her own aromatherapy clinic.
AMBITION
Grace's .... to start her own aromatherapy clinic.

3 Providing you look after it carefully, you can borrow my laptop.
LONG
You can borrow my laptop .... good care of it.

4 I wasn't surprised to hear that Martin had joined the gym.
CAME
It .... me to hear that Martin had joined the gym.

5 I will only try acupuncture if my doctor approves of the idea.
UNLESS
I won't try acupuncture .... my doctor's approval for the idea.

6 It's very unlikely that space tourism will take off in my lifetime.
HARDLY
Space tourism is ...., in my lifetime.

7 Clarissa told me how very good this anti-ageing cream is.
HIGHLY
This anti-ageing cream was .... Clarissa.

8 We arrived at the restaurant too late to order a full meal.
ABLE
Had we arrived at the restaurant earlier, ... order a full meal.

Writing

Cohesion

▶ CB page 94, WR page 200

Cohesion

1 Complete the text with cohesive devices from the list.

although   and   instead   or   others
rather than   these   too   whereas

The last few years have seen a rise in the popularity of alternative therapies. (1)................... do not use synthetic drugs (2)................... surgery. (3)................... , the emphasis is on maintaining health (4)................... dealing with the causes of illnesses (5)................... their symptoms. (6)................... some treatments are accepted by orthodox doctors, (7)................... are rejected as ineffective. Acupuncture is widely accepted, and homoeopathy is (8)................... . In time, more will become accepted, (9)................... it's hard to say which.

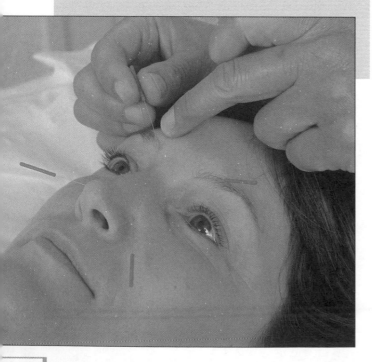

Substitution and omission

2 For each sentence, choose which option works best to make the sentence cohesive and natural. A dash (–) means that the sentence is already cohesive.

1 Acupuncture is very effective and shiatsu ....
   A is very effective too   B is too   C too
2 After my friend recommended the massage, I had ....
   A one too   B too   C the massage
3 I went to the same therapist that ....
   A my friend did   B my friend went   C my friend
4 I tried Indian head massage and reiki, but .... for me.
   A they neither worked   B both didn't work
   C neither of them worked
5 I find that shiatsu works much better than aromatherapy ....
   A works   B –   C is
6 I rang to make an appointment and .... for tomorrow.
   A made one   B made an appointment   C that's
7 I was told I'd have to take all my clothes off, but I wouldn't ....
   A take my clothes off   B take off   C do that
8 The treatment was expensive, but .... worth it.
   A it's   B it was   C the treatment was
9 I ended up having acupuncture, although I hadn't intended ....
   A to have   B to   C to do
10 Jenny said it was a fantastic treatment, but she didn't say ....
   A why it was fantastic   B why
   C why she thought it
11 I'd like a massage. I've heard that certain types .... are more suitable than others.
   A –   B of massage   C of it
12 I spoke to a therapist .... said she could help me.
   A . The therapist   B , who   C and

3 Complete the sentences. Use one suitable word in each gap.
1 I've just heard that there's an open day on Saturday at the alternative health clinic in town. You know, the .... on Malvern Road.
2 'Would you like to come to the cinema with us tonight?' 'Yes, I'd love ....'
3 Simon says he's going to resign from his job, but he always says .... when he's had a bad day.
4 She always says she'll help us clear up at the end of the evening, but she never ....
5 'I really enjoyed that film.' 'So .... I.'
6 Are you coming to the party on Saturday? If .... , don't forget to bring a bottle with you.

7 Annie and James need to know that we've changed the date of the trip, so I'll phone them .... tonight.

8 My car is being repaired at the moment, so do you mind taking us in .... ?

9 'We're meeting in the Black Bull pub in town at eight o'clock.' 'OK, I'll see you ....'

10 Phil is really into alternative therapies. You know, aromatherapy and other .... things.

4 Rewrite the following text to make it more cohesive either by deleting unnecessary words or by using substitution.

> **A**romatherapy uses fragrant oils. The oils are rubbed into the body. Aromatherapy is good for physical disorders and for emotional disorders as it works on a physical level and on an emotional level. You can have a whole course of treatments, but you don't have to have a whole course of treatments. Just one treatment is enough to feel some benefit. If relaxation is the aim, try aromatherapy; if it is not the aim, try something else.

....

....

....

....

....

....

....

....

....

....

....

....

Linking devices

5 For each sentence, mark the two options that are possible.

1 I think that your diet lacks fibre. .... , I am recommending that you eat more fruit.
A Consequently   B Furthermore   C That is why
D Nonetheless

2 Exercise is certainly a good thing for everyone. .... , you should never overdo it.
A In addition   B Nevertheless   C Furthermore
D Even so

3 I'm going to show you how to use the exercise ball. .... , you can have a go with it on your own.
A In the meantime   B Afterwards   C Later
D In the end

4 That's about all I've got to say about exercising. .... , I'd just like to remind you that exercise is meant to be fun, so try to enjoy it.
A Lastly   B Later   C Finally   D In the end

5 I spent ages looking for the right running shoes. I .... found a pair just like my old ones.
A eventually   B finally   C lastly   D in the end

6 I need to change my diet. I really should do some exercise ....
A besides   B moreover   C too   D as well

7 Running is a great way to get fit. .... , it can be very bad for your joints.
A Consequently   B On the other hand
C Meanwhile   D However

8 The club insists that all members have an induction before using the equipment. .... , the club is not responsible for injuries caused by incorrect use of the equipment.
A Besides   B That's why   C Furthermore
D Moreover

6 Use the underlined conjunctions to help match the sentence halves.
1 I think you should take vitamin C
2 You won't need to take iron tablets
3 I'm going to the health-food shop
4 Take one of these energy boosters
5 I eat a spoonful of yeast every morning
6 I've been taking multi-vitamins for years
7 You don't need expensive diet supplements
8 I got two of everything

a as soon as you start feeling tired.
b although I don't really know if they do any good.
c provided you eat a healthy balanced diet.
d in addition to the iron tablets.
e despite the fact that it tastes revolting.
f unless you are anaemic (short of iron).
g since they were on special offer.
h to get some brown rice.

Listening
Sentence completion (Paper 4 Part 2)
▶ ER pages 170–171

1 Read the instructions for the exam task below. Then read the sentences and think about the topic and what you expect to hear. Can you predict the type of information you will be listening for in each item? For example:
- Question 1: Is this likely to be:
  a) an activity?　b) an object?
  c) a person?
- Question 2: What is a *term*?
- Question 3: Is this word likely to be:
  a) a verb?　b) a noun?　c) an adjective?
- Question 4: Where could someone borrow money from?

2 ⌒ Listen to the recording once and complete the sentences. Use the Help clues if necessary.

3 Listen again to check and complete your answers. Remember to check your spelling.

HELP
➤ Question 2
Judy signals that she is going to use a term when she says *what people call*. Listen out for this phrase – the answer comes after it.
➤ Question 3
You are listening for the type of holiday Judy went on – in this case, it is an activity.
➤ Question 5
You are listening for a noun – something that Judy was using – but listen for a phrase that indicates her friends were *surprised* – the answer will come soon after that phrase.

4 Look at the following wrong answers that students gave to some of the questions. Listen again and decide why they are not correct.
1 oils
2 health fanatic
7 perfume
8 *The Easy Way to Health*

You will hear a woman called Judy Simpson, who is a complementary therapist, giving a talk about her life and work. For questions **1–8**, complete the sentences.

Complementary therapist

As an example of the work she does, Judy mentions a treatment which uses [1] at varying temperatures.

Judy uses the term '[2]' to describe herself as she was in her twenties.

It was during a [3] holiday that Judy made the decision to go self-employed.

Judy borrowed money from her [4] to finance her training as a complementary therapist.

Judy's friends were surprised to hear that she was using a [5] as part of her fitness programme.

Last year, Judy launched an unsuccessful online business selling [6].

Judy is currently planning to open a [7] of her own.

Judy recommends reading her book which is entitled [8].

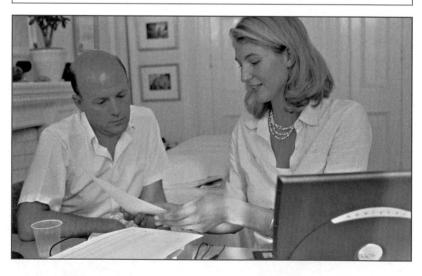

5 a Match the nouns in A and B to form compound nouns.

A	B		
1 health	a style	....	....
2 redundancy	b levels	....	....
3 energy	c fanatic	....	....
4 life	d payout	....	....

b Match the compounds in Exercise 5a to the definitions below.
1 an amount of money paid to someone when they are asked to leave their job
2 someone who is obsessed with staying healthy
3 the amount of energy that you have
4 the way that someone lives their life

B Unveiling the past

Language development
Verb complementation
▶ CB page 98, GR page 182

Verbs + *-ing*, *to*-infinitive or infinitive without *to*

1 Read the text and put the verb in brackets into the correct form.

A few years ago I spent a day **(1)**........................ (*work*) on an archaeological dig behind an old house. The location was believed **(2)**........................ (*be*) the site of an old Roman bathhouse.
First, I helped the archaeologists **(3)**........................ (*clear*) the site, then we began **(4)**........................ (*dig*). They instructed me **(5)**........................ (*remove*) the soil in 2cm layers. This involved **(6)**........................ (*scratch*) the earth very carefully with a tool no bigger than a small spoon. I suggested **(7)**........................ (*use*) something bigger but they didn't appreciate my **(8)**........................ (*say*) that, even though they seemed **(9)**........................ (*think*) that the ruins were at least a metre down.
I watched one person **(10)**........................ (*dig*) up a skeleton, but it turned out **(11)**........................ (*be*) a pet cat that someone had buried in the garden. That proved **(12)**........................ (*be*) the high point of the day.

2 Complete the sentences using the words in brackets. You may need to add a preposition.

1 The teacher asked ....
   (*me / wait outside*)
2 My friends warned ....
   (*me / not trust / her*)
3 I arranged ....
   ....
   (*some friends / help / me / move house*)
4 My parents refused ....
   (*let / me / stay out late*)
5 We all had to wait ....
   ....
   (*Jane / finish / her meal*)
6 He wanted ....
   (*her / go / with him*)

Verb + *-ing* form / *to*-infinitive with a change in meaning

3 Underline the most appropriate verb forms in italics. In some cases, both are possible.

1 a Most teachers don't allow *to eat / eating* in the classrooms.
   b The school doesn't allow students *to take / taking* books home.
2 a My grandfather teaches *to swim / swimming* in the local swimming pool.
   b My grandfather taught me *to swim / swimming* in a lake near our house.
3 a The museum guide advised us *to start / starting* in the Renaissance section.
   b The doctor advised against *to travel / travelling* so soon after the operation.
4 a I remember *him buying / him to buy* that watch. He got it in London.
   b I must remember *to buy him / buying him* a birthday present.
5 a I hate *to say / saying* this, but I think it was your fault.
   b I've always hated *to get / getting* my hair wet.

4 Complete the sentences using an appropriate verb from the list in the correct form.
arrive   ask   give up   inform   iron
pick up   read   show   study   tell

1 Unfortunately I stopped .... history books when I left school.
2 On Sunday evening I like .... all my shirts, ready for the week ahead.
3 The management regrets .... visitors that photography is not permitted in the museum.
4 Doing a Masters in Archaeology means .... for another two years.
5 Jackie forgot .... me that the museum is closed on Mondays!
6 My brother really regrets .... Latin when he changed schools.
7 On the way home, I stopped .... some information from the library.
8 I've been meaning .... you about your trip to Pompeii for ages.
9 I'll never forget .... in Venice on the Orient Express.
10 Mum likes .... people around the old town, pretending to be a guide.

Use of English
Gapped sentences (Paper 3 Part 4)
▶ ER page 170

1   Look at the example in the gapped-sentence task below and read the task rubric.
   1   How many sentences are there?
   2   How many words are missing?
   3   What do the missing words have in common?

2   a   Read all three sentences in the example carefully. What type of word is missing from all three (noun, verb, adjective, etc.)?

   b   Make a list of words that will fit in the gap in the first sentence. Think about both the grammar and the context. Which of these words would you include in your list?

   > willing   prepared   job   happy   delighted
   > ready   asked   required

   c   How many of the words on your list also fit the gap in the second sentence? Think about both the grammar and the context. Cross any words off your list which don't fit here.

   d   Look at the third sentence. Will one of the words left on your list fit here?

   e   Write your answer in all three gaps. Read the sentences again to check that it fits well in all three.

3   Now look at Questions 1–5 and repeat the procedure, using the HELP clues if necessary.

TIP

Check your answers carefully. For example, make sure that you've got the correct tense, that you've checked whether nouns are singular or plural, and that your spelling is correct.

HELP
➤ Question 1
   In all three sentences a verb is needed. All of these verbs fit in the first gap: *forget, ask, follow, take, seek, ignore.* Which of them fits in the other sentences?
➤ Question 2
   A past participle is needed in each of the gaps. It is followed by the preposition 'into' in the first sentence and so it describes a type of change.
➤ Question 3
   The words *amount, level, deal* all fit in the first sentence.

For questions **1–5**, think of **one** word only which can be used appropriately in all three sentences. Here is an example **(0)**.

0   Sarah is .... to show groups of visitors around the archaeological site in return for a small fee.
   Are you .... with the local history course that you're doing?
   Dora's mother was only willing to go and see films which had a .... ending.

1   I've decided to .... your advice about the best way of getting to the airport.
   Melanie likes to .... a relaxing herbal bath everyday after work.
   Lance has decided not to .... painkillers any more, but to try natural remedies instead.

2   The small fishing village has .... into a major resort in just a few years.
   The market for male beauty products has .... rapidly in recent years.
   I've .... used to the idea that some of my ancestors may have been criminals.

3   Fortunately for Grace, there was a good .... of support for her idea of organising a party to celebrate the school's centenary.
   If your school wants to save money, there's a special .... on English books on the Internet at the moment.
   As part of a reciprocal .... between the two governments, students on a gap year will no longer need to apply for a work permit.

4   Rules about non-student access to the university grounds only .... during term time.
   If Declan wanted to read an unfamiliar language like Japanese, he realised he'd have to .... himself to learning long lists of characters.
   Anyone interested in running a course covering the principles of acupuncture is invited to .... in writing, outlining any relevant qualifications and experience.

5   The local council had clearly underestimated the .... of local feeling about its plan to demolish the old building.
   Clara felt that she had researched the issue thoroughly and so could argue her point from a position of .... in the public debate.
   After last year's run of injuries, I'm happy to announce that the football team is now back to full ....

Writing
Guidebook entry (Paper 2 Part 2)
▶ CB pages 100–101, WR page 194

Exam strategy

When you write an informational text, your writing may be purely factual, but sometimes you may need to make it more interesting to persuade the reader about something. Think about your target reader and decide which approach is required before you plan and write your answer.

1 **Look at the two tasks below and answer the questions.**
  1 Which reader (A or B):
    a) is aged 30–40?   b) is aged 18–25?
  2 Which reader (A, B or both) will be interested in:
    a) beaches? c) safety?   e) nightclubs?
    b) pubs?   d) museums? f) shops?
  3 Which text (A or B) should be:
    a) informative and exciting to read?
    b) informative and gently persuasive?

A

Your local tourist authority wants to attract more family visitors to the town, and is planning to publish a special page advertising the town in the general guidebook to the whole region. You have been asked to write this page. You should say why the town would be interesting for families to visit, what they can do there and give some practical advice on finding places to stay.

Write your **entry for the guidebook** in 220–260 words.

B

You have been asked to contribute a page in a brochure advertising things for young people to do in your town. You should explain what facilities there are for young people and describe what they can do there. You should also include information on cafés and restaurants and easy ways of getting round the town.

Write your **entry for the guidebook** in 220–260 words.

2 **Look at a student's incomplete answer to Task A. The writer has some problems with cohesion and repetition.**

  a Correct three reference words.

  b Delete one repetitive sentence in each of the first two paragraphs.

Ⓐ
Come to sunny Compton!

There are many reasons why Compton should feature on your list of places to visit in this region, and not the least of this is its family orientation. It's a great place for families to spend time together. Families will have a good time here and there are some really interesting places for him to visit.

  Known locally as the jewel of the coast, its golden sandy beaches are delightful and are also extremely safe for small children. The beaches are beautiful and not dangerous. Compton also has a lifeguard station within easy reach.

  The town has something for everyone. For the best view of the picturesque old buildings, it's a good idea to take the sightseeing bus tour – it takes two hours and is well worth it.

- Museum of the history of Compton
- Zoo
- Castle with beautiful gardens and play area
- Accommodation – lots of small hotels ideal for families

3 **Now look at a student's incomplete answer to Task B, which is informative, but not very interesting or exciting to read.**

  a Add these adjectives to the text to replace *nice* and make the text more interesting to read:
  lively   thriving   trendy   exclusive

  b Insert the following rhetorical questions into the best places in the text, to involve the reader more.
  What's the town like?
  So what is there to do in the evenings?

Ⓑ
Compton is a nice place to have fun with friends – it's a nice town with lots going on.

The town itself is interesting, with good shops – these include not only extremely nice boutiques selling expensive designer clothes but also cheaper chain stores. You won't have any trouble finding what you want in Compton, and you can be sure of finding the most up-to-date merchandise there.

Compton has a good night-life, too, including nice clubs and a cinema complex which shows the latest films.

- Lots of cafés/restaurants
- Friendly pubs/nightclubs
- Good public transport, even late at night

4 Now complete the answer to either Task A or Task B, using the student's notes.

Reading

Gapped text (Paper 1 Part 2)

▶ ER page 168

1 Read the title and subtitle of the text, to identify the topic of the text. Then read the base text quickly, ignoring the gaps for the moment. Answer these questions to check your comprehension.

  1 It had been generally believed by scientists that Tyrannosaurus Rex

    a) was a predator, which killed other animals for food.

    b) ate the dead remains of other animals.

    c) ate only plants.

  2 Why have Jack Horner's ideas caused a lot of disagreement?

  3 What three pieces of evidence does Jack Horner give for his theory?

2 a Look at question 1.

  • Read the text before and after the gap. Use the highlighted words and phrases to help you choose which option A–G fits the gap.

  • Now read option D. Find the words and a phrase that relate to the first paragraph, showing that Horner is prepared to argue with conviction.

  b Read the options A–G and underline words and phrases that might help you to match them to the text.

3 Now look at questions 2–6 and follow the same procedure. Words have been highlighted around questions 2 and 3 to help you.

4 When you have finished the task, read the whole text through to check it makes sense.

5 a Scan the text to find these words and any related forms.

    1 controversy

    2 predator

    3 carnivore

    4 scavenger

    5 herbivore

  b Use your dictionary to complete a word family for each item in Exercise 5a in your vocabulary notebook.

You are going to read a magazine article. Six paragraphs have been removed from the article. Choose from the paragraphs A–G the one which fits each gap (1–6). There is one extra paragraph you do not need to use.

DIGGING FOR DINOSAURS

Jack Horner's ideas about the dinosaur, Tyrannosaurus Rex, have created some controversy. Lucy Winston meets him to discover why.

Jack Horner, one of the world's most prominent dinosaur experts, looks very North American, in a grey-blue, short-sleeved shirt and blue jeans. His bald crown is fringed by longish grey hair, and creases crinkle the corners of his eyes from years of squinting at the sun. He has a humorous, wry smile, but beneath this unassuming exterior is someone prepared to argue his point with conviction and intelligence.

He's talking about the controversial theory he's been working on for the last ten years – that Tyrannosaurus Rex, the predatory king of the prehistoric world, was in fact a scavenger more akin to a vulture; the big black bird that feeds on the dead flesh of larger wild animals. It's an idea that has met with considerable scepticism over the years, but it has recently been gathering momentum.

2

Jack Horner is not your typical academically gifted palaeontologist. Growing up with dyslexia, he struggled hard at school. 'I liked digging in the dirt when I was a little kid, and discovering things,' he remembers. 'I came across my first piece of dinosaur bone sticking out of the rock when I was only eight, and I've kept it,' he adds with a laugh. Much to his surprise, a high-school project on dinosaurs led to his being offered a place at university to study palaeontology. Yet, after persevering with his studies for four years, he decided he had taken all the courses he needed to be a palaeontologist, so left without a degree.

3

I challenge him, saying that Tyrannosaurus Rex does share certain characteristics with predatory reptiles, and he looks at me appraisingly. 'Like what?' he questions. 'Well, it's got a big mouth full of sharp teeth,' I reply. 'No, it hasn't,' he counters. 'It's got a mouth full of blunt teeth. There's a big difference.'

I try again: 'What about its big hind legs?'

35 'Yes, Tyrannosaurus Rex has big hind legs,' he concedes. 'So? That doesn't mean he can run fast.' Humans and other animals that are adapted for walking have longer thigh bones and shorter shin bones. On the other hand, fast-running animals such as the cheetah have short

40 thigh bones and long shin bones. Based on this, the leg bones of all known predatory dinosaurs seem to be designed for running after their prey. Tyrannosaurus Rex was, he believes, a walker.

| 4 | |

'Scavengers are much more common than predators, but

45 still less common than their prey.' Horner explains. 'If you look at how many meat eaters there were and how many prey animals, then you add up the huge numbers of Tyrannosaurus Rex, being the most common meat-eating dinosaur, compared with the scarcity of the

50 herbivorous dinosaurs, the numerical proportions are similar to those you find in some African national parks where the flocks of vultures wait to feed on animals killed by hyenas.'

| 5 | |

'Each of these points is based on scientific data that can

55 be falsified,' he concedes. 'Yes, one is a mammal and the other a bird, and somebody else could study this and find out that there's something weird going on. But nobody has done it yet.'

| 6 | |

'Just because Tyrannosaurus Rex had vicious-looking

60 teeth and looked intimidating, doesn't make it a lethal predator by default. This is the first hypothesis to be based on science. So I'm not going against the grain. Science is about evidence, not egos.'

A Horner frequently likens Tyrannosaurus Rex to these scavenging birds, and he recently scanned the brain of one in search of evidence to support his theory. He compared the size of its olfactory lobes, the parts used for scent detection, with those of a bloodhound. This dog has a highly sensitive localised sense of smell, but can't smell over large distances. Vultures, on the other hand, can sniff out a dead animal several miles away. He found the vulture had enormous olfactory lobes in its brain, as did the Tyrannosaurus Rex, but the bloodhound did not.

B Ironically, Horner has now become one of the world's foremost dinosaur experts. He found the first dinosaur eggs in the world, and it was he who discovered the largest, oldest and most complete Tyrannosaurus Rex skeleton. Yet the more he has learned, the more he has become convinced that, far from hunting its own food, Tyrannosaurus Rex survived on the scavenged meat of animals killed by other predators.

C As a result, he was later appointed as the scientific consultant for the *Jurassic Park* films, a position Horner views with amusement. The whole theme of the blockbuster films seems contrary to his personal theory of Tyrannosaurus Rex as a scavenger, and I questioned his reaction. 'I was glad that the lead character did not get eaten by the dinosaurs,' is all he'd say.

D 'When you do historical science, you come up with a supposition,' he says in a pleasant Montana drawl. 'But each piece of information should be backed up by a body of evidence. You can't just overturn a hypothesis with one piece of information, when there exists a large body of data that supports something else.'

E 'I admit that comparing only two different species is not the strongest possible hypothesis, and obviously it could be more rigorous, but in the absence of a more wide-reaching study, it's going to stand,' he states firmly. His main argument for those who think Tyrannosaurus Rex could have been a predator is that you still need some evidence of this, and he remains adamant that there is none.

F It has now reached the point where a leading natural history museum in the UK has put together an exhibition presenting evidence to support the argument and is inviting people to make up their minds. Tyrannosaurus Rex can now be viewed in a new light, as a scavenger, compared with the more popular view of it as a predator.

G By far the most convincing evidence, however, Horner maintains, is what he terms the 'biomass' of Tyrannosaurus Rex compared with that of other dinosaurs of its era. By calculating this biomass, or the proportion of dinosaurs over a given area, it's possible to work out how many of each type existed.

A | Against the odds

Use of English
Multiple-choice cloze (Paper 3 Part 1)

▶ CB page 106, ER page 169

1 Read the title of the text, then read the whole text quickly for general understanding, ignoring the gaps for the moment.

1 Where did the family sail to?
2 Which family members continued to work during their trip?

2 Read the text again carefully and try to predict what each answer will be. Then look at the options **A–D** and complete the task. Use the Help clues if necessary.

3 Read through the text again when you've finished to check your answers.

HELP

➤ Question 2
Which verb completes the expression with *out of their system*?

➤ Question 7
Read the whole sentence carefully. Only one of the options creates meaning in the context.

➤ Question 11
Only one of the options combines with *out* to make a phrasal verb.

For questions **1–12**, read the text below and decide which answer (**A**, **B**, **C** or **D**) best fits each gap. There is an example at the beginning (**0**).

A family gap year

When Jonathan and Claire Spencer, **(0)** ..A... by their two children aged eight and 11, set off on a 17,000-mile voyage from England to Australia in their 51-foot yacht *Attitude*, Jonathan **(1)**....... the year-long voyage as 'the gentlest way of having an extreme experience'. But the couple were not trying to **(2)**....... anything out of their system, and certainly didn't see the trip as something which had to be achieved at all **(3)**....... . Indeed, in spite of the enormity of their adventure, the Spencers were in no sense dropping out. Both are **(4)**....... sailors, and regarded their adventure as a career break, as a kind of family gap year.

Claire had been **(5)**....... a year's unpaid leave from her job, and the family rented out their home in London. Meanwhile, arrangements were made for the children to return to school after a year's **(6)**....... ; this had the school's blessing, **(7)**....... a private tutor was employed to keep them up to **(8)**....... with the curriculum.

Jonathan, the managing director of a property company, was able to take his job with him. He worked out a way of **(9)**....... his duties without actually **(10)**....... foot in the office. As you might imagine, the arrangement was entirely dependent on technology, and the cabin on *Attitude* was **(11)**....... out with a communications satellite which **(12)**....... him to keep in phone and email contact with his workplace. Could this be the gap year of the future?

	A	B	C	D
0	accompanied	escorted	supplemented	attended
1	expressed	described	explained	outlined
2	let	take	remove	get
3	costs	events	accounts	lengths
4	fond	keen	eager	doting
5	granted	conferred	consented	yielded
6	omission	truancy	absence	default
7	so that	as well as	even if	as long as
8	pace	speed	rate	stride
9	functioning	achieving	fulfilling	satisfying
10	placing	setting	putting	stepping
11	stocked	equipped	fitted	furnished
12	enabled	enforced	ensured	engaged

Language development

Spelling

▶ CB page 108, WR page 202

Spelling changes

1 **Complete the sentences with the correct form of the words in brackets.**

1 We have had a lot of .... about our new product range. (*enquiry*)
2 Watching the artist at work was a deeply .... experience. (*satisfy*)
3 The only .... character in the whole book is the detective's wife. (*like*)
4 The island of Java has a number of .... that could erupt at any moment. (*volcano*)
5 His room was like a library with .... of books on every wall. (*shelf*)
6 I have no .... in recommending Juan as an honest and reliable employee. (*hesitate*)
7 Flooding on this area of the coast is a common .... (*occur*)
8 I'd .... you to be more careful with your money in future. (*advice*)
9 I was .... to ask Kevin where he'd been, but I resisted the temptation. (*die*)
10 When I was younger I .... to go out with friends, but now my .... would be to spend time at home. (*prefer*)

Endings often misspelt

2 **Add the missing letter(s) to complete the words in these sentences.**

1 Crossing the Atlantic in a canoe would be virtually imposs__ble.
2 To ski down Everest is a remark__ble thing to attempt.
3 The government minister was embar__a__sed by the stories in the press.
4 You should not exc__ __d the speed limit.
5 If you wish to take up the place, you will have to write a letter of accept__nce.
6 Some of the excuses James came out with were unbeliev__ble.
7 It is incred__ble that he managed to survive at sea for so long.
8 After the earthquake, I wanted to help, so I volunt__ __red my services as a driver.

Commonly misspelt words

3 **Complete the nouns in these sentences. Some of the letters have been given.**

1 In order to exchange goods in a shop, you need your r__ __ __ __ __ __ .
2 Hard work and preparation are no g__ __rant__ __ of suc__ __ __ __ __ .
3 Another word for your job is your o__ __ __ __ __ __ __ __ __ __ .
4 Winning a medal gives someone a great sense of ach__ __ __ __ __ment.
5 Looking at your injuries, I think you should seek im__ __ __ __ __ __ __ __ medical attention.
6 Lost in the fog, I was sep__ __ __ __ __ __ __ from the rest of the group.
7 I'm not sure how big the room is exactly, but it's a __ __ __ __ __ __ __ __ __ __ __ __ __ y 15 metres^2.
8 If you let me think about it, I'll give you a de__ __ __ __ __ __n in a few minutes.
9 Just because the restaurant is expensive, it isn't nec__ __ __ __ __ __ __ __ __ the best.
10 After lunch, we went for a le__sure__ __ stroll.

4 **It is important to check your work for spelling mistakes. There are 24 mistakes in this letter. Read it carefully to find and correct all the mistakes.**

Dear Sir/Maddam

I am writting to complaine about the service I recieved in your restaurant last night. Generaly the food was poor and the service was awfull.

The potatos were nearly raw, and the source that the chicken was cooked in was much saltyer than was neccessary.

The waitor kept droping thinks, including two knifes, which he then put back on the table for us to use.

In additition, we were forced to wait nearly an hour between the main course and the desert. When we pointed this out to your staff, they became rude and aggresive.

I don't think you realise how much distres this causes to a person like myself who allways trys to maintain the highest standads in all aspects of my live.

I look forward to hearing your explainations and how you propose to compensate us.

Yours sincerly

D. Smith

Use of English
Word formation (Paper 3 Part 3)

▶ ER page 169

1 a Read the title of the text. What sort of people are *iron men* likely to be?

   b Read the rest of the text quickly for general understanding, ignoring the gaps for the moment. What do you think a *spoof sport* is?

2 Read the text again carefully and try to decide what kind of word will fit in each gap. Then fill in the gaps using the Help clues if necessary.

3 Read through the text again when you've finished and check that the words you've written fit in with the overall meaning of the text and are spelled correctly.

HELP
➤ Question 1
   Add a prefix to this adjective to make a verb meaning *to get over*.
➤ Question 3–4
   One of these questions requires a plural noun and one a singular noun. You have to read the surrounding text carefully to be sure.
➤ Question 8
   Add a suffix to create an adjective meaning *not given very willingly*.
➤ Questions 9
   Add a prefix to create a compound adjective which means *in the open air*.

For questions **1–10**, read the text below. Use the word given in capitals at the end of some of the lines to form a word that fits in the gap in the same line. There is an example at the beginning **(0)**.

Iron men let off steam

What are known as extreme sports have become **(0)** ...increasingly... popular in recent years. But what if you've already tried bungee jumping, paragliding and all the others, but still haven't **(1)**........................... the urge to prove yourself by taking part in **(2)**........................... challenging activities? The answer could lie in a new activity which goes by the name *extreme ironing*. **(3)**........................... describe themselves as 'ironists' and what they like to do is to climb mountains, go surfing or trek cross-country, doing their ironing along the way.

It all started in 1997, when Philip Shaw, a mountaineering **(4)**........................... from Leicester in the English midlands decided to iron his shirts in the garden on a hot day. His flatmate **(5)**........................... described this as 'extreme ironing' and the idea of the spoof sport was born. The sport's worldwide **(6)**........................... body, the Extreme Ironing Bureau, has received twenty thousand hits on its website, and future expeditions include such **(7)**........................... activities as hang-gliding ironing and white-water ironing.

For ironists, who are now earning the **(8)**........................... respect of some mainstream extreme-sports fans, the motivation for the sport comes from the chance to combine the thrill of an extreme **(9)**........................... activity with the **(10)**........................... of a well-pressed shirt.

Word
INCREASE
COME
PHYSICAL
PARTICIPATE
ENTHUSE
JOKING
GOVERN
LIKELY
GRUDGE
DOOR
SATISFY

Writing
Paraphrasing
▶ CB page 110

Exam strategy

In Paper 2 Part 1, you have to paraphrase words and phrases from the input texts so that the ideas are the same, but the language is different. Sometimes you have to change the register, to express the ideas in a more formal or more informal way.

Using synonyms

1   One way to paraphrase is to use synonyms. For each of the words below, cross out the word (A–D) which is not a synonym.

Adjectives

1 expensive   A pricey   B dear
              C costly   D fortunate
2 important   A necessary   B convinced
              C required   D essential
3 unusual   A bizarre   B weird
              C outstanding   D strange
4 boring   A prestigious   B dull
              C tedious   D dreary
5 ordinary   A standard   B run-of-the-mill
              C genuine   D typical

Nouns

6 solution   A answer   B verge
              C remedy   D way out
7 problem   A frenzy   B hiccup
              C difficulty   D hassle
8 effect   A consequence   B implication
              C attribute   D end result
9 plan   A vision   B timetable
              C schedule   D programme
10 reason   A explanation   B motive
              C pretension   D justification

Verbs

11 employ   A hire   B order
              C take on   D contract
12 find out   A check out   B investigate
              C accuse   D ascertain
13 repay   A reimburse   B pay back
              C refund   D repair
14 prevent   A seize   B impede
              C thwart   D obstruct
15 solve   A put right   B conceive
              C remedy   D sort out

Using opposites

2   Complete the second sentence of each pair so that it paraphrases the first.

0   The family is poor.
    The family is <u>not well-off</u>.
1   The food is cheap.
    The food doesn't .... much.
2   I refuse to take part in the discussion.
    I'm not .... to take part in the discussion.
3   We reject the suggestion that the facilities are underused.
    We don't .... the suggestion that the facilities are underused.
4   Students here are quite poor.
    Students here are not .... of money.
5   The residents are very unhappy about the proposals.
    The residents are far from .... about the proposals.
6   It's well known that the centre is going to close.
    It's no .... that the centre is going to close.
7   For us, the closure of the factory is very serious.
    For us, the closure of the factory is no .... matter.
8   The principal's suggestions are totally predictable.
    The principal's suggestions come as no .... to us.

Changing the form

3   Complete the second sentence so that it paraphrases the first.

0   You are more likely to succeed if you have help.
    You are more likely to <u>be successful</u> if you have help.
1   You may be surprised by this.
    This may come as a .... to you.
2   I've decided to sell my car.
    I've decided to put my car up for ....
3   I'd like to apologise to you.
    I'd like to offer you my ....
4   It's more suitable for children.
    It would .... children.
5   It showed how generous people can be.
    It showed the .... that some people have.
6   I was assisted by some passers-by.
    Some passers-by came to my ....
7   He is a person I can trust.
    He is a totally .... person.
8   The manager still insists on staff wearing uniforms.
    The manager is still .... on staff wearing uniforms.

Listening

Multiple choice (Paper 4 Part 1)

► ER page 170

1a Read the instructions for the task.
1 How many extracts are you going to hear?
2 What is each extract about?

b Look at the questions for Extract One. How much do you find out the topics and speakers
  a) from the rubric? b) from the questions?

c Highlight the most important ideas in each question stem and in the options (A, B or C).

2 ⌒ Listen to the recording and choose the correct option A, B or C. Follow the same procedure for Extracts 2 and 3.

TIP

Read the questions stems carefully. They tell you which speaker's view you are listening for and what the focus of the question is, e.g. opinion, feeling, agreement, etc.

HELP
➤ Question 1
  To answer this question you have to listen to both speakers. The woman says: 'I take your point on that'. What is she referring to when she says this?
➤ Question 2
  This question focuses on the man's opinion. Listen to everything the man says – which option best summarises his opinion?
➤ Question 3
  The presenter tells you about tonight's programme before he hands over to the female speaker.
➤ Question 4
  The female speaker tells us about Dr Senik. Which option best summarises the doctor's views?
➤ Question 5
  The female speaker says 'I'd certainly go along with that', what is she referring to?
➤ Question 6
  When the female speaker says 'Exactly', what is she referring to?

You will hear three different extracts. For questions **1–6**, choose the answer (**A**, **B** or **C**) which fits best according to what you hear.

Extract One

You overhear two friends talking about a record-breaking round-the-world sailor.

1 What do they agree about the sailor?
   A She's a good role model for young people.
   B She should pay more attention to safety.
   C She's not as innocent as she appears.

2 What is the man's opinion of the sailor?
   A He admires her determination.
   B He distrusts her motives.
   C He doubts her sincerity.

Extract Two

You hear part of a radio programme on the subject of motivation.

3 What is tonight's programme going to focus on?
   A the findings of economists
   B the work of one researcher
   C the views of philosophers

4 Dr Senik's theory suggests that people
   A tend to set themselves false goals.
   B are happier if they do set themselves goals in life.
   C become frustrated if they fail to set themselves realistic goals.

Extract Three

You hear part of a programme in which two reviewers are talking about a new book.

5 They agree that the main strength of the book is the fact that
   A it gets off to a very good start.
   B it will be a useful guide for travellers in the area.
   C it deals equally well with both history and the landscape.

6 They feel that the description of the modern-day journey
   A contains unnecessary detail.
   B captures the essence of the region.
   C could have explored some issues more deeply.

B Kicking the habit

Vocabulary
Obsessions
▶ CB page 111

1 a Match each verb with the phrase that creates a common expression.

1	to conceal	a	over your life
2	to tear	b	yourself something
3	to take	c	something for the sake of it
4	to do	d	something from someone
5	to feel	e	short of something
6	to tell	f	nervous without something
7	to fool	g	yourself away from something
8	to not be	h	yourself

b Rewrite the following sentences using the correct form of expressions from Exercise 1a.

1 I used to buy shoes in the sales, *even though I didn't need them.*

....

2 The exhibition was excellent, so *it was hard for me to leave* and get the train home.

....

3 I keep *trying to make myself believe* there was nothing I could have done to help.

....

4 You can never get served, even though *the shop has plenty of staff.*

....

5 Although Alice was pregnant, *her friends didn't know her secret.*

....

6 She pretended that she was in control of the situation, but *she knew it was not true.*

....

7 I'd *be worried if I didn't have* my address book with me when I went out.

....

8 I spent so much time playing and thinking about chess that *it controlled my life.*

....

2 In each sentence, choose the correct word to complete the underlined expression.

1 I first went to play bingo for a joke, but it wasn't long before I'd got the *germ / infection / bug*, and now I play every week.

2 At first I wasn't much of a soap opera fan, but after a while, I was *hooked / trapped / caught.*

3 Gus is a bit of a fitness *fellow / freak / fan* and goes to the gym at least four times a week.

4 When my friends surprised me, I was feeling angry and was in no *feeling / sense / mood* for a joke.

5 For years I had put sugar in my tea, so it was hard to *break / crack / snap* the habit.

6 After a hard day at work, I like to come home and *fall / collapse / plunge* in front of the TV.

7 Given a *dilemma / decision / choice* between bingo or cards, I'd much rather play bingo.

8 The bus is quick and cheap. Taking a taxi is simply *throwing / passing / sending* money away.

9 Sometimes I log on just to check my email, but one thing *brings / leads / comes* to another, and before I know it I've been there five hours.

10 I didn't intend to join the drama society, I just seemed to get *pulled / blown / sucked* in.

3 Complete the text with a suitable word in each gap.

My obsession with DIY started a few years ago when I needed to get a wall painted before I had new carpets fitted. Unable to find a decorator, I decided to do it myself. Within a few weeks, I'd (1)................ the bug. When I wasn't working on the house, nothing could (2)................ me away from the makeover shows on TV.

The thing about DIY is that it's easy to get sucked (3)................ . For example, you see a nasty mark on a wall, and one thing leads to (4)................ , and before you know it the whole room needs redoing. I wouldn't call myself obsessive, but (5)................ the choice between going away for a week's holiday and spending a week at home decorating the spare room, I'd much rather do the latter. Once I replaced the glass in a window just for the (6)................ of it.

It's not that I was (7)................ of money. In fact, I spent a fortune on fancy tools, but I (8)................ myself that it was all right because of the money I was saving not getting people in to do jobs. I also thought of myself as a bit of a craftsman, but in actual fact I was just fooling (9)................ .

Eventually, my wife realised it had taken (10)................ my life and she moved out. Sadly, when we split up, we had to sell the house, so I lost all my hard work. Perhaps I should have had a solicitor at the divorce hearing instead of trying to do it myself!

B

Language development
Unreal tenses

▶ CB page 115, GR page 183

wish/if only

1 Read the text and complete the gaps with an appropriate auxiliary verb.

My boyfriend spends hours every day on the computer. I hate the computer, and I wish he (1)...................... spend so much time on it every day. He's tried to break the habit, but he says he can't. If only he (2)...................... break the habit, then we'd be able to spend our evenings together. He keeps saying he'll restrict himself to an hour a day, and I wish he (3)...................... do that. If only he (4)...................... pay as much attention to me as he does to that machine of his! He upgraded it last month to a more powerful machine, and I really wish he (5)...................... , because now he's even more obsessed with it than before.

2 Correct the mistakes in these sentences.

1 I wish that chocolate doesn't bring me out in a rash.

2 I wish I would remember where I've put my keys.

3 He talks as though he would earn a huge salary, but I know he doesn't.

4 I'd sooner spent my money on clothes than food.

5 If only travel would cost less, I'd travel a lot more.

6 It's time we stop messing around and start work.

7 I'd rather you speak to James because you know him better than I do.

8 I wish I didn't spend all my money yesterday, then I would still have some in my bank account.

3 Rewrite these statements using *I wish* or *If only*.

1 I'd like to be fitter.
   I wish ....

2 Not having my phone with me is very inconvenient.
   If only ....

3 I can't find a job that I really enjoy.
   I wish ....

4 I regret not studying French at school.
   If only ....

5 I worry about my daughter because she never tells me where she's going.
   If only ....

6 It's a pity that I left my sunglasses on the beach.
   I wish ....

7 I'd really like it if someone invented decent clothes that didn't need ironing.
   If only ....

8 I was stupid to call the shop assistant dishonest.
   I wish ....

9 These aeroplane seats are very uncomfortable – wider ones would be better.
   I wish ....

10 It's a shame that my parents couldn't come to the wedding.
   If only ....

Other expressions

4 Rewrite the sentences using expressions from the list. Use each expression once only.
*It's high time   He'd sooner   Suppose   as if it
Supposing   I'd rather   It's time I   as though he*

1 He talks to his dog in the same way as he talks to a human being.
   ....

2 Please don't wear your shoes in the house.
   ....

3 If you moved house, where would you go?
   ....

4 He thinks that moving is more hassle than staying where he is.
   ....

5 I really ought to settle down and get a place of my own now.
   ....

6 I've lived here six months, but it feels like longer.
   ....

7 We should have had this room redecorated ages ago.
   ....

8 Could you afford to stay if the rent went up?
   ....

5 Rewrite the sentences using the words in brackets.

1 She talks to me in the way that my mother would. (*though*) ....

2 I'd like you to drive, if that's OK. (*sooner*)
   ....

3 We really should go to bed now. (*time*)
   ....

4 I don't want you to tell me how the film ends. (*rather*)

5 If the information turns out to be wrong, what will you do? (*supposing*)
   ....

6 She looked like someone who had been crying. (*as if*)
   ....

7 What if she had drowned? How would you have felt? (*suppose*) ....

8 You really should get a job and become independent. (*high time*) ....

Use of English
Key word transformations (Paper 3 Part 5)

▶ ER page 170

1 a Look at question 1. There are two sentences and a key word. Read the two sentences carefully and think about what they mean.

b What part of the meaning of the first sentence has not been included in the second sentence?

c Look at the key word. How can you use this word to express the idea missing in the second sentence? Remember the key word cannot be changed.

d Write between three and six words in the gap including the key word. The words must complete the sentence logically and grammatically.

e Read both sentences again to check that they mean the same thing.

2 Repeat the procedure for questions 2–8. Use the HELP clues if necessary.using the Help clues if necessary.

HELP
➤ Question 3
Be careful: You need to write at least three words. The last word is a verb that forms half of an idiom meaning 'to visit'.
➤ Question 6
Look at the word after the gap: which verbs take this as a direct object?
➤ Question 7
There's an infinitive after the gap; a negative form of a modal verb comes before it.
➤ Question 8
What is the noun formed from 'enthusiastic'?

For questions **1–8**, complete the second sentence so that it has a similar meaning to the first sentence, using the word given. **Do not change the word given**. You must use between **three** and **six** words, including the word given.

1 I regret upsetting my parents last weekend.
   WISH
   I .... parents last weekend.

2 I never intended to invite Miranda to the party.
   HAD
   I never .... Miranda to the party.

3 Tom wrote a novel about India, a country he had never visited.
   EVER
   Tom wrote a novel about India without .... foot in the country.

4 When she's out of the office, Toni would rather contact her colleagues by email.
   TOUCH
   Toni prefers .... colleagues by email when she's out of the office.

5 From the woman's face you got the impression that she'd been crying.
   IF
   From the woman's face, it .... she'd been crying.

6 I don't want to hear all the details of your operation.
   RATHER
   I'd .... me all the details of your operation.

7 It annoys me that Ian is always leaving that door open.
   WISH
   I .... keep leaving that door open.

8 Deanna is clearly very enthusiastic about her new hobby.
   DEAL
   Deanna is showing .... for her new hobby.

Reading

Multiple matching (Paper 1 Part 4)

▶ ER page 168

1 Read the title and the subtitle of the text opposite. What do the four people have in common? Make a list of the types of personal ambitions that you think the four people might have.

2 Read the text quickly to find out about the ambitions of each person. Were your predictions correct?

3 a Read the instructions for the exam task below, then read all the questions and highlight the key words. The first two have been done for you.

   b Read section A (about Hannah Woodford) carefully and mark any sections of text that contain similar ideas or information to the questions 1–15. For example, look at question 9. Find the idiomatic phrase in section A of the text that means *taking on too much responsibility*. You have now found one question which matches option A. There are three more. Can you find them?

   c Now read section B (about Tamsin Jackson). Look at question 1 and find the phrase in the text that matches *soon able to get on with*.

4 Now complete the task.

5 Skim the text to find the idiomatic phrases in A below. Think about the meaning in the context of the text, then find the best paraphrase in B.

   A
   1 get something up and running
   2 set foot somewhere
   3 come up with something
   4 take up an offer
   5 the odds are stacked against someone
   6 give someone a push
   7 point someone in the direction of
   8 have all your eggs in one basket

   B
   a to accept something
   b to depend totally on one thing
   c to enter/arrive somewhere
   d to have an unexpected idea
   e to encourage/motivate someone
   f to make a useful suggestion about how to get something
   g to start a business
   h someone is very unlikely to succeed

You are going to read a magazine article about people who have realised a personal ambition. For questions **1–15**, choose from the people (**A–D**). The people may be chosen more than once.

Which person

was soon able to get on with their new neighbours?	1 ....
did not allow family criticism to divert them from their chosen course of action?	2 .... 3 ....
has discovered personal qualities that they were unaware of?	4 ....
required the practical assistance of business contacts in their field?	5 ....
was determined to succeed in their objective despite a lack of funds?	6 ....
is convinced that they will enjoy lasting job satisfaction?	7 ....
says they were searching for more flexibility in their daily life?	8 ....
realised they had taken on too much responsibility too quickly?	9 ....
took steps to remedy a lack of experience of dealing with business finances?	10 ....
appreciates that a strong personal relationship helped in seeing a project through?	11 ....
was surprised when a risky business venture began to succeed?	12 ....
realised the value of working as a part of a team in order to achieve their objectives?	13 ....
admits that the extent of their financial commitments made them feel insecure?	14 ....
has no particular wish to make huge profits?	15 ....

DON'T JUST DREAM IT ... DO IT!

Why do some people suddenly decide to take a risk in their lives and follow their personal ambition, when most of their friends are quite content to play it safe? We talk to four people who followed their dream.

A Hannah Woodford

I'd always loved the elegant lines of the beautiful 18th-century building in which I'd rented a room for my work as a freelance lecturer in interior
5 design. As a way of covering my costs, I'd hire it out on an occasional basis as a meeting room. People loved it, and I realised I'd stumbled across a possible business venture. The market was flooded with white-walled conference centres, but there was clearly a
10 demand for something more sumptuous. I realised I could offer my room, and others like it, as a practical, yet impressive location for top-level corporate events. There were several other rooms on offer in the same building, and being a designer, I had a clear vision of
15 the conference centre I could create, but had to draw on the experience of people I knew from the world of art and design in order to get it up and running. The project rapidly took off, and within months I'd taken over the whole building. I quickly realised that,
20 although I knew the demand was there, professionally I had bitten off far more than I could chew with this venture. The rent I was paying was astronomical, and I began to feel very exposed. Unless I sought proper guidance, I knew I'd be in trouble. Much to my
25 parents' relief, I invested in a comprehensive business course, which enabled me to get a better grasp of accounts. I'm now gaining a nationwide reputation in the corporate world – looking back, it was certainly worth the risk!

B Tamsin Jackson

30 Together with my husband, I was searching for an escape from the rat race, and when I heard about a small 'eco-village' – a community that is entirely self-sufficient in everything from food to energy – located on the west coast of Scotland, it sounded
35 exactly what we were looking for. The community lives rent-free on an island in return for caring for the environment. I knew from the first moment we set foot on the island that it was simply meant to be, and we hit it off with the locals in no time. We wasted no time
40 in abandoning our careers and selling our house in London, much to the horror of my parents, then settling down to life in a small cottage on the island. We knew that in order to succeed in our new life, we had to muck in with the others in the village, because
45 we all shared the responsibility for preserving the unspoilt beauty of the island. Our lives have changed out of all recognition; instead of struggling through traffic, I stroll down to tend the community organic garden, and we share all the household tasks. But the
50 biggest change was the arrival of our son, Joshua, now 19 months old. I used to think I wasn't cut out to be a full-time mother. But here I can combine work and childcare in a way that wouldn't have been possible before. It's a wonderful place to bring up
55 children.

C Adrian Dexter

Hitting 30 signalled a major life-shift for me. After years of dividing myself between my home on the south-west coast of England and my family's delicatessen business in London, I decided there must
60 be more to life than work. I came up with the idea of a mail-order business selling speciality food hampers, because it wouldn't tie me down to working shop hours. I would deliver a beautifully presented basket of high-quality food to the doorsteps of the busy
65 commuters, thereby saving them the trouble of a time-consuming shopping trip. At first, I just took a deep breath and called all my acquaintances working in large companies to see if they wanted to buy my hampers as a corporate gift; to my amazement,
70 several took me up on my offer. In fact, as far as the money side of the business was concerned, I had very little idea what I was taking on, but it seems to be working. After all, I didn't go into this to make a fortune; it was more so that I could take control of my
75 life, which I've certainly achieved.

D Jane Bartlett

Ever since we first met, my husband Peter and I had talked about restoring an old house. After years of looking at derelict cottages, we'd begun to give up hope, until one day driving down a country lane, we
80 caught sight of the castle and recognised it instinctively as the place where we were going to live. Even though the odds were stacked against us – given our cottage-sized budget, and the fact that the castle turned out to be a crumbling ruin – from the
85 moment we bought it, neither of us ever questioned what we'd taken on. The restoration was certainly a full-time job. If we'd listened to the pessimistic predictions of our relations, we'd never have carried on when the rain was pouring through the ceiling. But
90 Peter and I have always shared the same dream, and I couldn't have managed it without him. We've now opened the castle to the public, and our bed-and-breakfast business is growing, so I can't see us ever giving it up because we get so much out of it.

B

Writing

Letter (Paper 2 Part 1)

▶ CB pages 116–117, WR pages 195–197

Exam strategy

In a Part 1 task, don't 'lift' the words from the input texts. Keep the meaning, but use your own words wherever possible. Make sure that the words and expressions you use are in the correct register.

1 a Read the task on page 116 of the Coursebook again. Then read a student's answer on the right.

   b The underlined phrases in the answer have been 'lifted' from the input text. Which could be replaced by items from this list?

   In the first place   It was unsuccessful
   reverse their decision   opposed the idea
   without any warning

   c Rewrite the remaining underlined phrases using your own words.

2 The writer could improve the answer by using more formal words. Find these expressions (1–6) in the text and replace them with the more formal words and phrases in the list below.

   1 worried
   2 forced through
   3 say
   4 tried
   5 bring in
   6 seem

   appear   explain   introduce   implemented
   concerned   attempted

3 Rewrite the answer with all the changes.

I am writing to complain about the suggested ban on smoking in public places. I work in Café Noir, a well-known restaurant popular with visitors in the centre of town.

I am very worried about this proposal, for a number of reasons. Firstly, I don't understand why this is being forced through **(1)** <u>at such short notice</u>, and why there has been no discussion – there is no time for anyone **(2)** <u>to get used to the idea</u>. And secondly, **(3)** <u>it is ridiculous</u> to suggest it in outdoor bars and restaurants – such an idea is **(4)** <u>totally unenforceable.</u>

To support my argument against the proposed ban, I would like to say what happened when the authorities tried to bring in a ban on smoking in my home town. **(5)** <u>It failed</u>, and the politicians had to **(6)** <u>change their minds</u>. **(7)** <u>For a start</u>, few people **(8)** <u>took any notice of the law</u>. Of course, most businesses **(9)** <u>were against it.</u> A small number of restaurants tried to implement a no-smoking policy, but **(10)** <u>half their customers disappeared overnight</u>. If the same thing happened here, **(11)** <u>I could lose my job</u>.

As a suggestion, **(12)** <u>why not encourage workplaces</u> to introduce specific non-smoking areas instead? This would seem to be a better solution.

A A changing society

Use of English
Word formation (Paper 3 Part 3)

▶ CB page 122, ER page 169

1 a Read the title of the text to identify the topic. How might people in different cultures be influenced by international television?

  b Read the text through quickly ignoring the gaps for the moment. Does the writer mention your ideas? Does anything surprise you?

2 Read the text again carefully and complete the task, using the Help clues if necessary.

3 Read through the text again when you've finished to check your answers.

HELP

➤ Questions 2
  Add a prefix to this word – but it's not a negative one.

➤ Question 5
  Be careful – a spelling change is needed here.

➤ Question 6
  Two changes are needed in this word: a prefix and a suffix.

➤ Question 8
  Is a noun or an adjective required here? Read the surrounding text carefully to check.

For questions **1–10**, read the text below. Use the word given in capitals at the end of some of the lines to form a word that fits in the gap in the same line. There is an example at the beginning **(0)**.

What the world watches on TV

Over 2 billion people in developing countries now have access to **(0)** Western television. There are, however, few **(1)**............... statistics to give us information about the pattern of television viewing in Africa and Asia. We know a great deal, for example, about the programming strategies of international broadcasters, but very little about what is actually watched, and there hasn't been very much **(2)**............... into the impact of the programmes.

There is, however, a **(3)**............... to assume that the world's poor people, unlike the media-aware rich, will be **(4)**............... influenced by what they see. But studies have shown that across cultures, the **(5)**............... to well-known programmes can be as diverse as it is **(6)**............... , because we all bring our own experience to bear on what we see.

For example, one study revealed that in rural Algeria people watching the US soap opera *Dallas* were not particularly impressed by its capitalist values, or indeed by the **(7)**............... lifestyle enjoyed by the characters. What made the greatest **(8)**............... on them was another aspect of the series entirely: its **(9)**............... of a close-knit family in a patriarchal world, something fast disappearing in Algerian culture. People were therefore inclined to view the programmes through rather **(10)**............... eyes.

	WEST
	RELY
	SEARCH
	TEND
	EASY
	RESPOND
	PREDICT
	LUXURY
	IMPRESS
	PORTRAY
	NOSTALGIA

Language development
Emphasis (inversion and fronting)
▶ CB page 124, GR page 183

Negative introductory expressions

1 **Decide whether the verb should be inverted or not and mark the correct option in each pair.**
   1 If I'm short of time, *I will / will I* stay up all night working.
   2 Only if I'm short of time, *I will / will I* stay up all night working.
   3 Rarely these days *I get / do I get* to bed before midnight.
   4 Sometimes these days *I get / do I get* to bed before midnight.
   5 Since I was a student, *I have / have I* lived alone.
   6 Not since I was a student *I have / have I* lived alone.
   7 Only after six months of study *I could / could I* speak Japanese.
   8 After only six months of study, *I could / could I* speak Japanese.
   9 Hardly *she had / had she* spoken when Jim arrived.
   10 *She had / Had she* hardly spoken when Jim arrived.

2 **Rewrite the following sentences beginning with one of the expressions in the list.**
   Not only … but also   Not since   No way
   Rarely   Not a   Only now   No sooner … than
   Under no circumstances

   1 The company will not give a refund without a receipt in any situation.
   ....
   2 The new computer system is both safer and more reliable.
   ....
   3 We hadn't been anywhere so interesting since we visited Nepal some years ago.
   ....
   4 We hardly ever come across such a hard-working student these days.
   ....
   5 We had only just started dinner when she suddenly said she had to leave.
   ....
   6 At the time, I didn't realise how dishonest she was, but I do now.
   ....
   7 We spent nothing, not even a penny, on food all the time we were there.
   ....
   8 I refuse to work on the afternoon of the Cup Final.
   ....

Emphasis through fronting parts of the sentence

3 **Rewrite these sentences, moving the underlined objects before the subjects.**
   1 It took <u>years</u> to complete the building of the tunnel.
   ....
   2 I'm going to enjoy <u>this</u>!
   ....
   3 We waited <u>weeks and weeks</u> with no news from them.
   ....
   4 Jerry's going to run a marathon? I'd like to see <u>that</u>!
   ....
   5 They say the health service is improving? I find <u>that</u> difficult to believe.
   ....

4 **Rewrite these sentences, putting the adverb/adverbial phrase of the second sentence in each case before the subject. Make any necessary changes. The adverb has been underlined in the first one for you.**
   1 The door suddenly opened, and Stella came <u>in</u>.
   ....
   2 I begged the boy to get help, and he ran off as fast as his legs would carry him.
   ....
   3 Hearing a noise, they opened the cellar door, and a black dog sprang out.
   ....
   4 There was a sudden gust of wind, and the balloon flew up into the treetops.
   ....
   5 There was an outhouse behind the main building. There was an old well in front of it.
   ....

5 **Rewrite these sentences beginning with *so* or *such* and making any necessary changes.**
   1 He was so tired that he could hardly walk.
   ....
   2 There was such danger in the streets that we dared not go out.
   ....
   3 Their anxiety was such that they did not sleep at all for three days.
   ....
   4 They were so confident of victory that they planned the celebrations before the election had taken place.
   ....
   5 His ability on the football field was such that no one could stop him scoring goals.
   ....

Use of English

Multiple-choice cloze (Paper 3 Part 1)

▶ ER page 169

1 Read the title of the text below, then read the whole text quickly for general understanding, ignoring the gaps for the moment.
   1 What is *eBay*?
   2 How do you buy something on *eBay*?

2 Read the text again carefully and try to predict what each answer will be. Then look at the options **A–D** and complete the task. Use the Help clues if necessary.

3 Read through the text again when you've finished to check that the options you've chosen fit in with the overall meaning of the text.

HELP
➤ Question 1
Only one of the options completes the expression with *by*.
➤ Question 2
Which of these adverbs collocates with *regarded* to tell us that this opinion is commonly held?
➤ Question 9
Which of these phrases captures the idea of *personal recommendations*?
➤ Question 12
Does this adverb signal a reinforcement of the ideas in the preceding sentence, or a contrast to them?

Language development
Read the text again. Can you find two sentences which contain examples of fronting and inversion? Underline them.

For questions **1–12**, read the text below and decide which answer (**A**, **B**, **C** or **D**) best fits each gap. There is an example at the beginning (**0**).

The *eBay* Phenomenon

Located in an elegant 18th-century building in London is the nerve (**0**) A of one of the world's most prolific companies. It (**1**)........ by the name *eBay*. Not only has the company gone from Internet hobby site to potent economic force, with 95 million users in just ten years, it is (**2**)........ regarded as having altered the (**3**)........ of commercial life as we know it.

If you want to buy anything, from a nail file to an airliner, *eBay* is the Internet site to go to. A million items appear for sale each day in what is (**4**)........ an online auction. If you like the description of an item, you make a bid within a given time limit; if you (**5**) .... to be the highest bidder, you become the (**6**)........ owner of the goods in question. But the most astounding factor behind *eBay* is not the range and value of the goods on (**7**)........ , but the fact that the whole business is based on mutual trust. Rarely do you find people so willing to buy unseen goods from an unknown source.

Part of the explanation for this (**8**)........ in the fact that 95% of *eBay* buyers and sellers are private individuals. The company has expanded through (**9**)........ recommendations rather than smart marketing, and there's a real (**10**)........ of community about it. What's more, using *eBay* (**11**)........ to that instinctive sense of satisfaction people get from the process of bargaining – and from actually getting a bargain at the end of it. (**12**)........ , it puts the fun back into shopping.

	A	B	C	D
0	centre	heart	focus	middle
1	calls	goes	knows	greets
2	largely	deeply	greatly	widely
3	course	route	flow	trend
4	precisely	effectively	absolutely	exactly
5	turn out	check in	show up	send off
6	proud	conceited	boastful	vain
7	issue	supply	question	offer
8	finds	draws	lies	comes
9	matter-of-fact	man-to-man	tell-tale	word-of-mouth
10	sense	feel	touch	mood
11	entices	attracts	tempts	appeals
12	Otherwise	In short	Instead	Despite that

Language development
Attitude clauses and phrases
▶ CB page 126, WR page 203

1 Underline the most appropriate word in italics.

1 Many people think young men love gadgets. But *actually, / rightly,* it is women who now spend the most money on technology.

2 *Not surprisingly, / Strangely,* the advent of TV has had a major impact on modern society.

3 The 24/7 society has benefits, but *doubtless, / honestly,* who wants to go shopping at three in the morning?

4 *Annoyingly, / As a matter of fact,* some of the original data from the study is missing, so we cannot draw firm conclusions.

5 *Hopefully, / Obviously,* something must be done about the litter problem immediately before it gets out of hand.

6 *Indeed, / Naturally,* everyone we interviewed in our survey said cheaper food would be a benefit.

7 Because accommodation is so vital, the shortage of decent housing is, *arguably, / personally,* the most important issue facing the city at present.

8 A lot of people complain that our facilities are too expensive, so *admittedly, / presumably,* if prices were reduced, more people would use them.

2 Complete each gap with a suitable expression from the list. Use each expression only once.

frankly   funnily   granted   indeed   of course
surely   understandably   worryingly

1 You know we were talking about Sandra on Friday? Well, ... enough, I bumped into her on the street on Saturday!

2 We don't mind at all if you join us. .... , we will be delighted.

3 .... , the level of air pollution in the city is increasing every year.

4 You must have heard of him, ... ? He's one of our best writers.

5 Well, quite .... , I think he is overrated.

6 They were pretty angry when they heard he had crashed the car, ... enough.

7 Most people enjoy shopping, but .... there are exceptions to every rule.

8 'Our products are the best on the market.'
'.................... , but they are also the most expensive, so not many people can afford them.'

3 Complete the expressions used for generalising with one word from the list.

considered   generally   large   main   rule   whole

1 .... speaking, we don't have much of a problem with crime in this area.

2 All things .... , I think we made the right decision.

3 On the .... , the children were very well behaved.

4 By and .... , the event was a success.

5 As a .... , I don't eat very much during the day.

6 In the .... , the weather here is pretty good in summer.

4 Complete the expressions used for indicating an attitude or feelings with one word from the list.

afraid   believe   far   honest   judging   speaking
truth   turned

1 Strictly .... , tomatoes are not vegetables but fruit.

2 .... it or not, the figures show that crime is decreasing.

3 To be .... , I didn't enjoy the party very much.

4 As .... as I know, he's still living in Manchester.

5 To tell the .... , we have no idea how the burglars got in.

6 .... by his accent, he must come from the north of England.

7 I completely forgot to tell them we'd be late, I'm ....

8 I thought I was going to fail the test, but as it .... out, I did very well.

5 Complete the text by putting an appropriate word or expression from Exercises 1–4 in each gap. There may be more than one possibility.

(1).................... , older people are more concerned about burglary than younger people. Yet, (2).................... , incidents of theft have not increased sharply in our neighbourhood in recent years. (3).................... they do occur from time to time. (4).................... , a bag was stolen from the local library just last week. (5).................... , the incident was not a theft. (6).................... , the owner's friend had hidden the bag as a joke. But (7).................... , it seems that a lot of thefts take place during daylight hours, something you wouldn't necessarily expect. (8).................... , there is no one around to check who is entering the building at that time. (9).................... the library should ensure that there is a receptionist on duty at all times?

Listening
Multiple matching (Paper 4 Part 4)

▶ ER pages 170–171

1 a Read the instructions for the task.

   b Read Task One carefully. Think about the vocabulary and expressions you would expect to hear connected with each of the social changes.

   c Read Task Two carefully and highlight the key words in the options. The first two have been done for you.

2 ○ Listen to the recording twice. The first time you listen, do Task One. The second time, do Task Two. Use the Help clues if necessary. Remember that you are listening to understand the speakers' main points, attitudes and opinions.

HELP
➤ Question 1
The speaker tells us that he now has to leave home early to *avoid the jams*. Which of the options A–H could this relate to? Listen to the rest of the text to hear confirmation of your chosen option.
➤ Question 2
At the beginning, the speaker tells us that she *gets in front of the screen*. Which of the social changes could this refer to? Be careful, there are three possibilities. Listen to the rest of the text for confirmation of which one matches exactly.
➤ Question 6
Listen for why the speaker no longer goes running. How has this affected his health?
➤ Question 7
The speaker says *it's a lot cheaper than calling them on their mobiles*. Which option does this match?

You will hear **five** short extracts in which various people are talking about current trends in society.

TASK ONE
For questions **1–5**, choose from the list **A–H** the social trend that each speaker is talking about.

TASK TWO
For questions **6–10**, choose from the list **A–H** how each speaker has been affected by the social trend they are talking about.

You will hear the recording twice. While you listen you must complete both tasks.

A the habit of viewing television while eating

B the growing number of open-plan offices

C the increasing consumption of take-away meals

D the build-up in the volume of traffic

E the expanding use of mobile phones

F the growing popularity of computer games

G the increasing reliance on email

H the tendency for people to make regular use of a gym

Speaker 1	1
Speaker 2	2
Speaker 3	3
Speaker 4	4
Speaker 5	5

A It has created difficulties for me at work.

B It has saved me a certain amount of money.

C It has helped me manage my time better.

D It has enabled me to make new friends.

E It has caused tensions within my family.

F It has had a bad affect on my health.

G It has helped me to be more efficient in my job.

H It has forced me to rethink my finances.

Speaker 1	6
Speaker 2	7
Speaker 3	8
Speaker 4	9
Speaker 5	10

Vocabulary
Law and order
▶ CB pages 127–130

1 Match a word in column A to a word in column B and write the names of the crimes on the lines below. Which are written as one word?

A	B
1 joy	dealing
2 armed	lifting
3 drunk	riding
4 drug	hacking
5 computer	robbery
6 shop	driving

1 ....
2 ....
3 ....
4 ....
5 ....
6 ....

2 Read these definitions and write the names of the crimes. Choose from Exercise 1 and the following list.

arson   burglary   forgery   manslaughter   slander

1 a false spoken statement about someone, intended to damage the good opinion that people have of that person: ....
2 deliberately making something burn, especially a building: ....
3 getting into a building to steal things: ....
4 stealing from a shop: ....
5 killing someone illegally but not deliberately:
....
6 stealing a car and driving it in a fast and dangerous way for fun: ....
7 secretly using or changing the information in other people's computer systems: ....
8 copying official documents, money, etc. illegally:
....

3 Complete the table.

Verb	Noun	Person
mug	1	2
3	burglary	4
murder	5	6
–	arson	7
steal	8	9
10	forgery	11
rob	12	13
14	joyriding	15

4 a Complete the text with words from the list. Use each word once only.

*acting   catch   commit   detect   fight   liaise
maintain   scene   search*

The police policy of 'Stop and (**1**).....................' is a controversial one. On the one hand, the police see it as a useful technique in the (**2**)..................... against crime and claim that it helps them to (**3**)..................... law and order. They point out that it makes good sense to stop people near the (**4**)..................... of a crime, as they may be involved. The policy also allows them to target people who are (**5**)..................... suspiciously, and look as if they are about to (**6**)..................... a crime. If they stop someone and discover that they are carrying drugs or stolen property, they are able to both (**7**)..................... crime and (**8**)..................... criminals.

On the other hand, the policy results in some sections of the population being stopped much more often than others, with the result that the police are seen as being prejudiced. They therefore have to work hard to (**9**)..................... with local communities, explaining why they stop the people that they do.

b Do the same with the following text.

*amnesty   anonymity   arrest   clamp down
come forward   penalty   schemes   tackle*

Another controversial subject is the idea of offering the public a weapon (**1**)..................... . At such times, people can take any illegally held weapons to a local police station and no questions will be asked about them. Such (**2**)..................... have resulted in thousands of weapons being removed from the streets, and the police see it as a useful way to (**3**)..................... crime in general, and gang crime in particular.

However, as the (**4**)..................... of the people handing in the weapons is maintained, the police cannot (**5**)..................... anyone for having them. Some people argue that the people who (**6**)..................... and hand in weapons are unlikely to be real criminals. But if this policy is used, and the (**7**)..................... for possessing an illegal weapon is increased at the same time, the police can give a clear message that they mean to (**8**)..................... on people who carry weapons.

Language development

Comparison

▶ CB page 132, GR page 184

Comparatives and superlatives

1 **Identify and correct the mistakes in the following sentences.**

1 Nirvana are still my most favourite band of all time.
2 James is slightly taller as his brother.
3 Life is a great much noisier nowadays.
4 This is easily the worse murder we have ever had to deal with in this city.
5 The job now is nothing like dangerous as it was.
6 Some people think that shoplifting is not such serious crime as burglary.
7 Murder is by far a most serious crime anyone can commit.
8 He is one of the most experienced officer in the police force.

so/such

2 **Combine the sentences using *so* or *such* and a *that*-clause. In some cases, both are possible.**

1 The trial was complex. Therefore it went on for weeks.

2 The cost of legal proceedings can be very high. Therefore some people cannot afford it.

3 Lawyers tend to earn a lot of money. Many people want to become lawyers.

4 Some laws are very outdated. They need to be rewritten.

5 The evidence was very strong. The jury reached a decision very quickly.

6 After the trial, there were many people outside the court. As a result, we couldn't see anything.

too/enough

3 **Combine the sentences using either *too* or *enough*. In some cases, it is possible to make sentences with both.**

1 The police arrived late. They couldn't catch the criminals.

2 There were not many officers on duty. They couldn't control the crowd.

3 We couldn't ignore the crime. It was very serious.

4 There was some evidence against him. Therefore the police could charge him.

5 Many crimes are committed. It is impossible for the police to solve all of them.

6 The joyrider drove faster than the police cars could go. Therefore they didn't catch him.

Double comparisons

4 **Match the sentence halves and rewrite them using a form of double comparison (*the -er … the -er* or *more and more …*).**

1 If they change the law soon,
2 Prisons are becoming
3 If we have more police officers on the street,
4 A growing number of police officers
5 Crimes that are more serious
6 In some places, criminal gangs

a generally receive tougher penalties.
b we will feel much safer.
c are becoming increasingly violent.
d it will be better.
e would like to carry a gun.
f increasingly overcrowded.

1
2
3
4
5
6

as/like

5 **Complete the sentences with *as* or *like*.**

1 .... a parent, I feel that more should be done to protect our children.
2 His parents treat him .... a child, even though he's 16.
3 The garden looked .... a jungle after being neglected for weeks.
4 When we went camping, we used a large flat stone .... a table.
5 Caroline moves and talks exactly .... her mother.
6 Tom Cruise appeared .... a lawyer in the film.

Use of English
Gapped sentences (Paper 3 Part 4)
▶ ER page 170

1 Look at the example in the gapped-sentence task below and read the task rubric.
   1 How many sentences are there?
   2 How many words are missing?
   3 What do the missing words have in common?

2 a Read all three sentences in the example carefully. What type of word is missing from all three (noun, verb, adjective, etc.)?

   b Make a list of words that will fit in the gap in the first sentence. Think about both the grammar and the context. Which of these words would you include in your list?

wait	keep	very	hold	stand
stay	remain	pose	sit	

   c How many of the words on your list also fit the gap in the second sentence? Think about both the grammar and the context. Cross any words off your list which don't fit here.

   d Look at the third sentence. Will one of the words left on your list fit here?

   e Write your answer in all three gaps. Read the sentences again to check that it fits well in all three.

3 Now look at Questions 1–5 and repeat the procedure, using the HELP clues if necessary.

TIP

Don't spend too long on each question. If you have no idea of what word is needed, go on to the next question and come back to this one later.

HELP
➤ Question 1
   In all three sentences a noun is needed. All of these nouns fit in the first gap: *manner, attitude, appearance, dress, qualifications, experience, looks.* Which of them fits in the other sentences?
➤ Question 2
   A verb is needed in each of the gaps. It is followed by an infinitive in the third sentence, and so has a slightly different meaning.
➤ Question 4
   If you're not sure about this one, try starting with the third sentence.

For questions **1–5**, think of **one** word only which can be used appropriately in all three sentences. Here is an example **(0)**.

0 Olga told Mario to .... still while she took his photograph.
   When finished, the modernist sculpture will .... in the town's main square.
   I can't .... the way Phil keeps interrupting me when I'm trying to explain something.

1 When interviewing applicants for jobs, you should be careful not to judge people by their .... alone.
   Dan's work has the .... of something done in a great hurry, because he never goes back and checks what he's written.
   Fiona asked the child actor how old he'd been when he made his first .... on television.

2 'Can you .... all those enquiries yourself, or would you like some help?' David asked the company's new receptionist.
   Having decided to reorganise their office space, the company needed to find somebody who could .... the project for them.
   Although afraid of offending her hosts, Stella simply couldn't .... to finish the enormous portions of meat she was given.

3 Tina was keen to buy a folding bicycle that would .... inside the boot of her car.
   Marius painted in a very individual style that didn't .... easily into any traditional category.
   Greg borrowed his brother's suit to wear at the wedding, but to be honest it didn't really .... him very well.

4 I'm not .... about Barbara's new hairstyle – it makes her look too serious.
   Steve didn't really know the answer to the last question in the quiz, so he just made a .... guess and to his astonishment got it right.
   It is now an offence to pick .... flowers in the countryside.

5 It was a rather .... day, with so much mist and low cloud that we hardly got to see any sunshine at all.
   Thelma explained to the doctor that what she felt in her knee was more a kind of .... ache than a sharp pain.
   The film is really action-packed from start to finish with never a .... moment.

Writing

Essay (Paper 2 Part 2)

▶ CB page 133

Exam strategy

In the exam, you may be asked to write an essay. An essay puts forward a point of view and is usually written for your teacher. You should use a neutral style, and make sure that you organise your points clearly in paragraphs with relevant supporting detail.

1 Read the task below, and think of three problems and three solutions you can suggest about the topic.

> Your class has been discussing what people can do to help develop a sense of community in a town or a residential college. Your teacher has now asked you to write an essay outlining what some of the problems of developing a sense of community are, and suggesting possible solutions.
>
> Write your **essay** in 220–260 words.

2 Look at the suggested approaches below, and then read a student's answer on the right. Which approach has the student taken? What three problems and three solutions has the writer described?

> A
> • Introduction stating topic
> • Problems
> • Solutions
> • Conclusion summarising points made

> B
> • Introduction stating topic
> • Problem 1 + solution
> • Problem 2 + solution
> • Problem 3 + solution
> • Conclusion summarising points made

3 An essay should be organised clearly and use good linking expressions that are also in a semi-formal register. Read the answer again and choose the best linking expression from each pair.

4 Now write your own answer to the task, but base it on life in a residential college. Think of three reasons why a sense of community is needed and might be lacking, and three things that the college could do to improve the situation. Then write your essay using one of the two models suggested in Exercise 2.

(1) *It is often said that/As you all know*, the pace of modern life has led to a breakdown in community spirit, and that (2) *as a result/in contrast* we are all more concerned with our own lives than with others. Is this true, and (3) *even if/if so*, what can be done about it?

There are certainly problems in many aspects of society today. The emphasis placed on material success and having a good life can lead people to ignore the needs of others less well off in their communities. Furthermore, families are more fragmented as children move away from their home towns to find work, and they may not feel the same loyalty to their new town. (4) *At the end/Finally*, the Internet has caused problems for communities as people spend so much time inside surfing the net that they live in a 'virtual' community rather than a real one.

(5) *Anyway/So* how can we create more of a community spirit? People need to realise that (6) *although/in spite of* money is important, there are other priorities. The media should give less publicity to celebrity lifestyles and more to community work. (7) *Obviously/Generally* people have to move to find work, but town councils could provide more social opportunities. (8) *In this way/Such as this* they could involve newcomers. (9) *Although/In spite of* the advantages of the Internet, it may be the biggest problem – so why not make it a social occasion by introducing Internet cafés where people can surf together?

(10) *To sum up/Therefore*, although things can be done, ultimately it is up to us all to put more back into our communities and take responsibility.

Reading
Multiple-choice questions (Paper 1 Part 3)
▶ ER page 168

1 Read the title of the text and the subheading.
   1 What is meant by the phrase *young offender*?
   2 What attitude do you think the young offenders will have towards drama sessions?

2 Read the text quickly to check whether you were right. As you read, make a note of why each of the following people is mentioned in the text.
   1 Nathan   2 Sally Brookes   3 Lou Heywood

3 Read all the questions and underline the key words in each question.

4 a Read question 1 and look at the first word of the options **A–D**. Each of them focuses on Nathan; this tells us that we need to read for what he says or does in relation to Feltham.

   b Read what Nathan says about the place in the text. Now read the options carefully. Which one is closest to your own understanding of what he says?

   c Read the paragraph again carefully to check that your answer is right and that the other options are definitely wrong.

5 Now continue to answer the rest of the questions, following the same procedure.

6 Match the words from the text in column A to a definition in column B.

A	B
1 loathe	a not convinced that something is true
2 innovative	b designed for someone particular
3 detained	c hate
4 constructive	d being likely to be hurt
5 sceptical	e hidden
6 irrational	f without reason
7 concealed	g with new ideas
8 vulnerability	h with a positive outcome
9 tailor-made	i held as a prisoner

You are going to read a magazine article about the use of drama with young offenders. For questions **1–7**, choose the answer (**A**, **B**, **C** or **D**) which you think fits best according to the text.

FACING FACTS

The Geese Theatre Group has a dramatic approach to helping young offenders stay out of custody.

Like many young offenders, 16-year-old Nathan loathes depending on a 'front'. He says: 'It's what landed me in here. I felt I had to be the "tough" guy or the "cool" guy to survive, and the next thing I
5 knew, I was in here for stealing cars.' 'Here' is Feltham young offenders' institution near London where convicted 14–18-year-olds are detained. As Nathan adds, 'Nobody says what they really mean here. It's a frightening place, so you just carry on
10 pretending that you're a particular kind of person because you believe that will keep you the safest. But acting in that way in here just makes you do it all the more when you get out, and so the cycle goes on.'

15 What does make Nathan stand out from other young offenders, however, is his willingness to admit this, and even to change it. It is, he says, the result of an innovative drama course that the Geese Theatre Company – a touring company based at the
20 Midlands Arts Centre in Birmingham – has extended to young offenders to help them examine their reactions to things and develop more constructive ways of handling challenging situations.

25 It works like this. Masks, representing a variety of 'fronts', are worn by the actors who then play out a scene according to the rationale of that behaviour. The mask for Cool ('Listen, you're all making a lot of fuss about nothing – if you want the TV, just
30 steal it') is an ominous, green face with dark glasses; Target ('I don't feel in control of this situation – it's everyone else's fault I'm doing this') has an archery target on the forehead. At various points in the performance, the audience of young offenders calls
35 out for the character to lift the mask and explain what he is really feeling — and how he might find ways to act on that feeling, rather than according to the front. The actor then tests out the consequences of that option.

40 'It's not about truth, but more about what is being
withheld – highlighting hidden vulnerabilities and
concealed thoughts and feelings,' says Sally Brookes,
the theatre company's programmes director. 'That's
why we use fragment masks because they display only
45 a fragment of behaviour. Few people are the Joker, the
Mouth, the Victim or any other front all the time.'
Through workshops lasting one day, and 'residencies',
which last several, the company focuses on the young
offenders, motivation and ability to change. Brookes
50 says: 'We recognise that wider social and economic
factors have a major influence on crime – particularly
when it comes to young offenders – but we work
from the premise that each person can nonetheless
make active choices and has a responsibility for their
55 actions. For us, that's the key point.'

She admits that many of the inmates are sceptical
about the idea of drama. 'They feel it's childish and
silly,' she says. 'But that's overcome fairly quickly –
not only because there is a clear logic to what we're
60 doing, but because they get to explore behaviour
patterns one step removed through the medium of an
actor. That means they themselves don't end up
feeling judged or interrogated. Young offenders are a
difficult group to measure in terms of the effects of
65 the course,' she admits, 'but the verbal feedback from
prison workers and probation workers, as well as the
young people themselves, is certainly positive enough
for us to be booked up for months ahead.'

Like all the trainers at Geese, Lou Heywood, the
70 company's touring director, comes from a background
of drama training, with a strong interest in issue-
based theatre. In addition, all staff receive six months'
training in teamwork, the criminal justice system,
probation services and aspects of offending behaviour.
75 Lou believes that each workshop must be tailor-made
to the needs of a particular group. One, for instance,
may focus intensively on aggression, while another
may explore a range of knee-jerk reactions and their
ramifications. One may focus on behaviour outside
80 prison, while another may include the experience of
prison itself. He says: 'The objectives must be clear.
One session we recently ran was for young offenders
who had been in the institution less than a week.
Many seemed confident, but you could tell that
85 almost all of them were frightened, particularly if they
didn't understand the system. The first part of the
drama involved acting out a scene in which a lad
went into his cell for the first time. Using the masks,
we explored what he might be thinking. The aim was
90 to let the group talk honestly about the kinds of
feelings they might have, rather than letting them out
through destructive behaviour.'

1 In the first paragraph, Nathan tells us that at Feltham
Young Offenders Institution,
  A he has to hide behind a certain image.
  B he is forced to adopt an unfamiliar role.
  C his behaviour has changed dramatically.
  D he is learning to be a more successful criminal.

2 The drama course he attended has enabled
Nathan to
  A consider taking up a career in the theatre.
  B realise why he has been behaving irrationally.
  C stand up to his fellow prisoners more effectively.
  D understand what makes him behave in particular
    ways.

3 During the sessions, the masks used by the theatre
company allow the young offenders to
  A conceal their real identities.
  B appreciate the funny side of their situation.
  C recognise their own failings in certain areas.
  D see that there are different ways of dealing with
    things.

4 Sally Brookes stresses that the drama workshops
aim to give young offenders
  A a chance to take control of their own lives.
  B an opportunity to discuss the causes of crime.
  C an understanding of why a life of crime is wrong.
  D an insight into their reasons for committing crimes.

5 Sally thinks that the main reason for the success of
the workshops is that young offenders
  A are unfamiliar with drama techniques.
  B can see what it is that the company is trying to
    achieve.
  C can recognise their own attitudes in the actors'
    performance.
  D are young enough to feel uninhibited about taking
    part in drama.

6 What do we learn about the trainers in the Geese
group?
  A They were all once young offenders themselves.
  B They all have experience of drama teaching.
  C They all studied law before taking up drama.
  D They all usually do their work in the theatre.

7 Lou Heywood stresses the importance of sessions
which
  A meet the needs of a wide range of participants.
  B reflect the experience of the particular group of
    offenders.
  C prepare the participants for life outside prison after
    their release.
  D take account of the behavioural problems of
    individual offenders.

A Something to say

Use of English
Multiple-choice cloze (Paper 3 Part 1)

▶ ER page 169

1 Read the title of the text, then read the whole text quickly for general understanding, ignoring the gaps for the moment. What is N'kisi able to do?

2 Read the text again carefully and think about the type of word which will fit in each gap. Then look at the options **A–D** and complete the task. Use the Help clues if necessary.

3 Read through the text again when you've finished to check.

HELP
➤ Question 1
Only one of the options makes sense if followed by *as*.
➤ Question 2
Which of these adjectives describes how you feel towards someone you like and spend a lot of time with?
➤ Question 10
Which of these words collocates with *life* to mean *the average length of time that something lives*?
➤ Question 11
Is it a consequence or a contrast which is needed here?

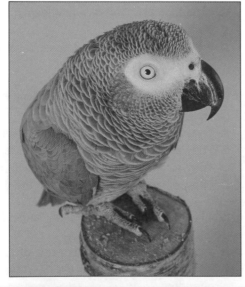

For questions **1–12**, read the text below and decide which answer (**A, B, C** or **D**) best fits each gap. There is an example at the beginning (**0**).

The world's most talkative bird

N'kisi is the name of a grey parrot, bred in captivity, which (**0**) A to the artist Aimee Morgana. Every day, Aimee speaks to her parrot, explaining what she does in simple sentences and encouraging him to develop what she (**1**)....... as a spontaneous and creative relationship with language. So successful has she been that N'kisi is now the world's most talked-about talking bird.

Parrots and people have been (**2**)....... companions for centuries, and everybody knows that parrots can be taught to talk. As Aimee explains, however, parrots can do more than just (**3**)....... back what is said to them. N'Kisi says what he wants, when he wants and, (**4**)....... most animals trained to perform human-like tasks, he receives no form of reward in return for his utterances.

N'kisi's vocabulary (**5**)....... to around 950 words which he uses in (**6**)....... and with past, present and future verb tenses. What is (**7**)....... impressive, however, is that N'kisi doesn't speak randomly, but actually (**8**)....... on what's going on around him, even inventing original expressions, for example calling Aimee's aromatherapy oils 'pretty smell medicine'. He also (**9**)....... exciting events, like his first ride in a car, and pesters Aimee to take him out again like a persistent toddler: 'Wanna go in a car right now!'

The life (**10**)....... of a parrot is roughly equivalent to that of a human being. Six-year-old N'kisi is (**11**)....... just beginning his education, and Aimee has (**12**)....... hopes that his communicative abilities will continue to increase as he matures.

0 A belongs	**B** possesses	**C** retains	**D** shelters
1 A illustrates	**B** describes	**C** demonstrates	**D** emphasises
2 A firm	**B** near	**C** tight	**D** close
3 A respond	**B** reply	**C** repeat	**D** replicate
4 A unlike	**B** dissimilar	**C** different	**D** unrelated
5 A climbs	**B** runs	**C** makes	**D** totals
6 A reference	**B** background	**C** context	**D** situation
7 A particularly	**B** largely	**C** chiefly	**D** importantly
8 A mentions	**B** discusses	**C** observes	**D** comments
9 A reminds	**B** recalls	**C** reminisces	**D** reviews
10 A expectancy	**B** assumption	**C** forecast	**D** anticipation
11 A otherwise	**B** therefore	**C** nonetheless	**D** instead
12 A wide	**B** deep	**C** high	**D** strong

Language development
Read the text again and find a sentence beginning with *so*. What happens to the verb?

Language development
Reporting structures
▶ CB page 140, GR page 185

Review of reported speech

Tenses in reported speech

1 Write up the minutes of a meeting held last week, using the reporting verbs given in brackets for each sentence.
1 John: 'Sales have increased by 20 per cent.' (*report*)
2 Dave: 'The new campaign starts in three days' time.' (*announce*)
3 Adam: 'We're getting a lot of positive feedback from consumers.' (*tell*)
4 Jenny: 'I met the clients yesterday and I'm sure they don't have any worries.' (*say*)
5 Adam: 'I haven't seen the new posters yet.' (*confess*)
6 Dave: 'Unfortunately I don't have them with me, but I'll get everyone a copy tomorrow.' (*admit / promise*)
7 Jenny: 'Well, guys, keep up the good work. I'll see you all here again this time next week.' (*encourage / remind*)

1 John reported that ....
2 ....
3 ....
4 ....
5 ....
6 ....
7 ....

Reporting questions

2 Report the following questions you were asked at a job interview.
1 Where have you worked before?
2 Why do you want to work for this company?
3 Have you ever worked in marketing before?
4 What is your favourite advertising slogan?
5 Are you a good communicator?
6 Where do you think you will be in ten years' time?
7 Do you work better on your own or as part of a team?

8 What did you least like about your old job?
9 What impression did you have when you came in here this morning?
10 Can you start next Monday?

The interviewer asked me:
1 where ....
2 ....
3 ....
4 ....
5 ....
6 ....
7 ....
8 ....
9 ....
10 ....

Reporting modal verbs

3 Put the following into reported speech.
1 'I might not be here tomorrow,' explained Harvey.
Harvey explained that ....
....

2 'I shouldn't have said what I did,' said Amanda.
Amanda said ....
....

3 'We can get it for you by next Tuesday,' promised the shop assistant.
The shop assistant promised that ....
....

4 'I can help if you need a hand,' said my neighbour.
My neighbour said ....
....

5 'You don't need to do any more; you've done enough,' I told the class.
I told the class ....
....

6 'I shan't be here next week. I'll be on holiday,' explained the teacher.
The teacher explained that ....
....

7 'Shall I put the lights on? It's getting dark,' asked Rachel.
Rachel asked ....
....

8 'I must admit; it's a great film,' said the critic.
The critic admitted that ....
....

Patterns after reporting verbs

4 **Underline the correct option. Only one option is possible.**

1 They recommended .... the train.
   A that I took   B to take   C me to take

2 He offered .... a lift home in his car.
   A that he would give me   B to give me
   C giving me

3 They reassured .... home safely.
   A me to get   B me that I would get
   C me in getting

4 They expected .... home before six.
   A me to get   B getting   C that I get

5 She accused me .... dangerously.
   A to drive   B that I drive   C of driving

6 I admitted .... over the speed limit.
   A to go   B going   C it to go

7 The police warned .... it again.
   A me not to do   B me don't do   C that I didn't do

8 I reassured .... go fast again.
   A that I wouldn't   B them not to
   C them that I wouldn't

5 **Rewrite the following sentences, using one of the reporting verbs in the list. Report the meaning of the sentence, not the actual words. Think about which of the patterns above to use.**

~~advised~~   beg   blame   deny   promise   refuse
remind   suggest   thank (for)

1 My classmate: 'If I were you, I'd ask him to speak more slowly.'
   My classmate _advised me_ ....

2 Dad: 'Don't worry, I will get a film on the way home.'
   ....

3 My colleague: 'There's no way I'm helping you tonight.'
   ....

4 My brother: 'I didn't read your private diary, honest.'
   ....

5 My secretary: 'Don't forget that you've got an appointment at 4 p.m.'
   ....

6 Anne's friend: 'Please, please tell me where you got that shirt.'
   ....

....
7 The driver: 'It was very kind of you to help me change the wheel.'

....
8 Julie: 'It was Gerald's fault that we got lost.'

....

Impersonal report structures

6 **Rewrite the news story using impersonal report structures. If two forms are possible, write both.**

1 Everyone knows that fake CDs are widely available.
   Fake CDs ....
   It is ....

2 A police spokesperson has announced that they have made a major arrest.
   It ....

3 Reports say that 100,000 CDs were confiscated.
   It ....
   100,000 CDs ....

4 The police believe the fake CDs were made abroad.
   It ....
   The fake CDs ....

5 They think that the CDs were smuggled into the country in boats.
   It ....
   The CDs ....

6 They suspect that the man arrested is the ringleader of an international gang.
   The man arrested ....

7 Reputedly, he has made millions of dollars from crime.
   He is ....
   It ....

8 There are rumours that he has homes on five continents.
   He ....
   It ....

9 Some people have suggested that fewer people would buy fake CDs if genuine ones were not so expensive.
   It ....
   ....

10 Some say that the industry is looking at new ways to prevent illegal copying.
   The industry ....
   ....

Use of English

Key word transformations
(Paper 3 Part 5) ▶ ER page 170

1 a Look at question 1. There are two sentences and a key word. Read the two sentences carefully and think about what they mean.

  b What part of the meaning of the first sentence has not been included in the second sentence?

  c Look at the key word. How can you use this word to express the idea missing in the second sentence? Remember the key word cannot be changed.

  d Write between three and six words in the gap including the key word. The words must complete the sentence logically and grammatically.

  e Read both sentences again to check that they mean the same thing.

2 Repeat the procedure for questions 2–8. Use the HELP clues if necessary.

HELP
➤ Question 1
You may need to add an adverb to make sure the idea of 'everyone' is also in the second sentence.
➤ Question 2
The key word is part of a common expression that means 'will do very soon'.
➤ Question 4
You need to use a phrasal verb here that means 'to refuse'.
➤ Question 6
Be careful: which auxiliary verb is needed here, 'does' or 'is'?

For questions **1–8**, complete the second sentence so that it has a similar meaning to the first sentence, using the word given. **Do not change the word given.** You must use between **three** and **six** words, including the word given.

1 Everyone thinks that man is dishonest.
  THOUGHT
  That man .... dishonest.

2 Rumours suggest that the couple will announce their engagement very soon.
  ABOUT
  The couple are .... announce their engagement.

3 'Don't forget that you need to phone the doctor, Ted,' said his wife.
  REMINDED
  Ted's wife .... needed to phone the doctor.

4 'Thank you for the offer, Roy, but I don't need any help,' said Suzy.
  TURNED
  Suzy .... offer of help.

5 'Please don't leave valuables in your rooms,' said the hotel receptionist to the tourists.
  ADVISED
  The hotel receptionist .... leave valuables in their rooms.

6 As well as playing the trombone brilliantly, Gus has also won competitions.
  BRILLIANT
  Not only .... trombone player, he has also won competitions.

7 For security reasons, you are asked not to keep a written record of your email password.
  INTERESTS
  In ...., you are asked not to keep a written record of your email password.

8 This door should be kept closed at all times.
  CIRCUMSTANCES
  Under .... left open.

Listening
Multiple-choice questions (Paper 4 Part 3)

▶ ER pages 170–171

1 Read the instructions for the exam task. Then read the multiple-choice questions and highlight the most important ideas in the question and options. This has been done for you in question 1.

2 🎧 Listen to the whole recording once, and try to answer the questions. Use the Help clues if necessary. Then listen again to check and complete your answers.

HELP

➤ **Question 1**
Jessica's answer comes after she mentions her mother meeting her from school. What is the multiword verb that means *to embarrass someone*? You will hear this in the part of the text which gives you the answer.

➤ **Question 2**
Listen carefully to how Jessica's mother reacted after she went to university, then you will hear the answer to this question.

➤ **Question 3**
Listen to the whole of Jessica's answer to the interviewer's question. You will hear a phrasal verb that means *to survive on very little money*. This will help you to choose the correct answer.

3 a Complete the sentences with the correct verb from the list in the appropriate form.
   attract   catch   make   take

   1 I didn't have much money, so was always struggling to .... ends meet.
   2 I had a go at modelling, and decided to .... it up professionally.
   3 When I was a child, modelling didn't .... my imagination.
   4 Her clothes always .... a lot of attention.

   b Match the phrases in Exercise 3a to their definitions.
   a to make someone feel excited and interested
   b to make people take notice
   c to have just enough money to buy what you need
   d to become interested in an activity and spend time doing it

---

You will hear an interview with the fashion model Jessica Hanson, who is talking about her upbringing and career. For questions **1–6** choose the answer (**A**, **B**, **C**, or **D**) which fits best according to what you hear.

1 Jessica says that when she was a child, she
   A found her mother's behaviour embarrassing.
   B was envious of her sister's sense of humour.
   C was fascinated by the glamorous world of fashion.
   D felt most at ease with people of her own age group.

2 Looking back at her schooldays, Jessica feels that her mother
   A expected far too much of her.
   B often caused family arguments.
   C sometimes criticised her unfairly.
   D showed little interest in her achievements.

3 Why did Jessica first take up modelling as a student?
   A It provided her with an additional source of income.
   B She was unable to cope with her university course.
   C It was a result of her mother's contacts in fashion.
   D She wanted to prove something to her parents.

4 In bringing up her own children, Jessica aims to
   A be completely honest with them.
   B teach them to communicate easily.
   C encourage them to be independent.
   D steer them towards worthwhile careers.

5 When asked about her decision to write a novel, Jessica says that she
   A intends to draw inspiration from her own close relationships.
   B suspects the commercial motives of her publisher.
   C is adapting an idea from an earlier short story.
   D is grateful for the support from her friends.

6 How does Jessica feel about her future career?
   A She's determined to make her children her first priority.
   B She's unsure whether she wants to remain in the public eye.
   C She's confident that her writing will bring financial security.
   D She's keen to maintain her contacts with the world of fashion.

B Making a statement

Vocabulary
Clothing and fashion
▶ CB page 143

1 a All of the words below can be used as nouns. Decide whether each word is countable or uncountable, and whether each is formal, neutral or informal. Use a dictionary to help you if necessary.

cloth   clothes   clothing   dress/attire   garment   kit   outfit   wardrobe   wear

b Use a suitable word from Exercise 1a in the correct form to complete the sentences.

1 I'm going to need a complete new summer .... to take on holiday.
2 The wedding dress was made from the finest silk ....
3 Only two .... may be taken in the fitting room at any one time.
4 After getting caught in the rain, their .... were soaked and they had to change.
5 There was nothing in the suitcase except a few items of ....
6 I chucked my sports .... into a bag and took it to work so I could go running at lunchtime.
7 My parents own a shop that specialises in leisure ....
8 It was an amazing formal party with all the men in evening ....
9 I spent a fortune on a new .... for the office party.

2 Complete the text with the words in the list. Use a dictionary to check if necessary.

brand   design   label   logo   pattern   style

Marketing clothes and accessories can be a difficult business. Customers want comfort and quality but are also buying a certain **(1)**..................... . An item bearing a designer **(2)**..................... can cost many times the equivalent item from a High Street shop, even if it is a classic **(3)**..................... such as a basic white T-shirt. Some companies, such as jeans manufacturers, generate strong **(4)**..................... loyalty so customers keep coming back to buy more. Some companies like Gap promote their product by producing many items bearing their **(5)**..................... in a prominent position. Other companies use an instantly recognisable **(6)**..................... , such as Burberry's distinctive black and brown check, on a wide range of items.

3 a Use the table to make phrasal verbs connected to clothes and match them to the definitions below. Use a dictionary to help you if necessary.

dress	grow	up	into
take	slip	down	out of
let	wrap	in	on
change	do/zip	out	off

1 make clothes larger/smaller
2 make clothes longer/shorter
3 wear very smart/casual clothes on a particular occasion
4 replace one set of clothes with another
5 put on warm clothes
6 put on/take off clothes quickly and easily
7 fasten clothes
8 become too big / big enough for some clothes

b Complete the sentences with the phrasal verbs above.

1 When I get home, the first thing I do is .... my work clothes and .... something more comfortable.
2 It's a casual party, so you don't have to ....
3 When I .... my clothes, I passed them on to my younger brother.
4 It's very cold, so .... well when you go out.
5 He .... a pair of shoes and left the house.
6 Since I've put on weight, I've had to .... my trousers by a couple of centimetres.
7 If the trousers are too long, you can always .... them ....
8 .... your coat .... , or you'll get cold.

4 Choose the correct word to complete the underlined phrases.

1 Whenever a new fashion <u>comes *in / on / over*</u>, you can be sure that Diane will be wearing it.
2 When I bought these shoes, they were <u>the *peak / top / height* of fashion</u>, but I'd never wear them now.
3 Long skirts seem to <u>come in and out of *style / mode / trend*</u> every few years.
4 I never imagined the fashion for tattoos would <u>*take / catch / get* on</u> the way it did.
5 I'm keeping my old flared trousers until the next time they <u>make a *return / comeback / reprise*</u>.
6 His i-pod is as much <u>a fashion *statement / comment / announcement*</u> as a music player.
7 I tend to avoid designer clothes as I don't want to end up looking like a <u>fashion *casualty / victim / sufferer*</u>.

Language development
Word formation
▶ CB page 147

For each word, complete the table. Use a dictionary if necessary. Then choose the correct form of the word to complete the sentences below.

1 desire

noun [C/U]	
verb [T]	
adjective (*describing something worth having*)	
negative adjective	
adverb (from adjective)	
noun [U] (from adjective)	
negative noun [C] (*somebody/something that isn't wanted*)	
adjective (from past participle)	

1 It is highly .... that we keep information about new products a secret.
2 Unfortunately the marketing campaign produced some .... side effects.
3 The shop is very exclusive and has strict security to keep out .... like me!
4 The advertising campaign had the .... effect of increasing sales by 20%.
5 The .... of many products depends as much on fashion as it does on appearance or functionality.

2 origin

noun [C]	
plural noun	
adjective	
negative adjective	
adverb	
verb [I, T]	
noun [C] (thing or person)	
noun [U] (from adjective)	

1 All products should be clearly marked with their country of ....
2 We need people who can come up with .... ideas.
3 A lot of their designs are rather dull and ....
4 I kept a copy of the letter and returned the ....
5 KitKat's slogan was .... used in the 1950s.
6 The company director likes to keep quiet about his humble ....

7 The products are well made, but lack ....
8 The Internet .... from an idea to connect universities.

3 secure

adjective	
negative adjective	
adverb	
negative adverb	
noun [U]	
negative noun [C, U]	
verb [T]	

1 For reasons of .... , we cannot say who is staying in the hotel.
2 With no one to chat to, Jenny felt lonely and .... when she first went off to university.
3 By sending messages in code, companies can communicate .... over the Internet.
4 Make sure you .... all the doors and windows before you leave.
5 Negotiators are still speaking to the kidnappers, trying to .... the release of the hostages.
6 Dan's deepest fears and .... stem from his having been abandoned as a child.
7 It is important to make sure you have a .... connection when shopping on the Internet.
8 The rope was .... fastened, and came loose.

4 popular

adjective	
negative adjective	
noun [U]	
negative noun [U]	
adverb	
verb [T]	
noun [U] (from verb)	

1 The most .... drink in the world is probably tea.
2 The company's .... has declined a great deal in the last ten years.
3 American comedy shows did a lot to .... coffee shops in the 1990s.
4 We stopped making the product because it was so .... with consumers.
5 The tax increases have added to the government's ....
6 In Britain, ball-point pens are .... known as biros, after their inventor.
7 TV programmes have tried to encourage the .... of science and technology.

Use of English

Open cloze (Paper 3 Part 2)

▶ ER page 169

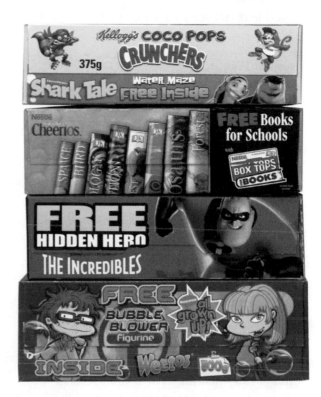

1 Read the title of the text to identify the topic, then read the whole text quickly for general understanding, ignoring the gaps for the moment. Which two things most affect consumers' decisions to buy a particular product?
a) the price b) free gifts c) special offers
d) the packaging

2 Read the text again and complete the task. Use the Help clues if necessary.

3 When you've finished, read the whole text again to check it makes complete sense.

HELP
➤ Question 2
Add a preposition to make a phrasal verb which means 'be easily noticed'
➤ Question 7
Add a preposition to complete this common expression.
➤ Question 10
Check the context carefully to see whether a word with a positive or a negative meaning is needed here.

For questions **1–15**, read the text below and think of the word which best fits each gap. Use only **one** word in each gap. There is an example at the beginning (**0**).

Special offers you can't refuse

Anyone (**0**)....who.... has ever done the weekly shop for an average British family will know that you come home with (**1**)............... sorts of free gifts and promotions. These might include a free toy or perhaps a bestselling novel or even the chance to win a holiday or a new house.

The free gifts, competitions and offers on packaged goods are designed to make those products stand (**2**)............... on the supermarket shelves. Clearly it's a marketing strategy that works, (**3**)............... companies wouldn't do it. (**4**)............... is more, for a large number of consumers, decisions about (**5**)............... brand to buy are clearly influenced (**6**)............... the promise of a free gift or the offer on a product's packaging. Over 70 per cent of British families with children visit a supermarket each week, and make over 70 per cent of their buying decisions (**7**)............... the spur of the moment.

(**8**)............... breakfast cereals targeted at children (**9**)............... an example. Manufacturers of these products know that people won't buy their product (**10**)............... there's a gift or an offer. So they (**11**)............... sure there always is one. (**12**)............... other words, the product with the most attractive offer picks (**13**)............... the most sales.

One couple who (**14**)............... married in London last year took this type of consumer behaviour to an extreme degree. Heinz, the food manufacturer, was running a 'win a free house' promotion, so the pair asked all their guests to bring along tins of food (**15**)............... of conventional presents.

Language development

Read through the text again and find all the nouns ending in -y. Which ones have a plural in -ies, and which have a plural in -ys?

Reading

Gapped text (Paper 1 Part 2)

▶ ER page 168

1 Read the heading and subheading of the text, to identify the topic. Then read the base text quickly, ignoring the gaps for the moment, and find out who the people (a–c) are, and what the numbers (d–f) refer to.
   a) Hamish Pringle
   b) David Graham
   c) Michael Winner
   d) 100
   e) 200,000
   f) 150

2 Look at question 1 and read the first two paragraphs of the base text again. Use the highlighted words and phrases to help you choose which option A–G fits the gap.

3 Read the options A–G and underline words and phrases that might help you to match them to the text. Then complete the task.

4 When you have finished the task, read the whole text through to check it makes complete sense.

5 a Match the words in list A to those in list B to form collocations used in the text.

A		B	
1	advertising	a	broker
2	crunching	b	endorsement
3	financial	c	order
4	insurance	d	campaign
5	pecking	e	adviser
6	product	f	numbers

   b Choose the phrase below which best matches the meaning of each collocation in Exercise 5a.
   a a way of ranking people according to importance
   b a personal assurance that a product is good
   c advertisements and other activities to persuade people to buy something
   d doing a lot of calculations
   e someone who advises people about how to save and invest money
   f someone who sells insurance to people

You are going to read a magazine article about celebrities and advertising. Six paragraphs have been removed from the article. Choose from the paragraphs **A–G** the one which fits each gap (**1–6**). There is one extra paragraph you do not need to use.

In celebrities we trust

Britain's obsession with celebrities means that people there are more likely to trust a soap star endorsing goods in advertisements than a qualified expert. Nick Higham asks why.

Celebrity sells. We all know that: it's one of the oldest clichés in advertising. But why? And why do some celebrities apparently sell more effectively than others? On April 5, the Institute of Practitioners in Advertising (IPA) is holding a
5 half-day seminar on the subject. It'll cost £100 to attend, but delegates will get a free copy of a new book, *Celebrity Sells* by IPA Director General Hamish Pringle. Who says advertising agencies don't understand sales promotion?

1	

Of course, the effectiveness or otherwise of an advertising
10 campaign is dictated by more than the shrewdness of the casting. The copywriting, the media planning, the amount spent and the aptness with which the advertisements themselves reflect the existing strategy for a brand are all significant factors. So eliminating all the other variables and
15 isolating the effects of a well-known name and face is not easy.

A But there is one potentially awkward implication in all this. It might strengthen the hand of those who maintain that light entertainment and soap operas are 'fast food for the brain', and that our predilection for them may be harmful.

B Nonetheless, if we all agree that celebrity does sell, one question immediately presents itself. Why? And a second follows. If we can work out why it sells, can we bottle it?

C Yet on television, the gossip about what is happening to the soap-opera families attracts millions more viewers than news documentaries on subjects which actually affect people's lives. And the irony of this is not lost on advertising executives when they're searching for a famous face to endorse a product.

D According to newspaper reports, the author believes the most successful celebrity ever to have appeared in a British advertising campaign is the actress Prunella Scales, whose advertisements for the Tesco supermarket chain have helped generate an additional £2.2bn in sales in the country since 1998.

E He proposes, if he can find partners or clients willing to sponsor a study, to start with soap operas, looking at those moments which produced the highest audiences, and which hold audiences for the longest periods, and seeing what elements they have in common and whether they connect up with the theory of evolutionary psychology.

F To be successful in such a social grouping requires a complex mix of co-operation and competition. It helps to know quite a bit about your fellow group members, especially those of high status in the pecking order. So, successful humans are those who are curious about friends, relatives, colleagues and anyone perceived to have high status – including, in the modern world, 'stars'.

G He thinks a partial answer to the puzzle of why celebrities sell – and also to why some TV programmes work better than others – may lie in the discipline of evolutionary psychology and the associated fields of neuroscience and genetics.

2

And here another expert thinks he may be on to something. David Graham has been crunching numbers and consulting strategically in the television industry for about 15 years. He's an expert in the analysis of television audience data, on the impact of broadcasting regulation and on the dynamics of the TV business.

3

According to Graham, academic evolutionary psychologists believe we may be genetically programmed to behave in certain ways – a belief they have come to partly by observing that certain parts of the brain are always associated with certain skills or behaviours. There may, for instance, be what Graham calls a 'gossip instinct'. It was a useful thing to have 200,000 years ago, when mankind lived in foraging bands of 150 or so and the modern human brain evolved.

4

This innate ability helps to explain why we pay extra attention to someone we recognise as a star in a TV advertisement or a poster – even though, rationally we would be better off paying attention to an expert. A financial adviser or insurance broker is likely to know more about insurance policies than the film director Michael Winner. But Winner is a celebrity, he draws our attention, and so an insurance company is willing to pay him a lot more than they would a financial expert to feature in its advertising. What intrigues Graham is the possibility of finding practical applications for this kind of theoretical work that go beyond the simple observation that celebrities attract attention.

5

But in due course, the same theoretical framework could obviously be applied to advertising as well. Graham rejects the suggestion that he's just trying to quantify the unquantifiable, or that a possible consequence of this work would be programmes and advertisements that were boringly similar. 'The comforting thing is that people do have an appetite for variety,' he says. 'That speaks against formulaic solutions and repeating oneself.'

6

The analogy here is with our taste for sweet and fattening treats. That developed when we were hunter-gatherers, and fruits and fats were in short supply: we have been programmed to stuff ourselves with sugars and fats whenever we find them. Our circumstances have changed, but our genetic make-up hasn't. Obesity is the result. Perhaps our gossip gene, which also evolved in circumstances rather different from modern society, may be equally damaging.

Writing Proposal (Paper 2, Part 1)

▶ CB pages 148–149, WR page 198

Exam strategy

One of the things your written work is assessed on is accuracy. When you check your work, think about the kind of errors you usually make, as you may not see these easily. Always remember to check grammar, spelling, punctuation and formality.

1 a Read the task on page 148 of the Coursebook again. Then read a student's answer on the right.

   b Find and correct four grammatical errors. Check:
   - verb tenses
   - subject/verb agreement
   - reference words
   - articles.

   c Find and correct four spelling mistakes.

   d Find and correct four punctuation errors.

   e The underlined words are too informal for a proposal. Replace them with suitable words or phrases.

2 Now write your own answer to one of the Part 2 tasks below. Remember that, in a report, the focus is on an existing situation, but in a proposal there is more emphasis on suggestions for the future. Remember to check your work for errors.

A

You are a member of the Board of Directors of an Adventure Centre. Your Managing Director wants to change the way the Centre organises its publicity, and has asked you to write a proposal suggesting ways in which the publicity could be improved.
Write your **proposal** in 220–260 words.

B

You are a member of the Board of Directors of an Adventure Centre. You have received complaints from customers unable to find out detailed information about the Centre. You have been asked to write a report explaining why the publicity is not satisfactory and recommending changes.
Write your **report** in 220–260 words.

Proposal suggesting ways of raising the profile of the Adventure Centre

Introduction

The aim of this proposal are to suggest ways of promoting the Adventure Centre to increase bookings, and make recommendations for action it is based on information gatherd from customer feedback.

Feedback

The Centre is generaly popular with those who come, but there is a problem with publicity. Some said that they have not heard of the Centre until a friend told them about them, and others complained that they could not find the website.

Suggestions and recommendations

In order to deal with the problems identefied in the feedback and to increase bookings; we recommend the following measures.

1 To address the problem of publicity:
   - journalists should be invited to special Open Days.
   - a specialist should be <u>taken on</u> to redesign the website, to make it more accesible.

2 To attract more bookings:
   - introduce a series of special offer's, including offering reduced prices in the low season, and special packages for school parties.

Conclusion

Implementing the measures above should lead to the general increase in awareness of the Centre and a subsequent increase in bookings. If the Centre is to <u>do well</u>, we urge the Directors to put them in place immediately.

A You have to laugh

Use of English
Word formation (Paper 3 Part 3)

▶ CB page 154, ER page 169

1 Read the title of the text to identify the topic. Then read the text through quickly, ignoring the gaps for the moment.

2 Read the text again carefully and fill in the gaps, using the Help clues if necessary.

3 Read through the text again when you've finished to check.

HELP
➤ **Question 3**
This word needs two suffixes to form the adverb.
➤ **Question 4**
Which negative prefix do we add to this word?
➤ **Questions 9**
Be careful. Two suffixes are possible here. Read the surrounding text to be sure which one is appropriate in context.

For questions **1–10**, read the text below. Use the word given in capitals at the end of some of the lines to form a word that fits in the gap in the same line. There is an example at the beginning **(0)**.

Laugh out loud (Radio 4: 8.30 p.m.)

If you tune into Radio 4 at 8.30 this evening, you will hear a delightful **(0)** _documentary_   DOCUMENT
programme on the subject of laughter,
presented by Nicola Green. **(1)**............................ ,   INITIAL
when she went out with her tape recorder
and started laughing in public places, people
were a little **(2)**............................ of her. But as   SUSPICION
she demonstrates rather **(3)**............................ on   CHARM
this short programme, once one person
starts laughing, it's not long before everybody
joins in. It seems to be an **(4)**............................   VOLUNTARY
response.

The scientific **(5)**............................ of humour is a   ANALYSE
rather serious subject, and Nicola wisely
doesn't go into this, concentrating instead on
what makes people laugh, which is not
(6)............................ the same thing. Children, of   NECESSARY
course, will laugh at almost anything: just an
(7)............................ noise or a funny name will   AMUSE
set them off and after that even the most
banal comment can seem hilarious to them.
Nicola's only slightly **(8)**............................   DEPRESS
conclusion is that we probably laugh less as
we get older. This is probably because if we
really give way to **(9)**............................ peels of   HELP
laughter, we start to feel vulnerable –
something we are less comfortable about with
increasing age and **(10)**............................ . I can't   RESPONSIBLE
help but think that's rather a shame!

Language development

How many other words can you form from the word *necessary*? Write them down and check their meanings in a dictionary.

A

Language development
Participle clauses
▶ CB page 156, GR page 186

-ing clauses

1 Rewrite these sentences using finite clauses and expressions from the list. Make any changes necessary.
and   and as a result   because   just as   when

1 I kept calling the box office, trying to get tickets.

....

2 Having bought my popcorn, I settled down to enjoy the film.

....

3 We stood at the back of the concert hall, trying to see what was happening.

....

4 On arriving at the theatre, I realised that I had left the tickets behind.

....

5 The lights went out, leaving the audience in total darkness.

....

2 Rewrite the following sentences using present participle *-ing* clauses.

1 Because she is growing up in Los Angeles, she dreams of becoming an actress.

....

2 Brad has had a busy year, as he has starred in three films.

....

3 I live in London, so it's easy for me to get to the theatre.

....

4 As I read the review, I realised that I had seen the film before.

....

5 He held a top hat in one hand and a cane in the other and performed an amazing tap-dance routine.

....

6 He couldn't swim, so he had to rely on other actors to do all his swimming stunts for him.

....

3 Rewrite these sentences using either present or perfect participle clauses and a conjunction where necessary.

1 Because she was an art lover, she was very keen to go and see the exhibition.

....

2 After we had packed the car up, we set off.

....

3 Because I had never been to Italy before, I was feeling slightly nervous.

....

4 Although I was pleased to be in New York, I missed my old friends.

....

5 I put the phone down, grabbed my suitcase and ran.

....

6 I hadn't performed on the stage before, so I didn't know what to expect.

....

Past participle clauses

4 Rewrite these sentences using finite clauses and one of the words from the list.
because   if   once

1 The cast chosen, they could start the rehearsals.

....

2 Booked solid for weeks, the show is hard to get into.

....

3 Carefully edited, the chase scenes look spectacular.

....

5 Rewrite these sentences using past participle clauses. Make any changes necessary.

1 I was bored so I fell asleep in the second act.

....

2 If Claudia is given the right coaching, she could be a great soprano one day.

....

3 The show has been rated by the critics as a 'must see' show, so it should be pretty good.

....

4 The set had been poorly constructed and was starting to collapse.

....

5 Had the show been better publicised, it would have been more successful.

....

6 Once the show had been properly advertised, it started to do better.

....

to-infinitive clauses

6 Rewrite these sentences using finite clauses and one of the words or expressions from the list.

and then   and as a result   if   so that

1 I bought a programme to see who else was in the show.

....

2 I sat down and started watching, only to realise I had seen the film before.

....

3 I've seen the Rocky Horror Show enough times to have learnt most of the words.

....

4 To hear her sing, you'd never believe she was totally untrained.

....

7 Rewrite these sentences using *to*-infinitive clauses.

1 We got seats at the front so we would have a better view.

....

2 They sold enough tickets that the production was a financial success.

....

3 If you heard her talk, you'd think she was a great actress herself.

....

4 We arrived at the theatre and discovered that the lead actor was sick.

....

5 I had had plenty of rehearsals and was therefore confident in the role.

....

6 If a new musical is going to be successful, it needs to have at least three great tunes.

....

All participle clauses

8 Correct the mistakes in the following sentences.

1 The plan was for the show transferred to Broadway after a few months in London.

2 The children jumped up, to shout, 'He's behind you!' when the villain appeared.

3 Not to have a ticket, I couldn't get into the concert.

4 Unsuccessfully, I searched the Internet finding the soundtrack.

5 I enjoyed the show, laughed all the way through.

6 Julie was the first person playing the role in the theatre.

7 Walking on stage, the audience greeted the singer with a loud cheer.

8 I'm very disappointed not have seen Elvis perform live.

9 She walked on stage, only realising she had forgotten her words.

10 Rising to their feet, the soloist bowed to the ecstatic audience.

9 Read the text and put the verbs in brackets into the *-ing* or *to*-infinitive form.

The old Theatre Royal had stood empty for many years, (1)........................ (*close down*) in the 1980s. But Simon Appleton, (2)........................ (*be*) a theatre lover and keen amateur actor, was determined to get it reopened. (3)........................ (*persuade*) a bank to lend him money for his scheme, he took on a team of skilled builders (4)........................ (*renovate*) the old building and (5)........................ (*restore*) it to its former glory. (6)........................ (*help*) by a team of willing volunteers, the builders completed the work within a year, and the theatre reopened under Simon's management.

Now, it is a thriving local theatre again, (7)........................ (*welcome*) touring theatre and dance companies from all over the world. The theatre also encourages amateur groups, regularly (8)........................ (*stage*) performances by local schools and amateur dramatics groups.

Use of English
Gapped sentences (Paper 3 Part 4)

▶ ER page 170

1   Look at the example in the gapped-sentence task below and read the task rubric.
   1 How many sentences are there?
   2 How many words are missing?
   3 What do the missing words have in common?

2   a Read all three sentences in the example carefully. What type of word is missing from all three (noun, verb, adjective, etc.)?

   b Make a list of words that will fit in the gap in the first sentence. Think about both the grammar and the context. Which of these words would you include in your list?

   > high   single   same   one   flat   low
   > standard   unique   minimum   top   student

   c How many of the words on your list also fit the gap in the second sentence? Think about both the grammar and the context. Cross any words off your list which don't fit here.

   d Look at the third sentence. Will one of the words left on your list fit here?

   e Write your answer in all three gaps. Read the sentences again to check that it fits well in all three.

3   Now look at Questions 1–5 and repeat the procedure, using the HELP clues if necessary.

TIP

Look at prepositions carefully. Is the missing word ever part of a phrasal verb?

HELP
➤ **Question 1**
   In all three sentences a verb is needed. All of these verbs fit in the first gap: *summon, organise, attend, arrange, call, hold*. Which of them fits in the other sentences?
➤ **Question 2**
   A verb is needed in each of the gaps. It is a rather formal verb that collocates with 'the services of' in the context of employment.
➤ **Question 3**
   Make a list of words describing the weather. From the context, this word doesn't describe an extreme weather condition.

For questions **1–5**, think of **one** word only which can be used appropriately in all three sentences. Here is an example **(0)**.

0   However much use you make of the city's public transport system, with this type of ticket you pay a .... rate of £10.00 per week.
    The printer needs to stand on a .... surface which will remain still when the scanner is in operation.
    The southern part of the island is rather .... and featureless, but much drier and sunnier than the mountainous area to the north.

1   The pop star has decided to .... a press conference so that she can put an end to rumours regarding her impending marriage.
    If you need a lift, I could .... in on my way to the party.
    After the heavy rain of last week, it was decided to .... off this year's garden party.

2   Because it was doing an increasing amount of trade in the Swedish market, the company decided to .... the services of a bilingual secretary.
    A politician needs to be a good public speaker who can .... the attention of an audience.
    I've tried to .... my new neighbours in conversation, but they always seem in a hurry to get away.

3   This week's weather will be mostly .... with temperatures about average for the time of year.
    I think it's only .... to say that the accident was completely my own fault and the other driver was in no way to blame.
    The rest of Gwenda's family live a .... distance away from her, so she doesn't get to see them very often.

4   The proceeds of the live aid concert will be .... equally between three international charities.
    Gordon was disappointed that his new suitcase .... along the seam the first time he used it.
    The group played together for three years, but when the lead singer decided to go solo, they .... up.

5   After leaving the expressway, take the road to Woodstock and continue to .... left until you get to the town itself.
    After spending years working as a chemist in the food industry, Des says he couldn't .... the thought of eating anything out of a packet.
    Although medical expenses are covered by their travel insurance, holidaymakers have to .... the cost of any non-urgent dental treatment themselves.

Listening

Multiple choice (Paper 4 Part 1)

▶ ER page 170

1 a Read the instructions for the task.
   1 How many extracts are you going to hear?
   2 What is each extract about?
   b **Look at the questions for Extract One. How much do you find out the topics and speakers**
   a) from the rubric?   b) from the questions?
   c) Highlight the most important ideas in each question stem and in the options (A, B or C).

2 Listen to the recording and choose the correct option A, B or C. Follow the same procedure for Extracts 2 and 3.

TIP

The word 'feel' has two meanings in English. Sometimes it means how someone feels emotionally as in question 5, and sometimes it means a feeling in the sense of an opinion as in question 4.

HELP
➤ Question 1
This is about the first question the songwriter is asked. Which of the three options summarises what he says in reply?
➤ Question 2
This question focuses on the songwriter's purpose when he answers the question. Which option best describes what he is saying?
➤ Question 3
Listen to the last word in the man's first turn – what does it mean in this context?
➤ Question 4
In the last part of the text, the female speaker tells us her opinion. What is the gist of what she says?
➤ Question 6
At the end of the recording, the woman starts to get a bit annoyed – what has annoyed her?

You will hear three different extracts. For questions **1–6**, choose the answer (**A**, **B** or **C**) which fits best according to what you hear.

Extract 1

You hear part of an interview with a singer-songwriter.

1 What does he say about the process of writing songs?
   A He likes to work to a formula.
   B He's always thinking about his work.
   C He finds it hard to settle down to work.

2 When answering the interviewer's second question, he is
   A describing the songwriter's craft.
   B denying that his later songs lack originality.
   C explaining what he finds hard about songwriting.

Extract 2

You hear part of a radio discussion about the environmental impact of rock music.

3 What point does the male speaker make about concerts?
   A They are becoming more financially important to bands.
   B They provide a chance for a band to show environmental awareness.
   C It's not easy to calculate how much damage they do to the environment.

4 The woman feels that some of the data relating to carbon emissions at rock concerts
   A has underestimated the problem.
   B has been based on questionable assumptions.
   C has failed to make people sufficiently aware of the issue.

Extract Three

You overhear two friends discussing a concert.

5 How does the woman feel about going to the concert?
   A unsure if she can afford it
   B reluctant to commit herself
   C doubtful about the sound in the venue

6 How does she react to the man's second suggestion?
   A She doesn't like the word he uses.
   B She doesn't agree with his reasoning.
   C She doesn't like the idea of eating out in London.

Vocabulary Music ▶ CB pages 160–161

Answer the following questions by choosing **A**, **B**, **C** or **D**. Look up any words that you do not know in a dictionary.

Music Quiz

How much do you know about music?

1 Which of the following is *not* a wind instrument?
  A saxophone
  B flute
  C bassoon
  D cello

2 What do you call the person who stands in front of a group of musicians or singers and directs their playing or singing?
  A director
  B conductor
  C concertmaster
  D principal

3 A piece of music for two singers or players is known as a
  A solo.
  B duet.
  C trio.
  D quartet.

4 A long piece of classical music, usually in four parts, written for an orchestra is known as a/an
  A symphony.
  B composition.
  C arrangement.
  D melody.

5 Musical instruments such as drums, bells, etc., which you play by hitting them, are part of which section of an orchestra?
  A string
  B woodwind
  C percussion
  D brass

6 Which of the following is a song that is sung by only one person in an opera?
  A overture
  B aria
  C hit
  D single

7 Playing jazz or rock music with other people in an informal way, without planning what you are going to play is called
  A jamming.
  B amplifying.
  C strumming.
  D plucking.

8 Which of the following is *not* a type of modern music?
  A R&B
  B house
  C garage
  D garden

9 The people who sing with someone in a pop group to accompany the lead singer are known as
  A backing singers.
  B chorus.
  C choir.
  D accompanist.

10 Music CDs are divided into
  A parts.
  B movements.
  C sections.
  D tracks.

11 The words of a song are known as the
  A score.
  B soundtrack.
  C lyrics.
  D notes.

12 A new recording of a song, piece of music, etc. that was originally recorded by a different artist is a/an
  A copy.
  B cover (version).
  C imitation.
  D revival.

13 A record, group, etc. that has sold the most records in a particular week is said to be at the top of the
  A charts.
  B lists.
  C tables.
  D sales.

14 Which of the following would best describe a performance by a musician or group playing modern popular music?
  A concert
  B show
  C gig
  D festival

Language development
Dependent prepositions

▶ CB page 163, GR page 186

Form

1 **Choose the correct option. One or two options may be correct.**
   1 Jenny has always been interested in ....
     A acting.   B becoming an actress.
     C to act.
   2 I .... to her joining a theatre company.
     A don't oppose   B have no objection
     C don't object
   3 There is something strange about .... to play villains.
     A he wants   B him wanting
     C his wanting
   4 Many people discourage their children .... actors
     A to become   B from becoming
     C become
   5 Be nice to the critics. Our success depends on ....
     A them.   B their reviews.
     C get a good review.
   6 When I started acting, I dreamt of .... an Oscar.
     A win   B me for winning   C winning
   7 I'd like to discuss ....
     A the plot with you.
     B about the plot with you.
     C you with the plot.
   8 He's accustomed to .... in rehearsals.
     A spend hours   B spending hours
     C the hours he spends

Prepositions after verbs and adjectives with related meanings

2 **Words with related or opposite meanings often take the same preposition.**

   a **Complete each sentence with a preposition that can be used with all three verbs.**
     1 My children both *hope / long / yearn* .... a part in the school play.
     2 Mike and Jeff are bound to *fall out / quarrel / squabble* .... who gets the best part.
     3 If I know Nicole, she'll *boast / brag / rave* .... getting the leading role.

   4 The preparations and rehearsals *culminate / end / result* .... a huge show for the public.
   5 William was *suspected / accused / convicted* .... stealing instruments from the theatre.
   6 We are planning to *campaign / demonstrate / protest* .... the closing of the old theatre.

   b **Complete each sentence with an alternative adjective that fits the preposition.**
   annoyed   deficient   pleased   perfect   rude   scared
   1 As a director, he was always very *polite /* .... *to* his actors.
   2 I was most *upset /* .... *at* missing the first part of the performance.
   3 Looking at his height and appearance, you'll soon realise he's *wrong /* .... *for* the part.
   4 The show was totally *lacking /* .... *in* drama and suspense.
   5 The director must be pretty *disappointed /* .... *with* the reviews he received.
   6 I could never be an actor, as I'm *terrified /* .... *of* going on stage.

Confusing pairs

3 **Read the text and underline the correct preposition in each pair.**

Years ago, I secretly dreamt (1) *of / about* becoming an actor. When I heard (2) *of / from* friends about a local drama group that was putting on a play, I went along for an audition. When I arrived at the theatre, I asked (3) *for / after* the show's director and was introduced to a young man called Gavin, who was known locally (4) *for / by* his modern interpretations of Shakespeare.
The audition seemed to go well and I was pleased (5) *with / at* my performance. A couple of days later, I heard (6) *about / from* Gavin and he told me that I would be just right (7) *about / for* the part of a fairy. I didn't really care (8) *about / for* the role, but had to accept it gratefully.
Gavin was anxious (9) *for / about* us all to learn our lines as quickly as possible so we could get started with the rehearsals. I was slightly disappointed (10) *in / at* the news that I had only one line to learn. I was, however, most impressed with my costume, which was made (11) *of / from* some old silk curtains, as wearing it really helped me to get into the character.
Unfortunately, every time I tried to say my line, Gavin got annoyed (12) *about / with* me and shouted (13) *at / to* me to speak with more emotion. Some of the cast gave me some tips, and I was glad (14) *for / of* the help, but I never got much better.
Two days before the opening night, I was so afraid (15) *for / of* going on that I decided to quit. I felt sorry (16) *about / for* Gavin, but what else could I do? I felt quite bad (17) *at / about* it at the time, but later I could laugh (18) *about / at* it.

B

Use of English
Open cloze (Paper 3 Part 2)
▶ ER page 169

1 Read the title and the text on the right quickly for general understanding, ignoring the gaps for the moment. Why do some people not approve of singers like Hayley Westenra?

2 Now read through the text again carefully and do the task. Use the Help clues if necessary.

3 Read through the text again when you've finished and check that the words you've chosen fit in with the overall meaning of the text.

HELP
➤ Question 1
Is the missng word going to be positive or negative? Read on in the text to see how popular Hayley's albums are.
➤ Question 13
Think about the sequence of tenses in the sentence.

For questions **1–15**, read the text below and think of the word that best fits each gap. Use only one word in each gap. There is an example at the beginning (**0**).

The voice of tomorrow causes a storm

Hayley Westenra, a pretty teenage soprano from New Zealand, has found (**0**) _herself_ at the centre of an unseemly row in the classical music world. Her latest album is about to be released, and there is (**1**)................... sign that it will make her into an even bigger star. This, however, will only serve to annoy further some purists in the world of classical music. These critics of (**2**)................... is known as 'crossover' classical music, (**3**)................... basically means classical hits marketed as easy listening, regard the popularity of artists (**4**)................... as Westenra, Charlotte Church and Russell Watson (**5**)................... a symptom of an inexorable cultural decline; a 'dumbing down' of a serious art form.

Hayley is dismissive (**6**)................... such people. 'I don't really understand their position,' she says, adding (**7**)................... anything which increases the appeal of classical music amongst the young must be a good thing. She has heard from many young fans who have (**8**)................... up the violin or piano as a result of enjoying her albums. They (**9**)................... , she argues, certainly never have (**10**)................... interested in classical music (**11**)................... it hadn't been made accessible to them.

She (**12**)................... well have a point there, of course. Until the recent spate of crossover releases, interest in classical music amongst young people (**13**)................... been in steep decline (**14**)................... decades. It's hard to believe this revival of interest can be sustained (**15**)................... there are young stars like Hayley Westenra to be its role models.

Language development
Read the text again and find one adjective which is followed by the preposition *of*, and one which is followed by the preposition *in*.

Writing
Review (Paper 2, Part 2)
▶ CB pages 164–165, WR page 199

Exam strategy

Try to use a range of sentence structures in your writing, to make it interesting. Don't always begin sentences in the same way, but do make sure that you express your ideas clearly. This is very important when you are writing a review, because you want to involve the reader in the topic and influence their opinion.

1 Read and analyse the task below.

> You have been asked to review two computer games for an international student magazine, and recommend one of them. Describe and evaluate each game and make your recommendation.
>
> Write your **review** in 220–260 words.

2 Read sections A and B of a student's answer on the right. The sentences always follow the same structure, so the text is not very interesting to read. Rewrite the underlined sentences, beginning with the words given below.

1 Having ....
   ....

2 Although ....
   ....

3 In my ....
   ....

4 In spite ....
   ....

3 Read section C of the answer. The student has used sentences that are too simple. Combine the groups of sentences so that they are more complex.

4 Which of these conclusions do you think is the best way to finish the review?

> 1 All in all, if you're looking for fast fun, challenge and value for money, then *Demons on the Loose* fits the bill.

> 2 All things considered, you should buy *Demons on the Loose*.

> 3 Quite simply, I would advise you to add *Demons on the Loose* to your collection of games if you come across it, although I wouldn't go out of my way to find it.

5 Read the complete review again. It is too short, so write it out again, adding some details of your own from the points below to make the correct number of words.
   - how to play the game
   - the graphics
   - who would enjoy the game
   - why you recommend it

Ⓐ I appreciate it when new games come on the market, but unfortunately, not all of them are equally good. I have recently tried out two games, and had mixed reactions to them.

Ⓑ The first game is called *Castle Raider*, and is a 'search and rescue' game. I enjoy playing computer games, but I want to be challenged by them. I did not feel that this game was challenging enough. There are 16 levels. Each level is more complex than the last, but I found they were easy to get through and took very little time. I like the graphics but they did not make up for the rather boring game.

Ⓒ (1) The second game is considerably more interesting. The game is called *Demons on the Loose*. (2) The game involved attacking villains and demons. The villains and demons are hidden among the graphics. The graphics are very realistic. (3) This game is better than *Castle Raider* because it is much more difficult to find the demons. The levels are difficult to get through. Imagine a game which takes four hours to complete a level! The game gives you value for money.

6 Do the following task.

> You have been asked to review two videos from your school library for the school magazine, and recommend one of them. Describe and evaluate each video and make your recommendation.
>
> Write your **review** in 220–260 words.

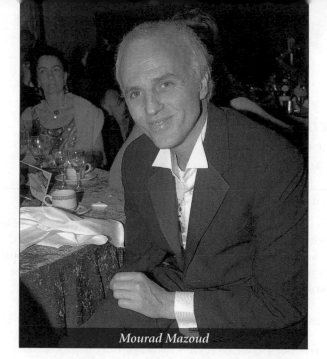

Mourad Mazoud

Reading

Multiple matching (Paper 1 Part 4)

▶ ER page 168

1 Read the title and the subtitle of the text.
- Where does the music being reviewed originate from?
- Which countries do you think will be mentioned?

2 Read the text quickly for general understanding. Were your predictions correct?

3 Read the instructions for the exam task. Then read all the questions and underline the key words in each question.

4 Now complete the task. Remember that:
- you should always read the relevant piece of text carefully, to check it has exactly the same meaning as the question
- many of the questions contain two points. The relevant piece of text must match both points in the question exactly, not just part of it
- when you have found a match for the question in the text, write the question number in the margin next to the relevant piece of text – you will need to go back and check it later.

5 Match the adjectives from the text in column A with their definitions in column B.

A	B
1 innovative	a of very good quality
2 cross-cultural	b difficult to explain or define
3 top-notch	c very different from each other
4 groundbreaking	d involving aspects from different cultures
5 disparate	e new and exciting
6 indefinable	f very beautiful
7 sublime	g trying something new that no one has tried before.

You are going to read some reviews of world music. For questions **1–15**, choose from the reviews (**A–F**). The reviews may be chosen more than once.

Which CD album

has an impressive sound despite some slight technical defects?	**1** ....
includes music that has been written by the artist or artists?	**2** .... **3** .... **4** ....
is produced by someone with diverse business interests?	**5** ....
features artists who are rarely heard outside their own culture?	**6** ....
is better organised than other albums of its type?	**7** ....
is influenced by the artist's multicultural upbringing?	**8** ....
has packaging which provides useful information?	**9** ....
was well received by critics when it was first released?	**10** ....
demonstrates a talent for performing in front of an audience?	**11** ....

Which artist or group

did not initially plan a career in the music world?	**12** ....
is praised for a consistently dynamic performance?	**13** ....
makes good use of instruments not normally associated with the type of music?	**14** ....
is said to show great musical potential?	**15** ....

World music

The best new CD releases from round the world are reviewed by Daniel Connolly.

A Jali Roll (revisited + 1)

In 1989, two West African masters of the kora sound teamed up with a group of English musicians to record an album that was praised in the British music press and was a big hit in their home
5 country. Now is certainly the right time for its rediscovery, with the renewed interest in kora music following releases by the likes of Toumani Diabate. What a hidden treasure this album is; Dembo Konte and Kausu Kuyuteh sing and play a
10 mixture of traditional songs and their own compositions, supported by a fine musical backing. The sound is primarily West African, with the unlikely but successful addition of accordion, trumpet and slide guitar. This is an early experiment
15 in cross-cultural music that deserves a second hearing.

B The Music of Mali

A fine collection of top-notch tracks by the stars of this musical nation. Putamayo is a US label with a forte for innovative compilations, backed up by
20 intelligent sleeve notes (the latest crop includes *Jamaica*, *Gypsy Caravan* and *Cajun*). My favourite tracks are those which showcase top-flight artists who have made this music so popular across Europe. As well as established stars such as
25 Khaled and Natacha Atlas, there are some excellent tracks from singers less well-known outside the Arab-speaking world. Highly recommended.

C Salsa Afro Cubana

Cuban born Osvaldo Chacon trained as a teacher in
30 Havana, but found music to be his true vocation. Rather unusually, he moved to London in 1997, formed a group and dedicated himself to salsa timba – a heavier and more varied style of salsa with an irresistible dance beat. With these eight
35 self-composed tracks, the young Cuban proves himself to possess a fast-developing talent; someone to keep a close eye on.

D Band of Gypsies

This exciting group has a formidable reputation as a live act, and this album of tracks recorded over
40 three concerts in their native Bucharest goes some way to showing why. It's a non-stop musical maelstrom, punctuated by odd moments of gentle recovery, before setting off again on the merry-go-round of gypsy reels and rhythms. Ironically, after a
45 decade of international success, these concerts were the first in the city, but judging from these performances, they should soon be making as much of a mark there as they have elsewhere. Some live albums suffer from inferior recording, but
50 the raw intensity of the music here makes up for the lack of studio polish.

E Próxima Estación: Esperanza

Following up the four-million-selling *Clandestino*, this magazine's record of the year, is no mean feat. The former front man of the indefinable anarchic
55 French rock band Mano Negra, Manu Chao has now created an individual style, reflecting his mixed ethnic background and the sounds he has collected on his travels in Latin America. *Next Station: Hope*, as the album title translates, is
60 very much a continuation of *Clandestino* in terms of music style and themes, with the songs gently flowing into each other, accompanied by a stream of everyday sounds. At the heart are Manu's melodic tunes sung in a mixture of French, Spanish
65 and English, though the music has more of a Caribbean feel to it this time, with reggae rhythms abounding. Not as groundbreaking as *Clandestino*, but a satisfying part two for Manu Chao fans.

F Arabesque 2

This is the second wonderfully crafted collection of
70 Arabic-influenced music put together by Algerian Mourad Mazouz, aka Momo (not to be confused with the band of the same name; he is in fact owner of, and inspiration behind, popular restaurants in London and Paris). While most
75 compilations sound like a disparate collection of tracks, *Arabesque 2* is an entity in its own right, with a groove that flows throughout, uniting the songs and instrumentals as if they were recorded as one. Songs from fairly well-known artists, such
80 as Khaled and Rachid Taha, are combined with sublime offerings from unfamiliar names. This is a must-have title.

Practice exam

Reading

Paper 1 Part 1

You are going to read three extracts which are all concerned in some way with travel. For questions **1–6**, choose the answer (**A**, **B**, **C** or **D**) which you think fits best according to the text.

Book Review

The Final Call: In search of the true cost of our holidays by Leo Hickman

Skiing and golf are dangerous activities: you can break limbs playing the one, and bore people talking about the other. But they harbour other, less obvious threats. Both pursuits draw millions of people across the globe every year, sending them to ecologically and environmentally sensitive communities, usually by air. And if you live on the Heathrow approach, as Leo Hickman does, you quickly become aware of just how many aeroplanes

5 that amounts to – about five hundred fly in and out of London's Heathrow every day, the vast majority carrying tourists. But despite the huge numbers involved, tourism remains largely unregulated, and for all its inevitable impact on the traditional areas of government – health, education, the economy – control of it mainly rests with Western corporations: hotel groups and tour operators, whose bottom line is always financial.

It's debatable whether this is the ideal way of managing the industry, and Hickman's investigation examines

10 how local communities suffer, or benefit, from being focal points of global tourism. His first stop is the Alps, where, for all the skiing that takes place, the busiest slope is that of aircraft descending into Geneva! It's also the one slope not wearing out. Snow is on the wane, and it isn't difficult to find data to back this assertion up: in one particular Swiss valley, snow levels have been measured daily since 1936. Every year, this archive is studied by a coalition of scientists, and its implications considered; and 'each year the frowns of concern deepen'.

1 What do we learn about Leo Hickman in the first paragraph?
  A He is in favour of self-regulation by western corporations.
  B His book deals particularly with the effects of sports tourism.
  C He has personal experience of certain effects of mass tourism.
  D His research has been funded by governments in various countries.

2 In the review, Switzerland serves as an example of a country
  A with a long history of tourism.
  B where it is hard to assess the impact of tourism.
  C in which detailed records have been kept of tourist numbers.
  D where there is growing concern about the depletion of a natural resource.

Letter to the Editor

In reference to Tony Burton's letter in the August issue about Ewan McGregor and Charley Boorman's latest journey, people undertake adventures for reasons that haven't altered for generations, nor are they likely to change. Some go for vanity, or to seek fame or fortune, or to further humanity's knowledge. But most do not. Most adventures are born from a love of the Earth, a curiosity to meet

5 new people and a desire to see what's 'out there'. But they are also designed to reveal what's really inside the individual: they want to challenge themselves and learn about themselves and make the most of their life. Unfortunately, such laudable goals don't pay the rent, nor do they cover the cost of today's increasingly expensive expeditions. Therefore, the adventurer tends to look for sponsorship, magazine articles and – if they are particularly talented, lucky or well-connected – perhaps a TV series and book

10 deal in order to fund their expeditions.

Perhaps McGregor and Boorman don't need the money to fund their adventures quite as much as some others, perhaps there are lengthier and more arduous ways to travel the length of Africa than a three-month motorcycle ride with entourage, and perhaps their book sold hundreds of thousands of copies more than most adventure books. But look at it another way: these are two men challenging
15 themselves to their own limits, making the effort to get out and do what most of us only dream about. We shouldn't begrudge them that. But on top of this, the enormous hype and publicity of their rides is raising lots of money and publicity for the charity UNICEF. They are still adventurers, whatever the frills and hype they choose to tack on to their expeditions. Hats off to them both.

3   The writer has chosen to write to the editor because
   A he agrees that the aims of adventure travellers are changing.
   B he wants to encourage companies to sponsor adventure travellers.
   C he thinks that a previous letter was unfair to the travellers mentioned.
   D he feels that adventure travellers need to start questioning their motives.

4   In the second paragraph, the writer suggests that what he calls 'hype'
   A makes little difference to the success of the trips themselves.
   B may be supporting the good intentions of the travellers.
   C undermines our respect for certain travellers.
   D is a poor way to gain funding for trips.

A Glimpse of Dreamtime

The rough ground pressed into my knees as I peered up the hollow log. Jacinta held her small pink hand-mirror to deflect the sunlight through the opening in the fallen tree trunk and spotlight the trembling captive. Out of the gloom shone a pair of wide eyes, encircled by tawny fur. The bandicoot's sanctuary had suddenly become his jail. I steeled myself against
5   sentimentality, knowing that this little rodent was about to become our lunch. Although I felt uncomfortable about the kill, I had to concede that the Aborigines had lived in harmony with their environment much longer than western cultures, where most wild species had been all but eradicated.

Jacinta is one of the Tiwi tribe of Aborigines living on Australia's Melville Island. Effectively
10 cut off from the mainland, the Tiwi's culture and heritage is still incredibly strong. Unlike urban Aborigines, many Tiwis have developed in relative isolation and retain the skills and crafts of their ancestors, without being seduced by mod cons – the little pink mirror that Jacinta used as a torch being an exception. Normally, this aboriginal land is off-limits to strangers but thanks to an initiative by the tribe, dubbed *A glimpse of dreamtime*, the Tiwis
15 have embraced a brand of tourism that couldn't be further from the kitsch wood carvings, plastic boomerangs and quaint bark paintings that represents the closest that most visitors ever get to aboriginal culture elsewhere in Australia. For me, the contrast could not have been more striking. Champagne and canapes on the Qantas flight one day, charred morsel of bandicoot the next.

5   From the text as a whole, we learn that the writer
   A accepts that the Tiwi know how to care for their natural environment.
   B fails to overcome strong feelings against the killing of wild animals.
   C doubts the wisdom of the Tiwi's decision to encourage tourism.
   D admires the way that the Tiwi use pieces of modern equipment.

6   Which phrase from the text is used to suggest what has happened to other Aboriginal people in Australia?
   A 'cut off from the mainland' (line 10)
   B 'seduced by mod cons' (line 12)
   C 'off-limits to strangers' (line 13)
   D 'embraced a brand of tourism' (line 15)

Paper 1 Part 2

You are going to read an article about fishing. Six paragraphs have been removed from the article. Choose from the paragraphs **A–G** the one which fits each gap (**7–12**). There is one extra paragraph you do not need to use.

FISHING FOR THE BIGGEST PRIZE

Boosted by television, tournament angling is rapidly becoming a thriving international business. Tony Harris reports.

If you were to consider which sports are the favourites of the media, fishing would not necessarily be the first one to spring to mind. Yet, in some countries today, angling is one of the most popular participant sports, following closely behind swimming and walking. Indeed, particularly in the USA, fishing is now one of the top favourites as a televised sport. On a Saturday morning, you can watch men, and the very occasional woman, catching fish on four different channels.

7

The willingness of anglers in the USA to watch fishing on screen, however, has brought a massive infusion of money from advertisers. In the frequent commercial breaks, every item of fishing equipment imaginable is promoted, from fluorescent plastic worms to electronic fish-finders. In addition, a whole range of products from the mainstream corporate world is marketed with the same level of enthusiasm, everything from biscuits to financial services.

8

At the centre of this rapidly growing business is a modestly sized fish called the freshwater bass, which can weigh four to five kilos when fully grown. A fiercely aggressive fish, in recent years it has become the most popular game fish in the country, mainly due to its tendency to fly out of the water when offered the bait at the end of a fishing line.

9

Nevertheless, for the television cameramen, this newcomer to the world of media sport is presenting a challenge. Fishing is not a pastime that easily holds the attention of today's television audiences. With a 20-kilo camera on his shoulder, the cameraman has to keep the tape rolling for eight hours

continuously, just in case he misses his assigned angler catching a fish. When it arrives, the moment lasts about ten seconds. With huge prize money at stake, the anglers will not risk losing the fish, they swing them into the boat with as little ado as possible.

10

On a cold February day in Alabama, USA, I have come to view just such a well-orchestrated spectacle. During the previous five-day tournament, the anglers have been using their skill and experience to compete against each other. I've watched them hurtling across the waters of the lake at insane speeds in their top-class speed boats, trying to be the first to reach the best fishing spots.

11

Despite all this, it is surprisingly difficult to catch the daily quota of fish needed to qualify for the weigh-in. In fact, many of the competitors may go all day without catching a single one. It is, therefore, inevitable that the less successful anglers are quickly eliminated from the competition. Today, the 175 initial entrants have been gradually whittled down to just ten finalists.

12

More recently, an angler called Darren Nixon, is said to have caught an even larger fish. This claim is still the subject of angry debate, but mainly, I feel, because Nixon used a cheap, unobtrusive plastic boat and maintained that stealth is the most important thing: because the biggest fish are the oldest and consequently the most suspicious. What if Nixon is right? Could it be that the $45,000, 125kph, seven metre-long modern bass boat is actually an impediment to catching the biggest fish?

A As a result, a peaceful rural pastime has been transformed into a marketing phenomenon; in chain stores and shopping malls you can buy leaping-fish T-shirts, and virtual fishing computer games. There are several bass-fishing websites. As a market for consumer products, bass fishing is rapidly becoming bigger than golf and tennis combined.

B Due to the growing commercialisation of the sport, once established in their position the fishermen use the very latest technology to assist them to catch the fish, the five largest of which they bring to the final weigh-in. They can employ electronic sonar depth finders and high-resolution display screens, which map out the topography of the lake bed and reveal any fish around the boat.

C This is in stark contrast to the image of fishing in other parts of the world. Although it has long been a much-loved hobby, there are few anglers who would attempt to support their families through the income they receive from fishing alone. In the USA, however, anglers are fishing a circuit of big-money tournaments, where not only can you be a professional, you can also acquire celebrity status through frequent appearances on the back of cereal packets.

D I watch the anglers standing apprehensively on the central stage, waiting to discover who will receive the winner's $110,000 cheque. It is worth reflecting in these days of electronic sonar fish-finders, that the world-record bass, weighing over ten kilos, was caught in 1932, by a keen amateur fisherman, from a home-made rowing boat using a $1.33 rod. He had the fish weighed and verified at a local fishing shop, then later cooked and ate it.

E The anglers have benefited from yet another technical evolution in the sport during the last ten years. They each have GPS navigation systems built into the consoles of their boats, and before the race, the professionals spend several days scouting the lake and logging co-ordinates of likely fishing areas.

F On each of these, it is possible to see tournament anglers catching endless fish from a lake, one after another. They do this for five minutes, followed by a series of adverts. In real life, what you see is the anglers standing on their boats with their lines in the water. After spending two hours standing doggedly not catching fish in one part of the lake, they then set off, in their high-speed boats, to spend a further two unproductive hours in a different area.

G To compensate for these visual shortcomings, the organisers of the bass-fishing tournaments make the ceremony of the final weigh-in, when the overall winner is discovered, the highlight of the whole broadcast. When constructing their programme, this showdown between the two leading anglers has the style of a TV quiz show, in an effort to liven up the sight of two fishermen totally absorbed in weighing plastic bags of fish.

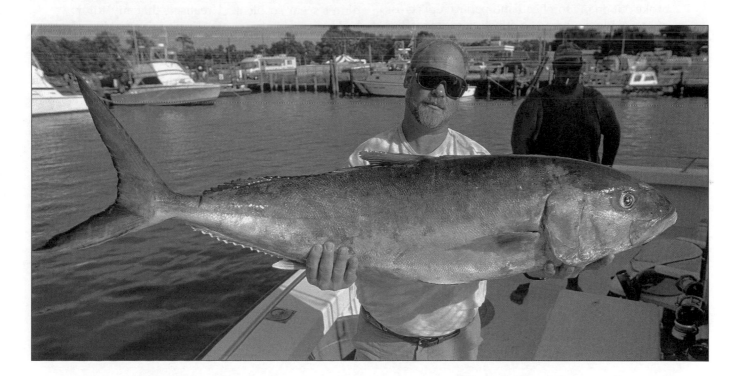

Paper 1 Part 3

You are going to read a magazine article. For questions **13–19**, choose the answer (**A**, **B**, **C** or **D**) which you think fits best according to the text.

What makes a good leader?

*Middle manager **India Gary-Jenkins** went on a course in leadership skills and got a few surprises.*

The tutor came into the room, coffee in hand, ready to teach. With a glum look on his face, he said: 'Leaders are born, not made. Who would want to be led by you?'
5 This was what I experienced when, in pursuit of personal growth, I recently completed a course on leadership and organisational development. I wasn't sure if the unsmiling tutor meant that the group of people sitting before him seemed a
10 pathetic group to be leaders, or if he really wanted to know the answer. I hadn't thought about who would want to be led by me, but it was a perplexing and humbling question.

I've learned that any
15 time a course begins with a rhetorical question, one should be prepared for self-reflection at dizzying
20 heights. I was quite nervous: the course was going to force me to ask questions of myself that I wasn't sure I wanted the answers to. Sweat broke out on my forehead and panic crept across
25 my face. I knew I was an effective manager, but I wasn't sure that I was a leader at all. I hoped that my fear of exploring my own weaknesses wasn't burrowing through the surface and betraying the confident stance that I usually
30 project.

The road to discovering leadership can be challenging. Some people really are born leaders. We all know them: the captain of the football team; the top manager who turns the
35 company round and the professor who stands in front of hundreds of students. There are, however, others, myself included, who have to dig deep to find the leader within. While born leaders naturally demonstrate their prowess by
40 larking about and being the life of the party, the quiet leaders are often overlooked and underdeveloped. On my course, I learned that the most competent leaders are not always the

ones that are obvious to us. They are people who
45 have the exceptional skill of making decisions that others want to follow, often without even knowing they are being led.

The tutor challenged us to observe people who demonstrate unconventional leadership skills. I
50 thought about the older brother whose younger brother follows his every move, the mother who leads her children by nature and the builder who is leading a team to complete a project. Leadership is all around us. There are born
55 leaders in every race, gender, community and industrial sector. Before I changed my frame of reference, I'd always thought of leaders as people standing on
60 podiums rallying the masses for change. I had been ignoring the beauty of change around me – including the benefit that
65 the leaders all around us contribute to our everyday lives. Suddenly, my future as a leader didn't seem so bleak. I realised that my tutor had been trying to get me to recognise that I was born a leader. He'd known it before I or anyone
70 else had come into his room. In reality, there was no skill he could teach me that I didn't innately know. He'd only facilitated my being able to recognise it. For years I'd been ignoring my own contribution to leadership.

75 I tell you this story, not to give you anecdotes about my coming into leadership, but in an effort to change your frame of reference about your own. You were born a leader with infinite possibilities. If your company is looking for
80 leaders, let them know they've got one. Evaluate the leadership skills that you demonstrate and concentrate on building them. The extent to which you demonstrate your leadership is up to you. So, now that you have the data you need, I
85 will pose the question to you. Who would want to be led by you?

> **Leaders are born, not made. Who would want to be led by you?**

13 The word 'unsmiling' in line 8 suggests that the writer's course tutor appeared to be

A unpleasant.

B pleased with himself.

C serious about his subject.

D keen to communicate with his audience.

14 What first impression did the writer gain of the course she attended?

A She was surprised by the tutor's casual appearance.

B She found the tutor's opening remarks rather offensive.

C She was intrigued to find out about the other participants.

D She realised that she was going to be made to think quite deeply.

15 In the second paragraph, we learn that the writer

A felt threatened by the issues raised on the course.

B doubted whether the course would be useful for her.

C lacked confidence in her ability to do her current job.

D realised that her feelings had been perceived by others.

16 In the third paragraph, the writer makes the point that the best leaders

A are those who take the trouble to learn the skills of leadership.

B may not actually be the people in the most prominent positions.

C are those who make us aware of their natural leadership abilities.

D may never be in a position to use the natural abilities they possess.

17 As a result of following the course, the writer came to appreciate that

A we all have the potential to be good leaders.

B she had nothing to learn from her course tutor.

C her course tutor had underestimated her abilities.

D leadership skills are very different from other skills in life.

18 The word 'it' in line 73 refers to

A a skill taught on the course.

B the writer's inherent ability.

C an approach adopted by the tutor.

D the attitude of the other participants.

19 In the final paragraph, the writer encourages us to

A support the leaders in the places where we work.

B demand that our leadership potential is recognised.

C develop the leadership qualities that we already possess.

D rethink our ideas about why it is necessary to have leaders.

Paper 1 Part 4

You are going to read an article containing reviews of photography books. For questions **20–34**, choose from the reviews **A–F**. The reviews may be chosen more than once.

A Walker Evans	**D** The Art of Seeing
B The Century of the Body	**E** Portraits
C Missing Link	**F** Around the World in Eighty Years

According to the article, which book

can be criticised for a lack of honesty in both text and photography?　　20 ...C...

celebrates the life of a photographer from another age?　　21 ...A...

shows images by a photographer who is renowned in a different genre?　　22 ...C...

sets out to be an historical record by portraying people over a period of time?　　23 ...B...

reflects one photographer's fascination with a particular group of artists?　　24 ...E...

features photos from a number of sources with a clever technical design?　　25 ...A...

has a title which is more impressive than the photos it contains?　　26 ...D...

is a visual record of the photographer's personal life?　　27 ...F...

depicts a lively period of history using traditional photographic techniques?　　28 ...A...

includes an informative narrative which links the work with broader themes?　　29 ...F...

presents pictures from photographers who are seen as leaders in their field?　　30 ...D...

is suitable for the less-experienced photographer?　　31 ...D...

shows that one photographer's best work was produced while he was in journalism?　　32 ...F...

features professional photographs from a well-respected organisation?　　33 ...D...

shows one photographer's ability to improve the appearance of ordinary locations?　　34 ...A...

PHOTOGRAPHY BOOKS
Nigel Stanton reviews the best of today's books on photography.

This year's collection of photography books is led by the multi-authored study of photographer **Walker Evans.** Many people will be familiar with his best-known work
5 which recorded the lives of poor Alabama sharecroppers in the early 20th-century. He did much more in his lifetime, however, so this retrospective tribute is well deserved. Evan's dates were 1903–1975, and he was a
10 photographer from 1928 until his death. Some of his last photos, which are in colour and have still-life subjects, look rather like the work of contemporary urban pop artists. Seen as a whole – there are 200 plates in this
15 magnificent volume – Walker Evans' career impresses by virtue of its diversity and simple love of mundane, man-made things. As is clearly illustrated here, his camera lens transformed the humdrum billboards,
20 shacks, garages and subways of American cities by delicate use of light and quietly monumental composition. Evans was also a subtle portraitist of working men and women, though his interest in faces seems to
25 have declined in the latter part of his life.

Two large survey books are useful introductions aimed at novices and students of photography. William Ewing's **The Century of the Body** is chronological. There
30 are 100 photographs, one for each year of the 20th century. Each of them is concerned with the human form, while the book's commentary makes a connection between the examination of the body and wider
35 cultural issues. An excellent present for any concerned young person. **Missing Link** is subtitled *The Image of Man in Contemporary Photography.* There are plenty of pictures of women, so one can't help but find this
40 somewhat misleading. Almost all the photos, by 60 artists from American and European countries, are manipulated. They are posed, hi-tech and ingeniously constructed. Yet no portrait in **Missing Link** is candid, and none
45 of its documentary aims to reveal the truth.

Many of today's photographers have rejected the traditions of humanist photography. Even news camerawork has been affected. Ulli Michel's mistitled **The Art of Seeing**
50 displays favourite shots by two dozen staff photographers from Reuter's, the long-established international news agency. Although the name is venerable, this photography business was founded as
55 recently as 1985. The book is rich, powerful and particularly contemporary. More sedentary journalists correctly regard photographers who record events in war situations as the heroes of the profession. Yet
60 something is wrong with these pictures. Even the most dramatic of them look staged, or resemble stills from a movie, and there's no essential difference in style between these pictures and photos of international sports
65 events.

The use of black and white, sometimes in stark contrasts and with hard silhouettes, gave a particular manner to 1960s photography, especially in London. A
70 handful of new books turn their backs on the colour technology to remind us of swinging days. John Hedgecoe's **Portraits**, records four decades of work. But surely he was at the peak of his professional career during his 14-
75 year association with *Queen* magazine. His portraits are full of detail and are often of domestic contexts. The most effective of them show a real curiosity about classical musicians and writers, especially the
80 scruffier ones, whereas he's over-respectful of painters and sculptors.

Photography also provides us with souvenirs of precious moments and sights. Eric Newby's **Around the World in Eighty Years**
85 is an excellent photographic autobiography. We all know that he's been one of the best of our travel writers, and it is very good to find how his skills with a camera lens complement his personal journeys and
90 precise reminiscences.

Writing

Paper 2 Part 1

You **must** answer this question. Write your answer in **180–220** words in an appropriate style.

1 You are the secretary of your local international student club, which organises a trip abroad every year. Last year, you were one of a group of students who went on a two-week visit to the UK. The president of the club has asked you to write a report about the trip.

Read the extract from the president's memo below, and the extract from the brochure describing the trip, together with your comments. Then, **using the information carefully**, write your report for the president with any recommendations you may have.

MEMO

Could you write a report for the committee about the trip to the UK? We are particularly interested in the general opinion about the accommodation which was provided.

Please make any recommendations you may have about the way in which the trip could be improved.

Thanks

Tim Belman

Visit UK

This year's programme:

Week 1:

Monday   Travel to UK

Tuesday   Stay in central London hotel
Open-air bus tour of London, with commentary in own language

Wednesday to Friday   a.m.: Language classes
p.m.: Sightseeing visits in London

Saturday   Train journey to Edinburgh, Scotland
Stay with families

Week 2:

Sunday   Tour of Edinburgh, the city and castle
Evening: display of traditional dancing and music

Monday to Friday   Stay in country hotel
Hill-walking in the Highlands.

Sunday   Travel home

Handwritten annotations:
- staff unfriendly
- 9 a.m. start too early
- some younger students found museums boring. The older students wanted to go out in London in the evening.
- good for language
- enjoyable

Now write your **report** for the president (180–220 words). You should use your own words as far as possible.

Paper 2 Part 2

Write an answer to **one** of the questions **2–5** in this part. Write your answer in **220–260** words in an appropriate style.

2   You see this announcement in an international student magazine.

> **LANGUAGE LEARNING**
> We would like you to write an article about language learning in your country.
>   Describe how learning a language 20 years ago was different to learning one now. Explain why these changes have occurred and say how you think language learning might change in the future. The best article will be published in a special edition of the magazine.

Write your **article**.

3   The director of an international sports centre has asked you to provide a reference for a friend of yours who has applied for work as a sports instructor with the teenagers who attend the centre. The reference should include relevant information about your friend's:

- character
- previous experience
- skills and interests
- suitability for working with teenagers

Write your **reference**.

4   You see this advertisement in an international student magazine.

> We are a travel organisation and we are planning to hold an International Cultural Exhibition in London. This exhibition will give visitors information about the culture and customs of different countries. Tell us what your country should include. Write us a proposal, suggesting what should be included in your country's display and explaining why your choice for the display best represents your country.

Write your **proposal**.

5   An international magazine for English language students has a page where novels in English are reviewed. You have been asked to provide a review of a novel in English which you have read recently. It should be a book which would appeal to English learners of different ages in different countries. In your review include:

- your reasons for choosing to read this book
- what you feel are the book's strengths and weaknesses
- why people of different ages in different countries would like it

Write your **review**

Use of English

Paper 3 Part 1

For questions **1–12**, read the text below and decide which answer (**A**, **B**, **C** or **D**) best fits each gap. There is an example at the beginning (**0**).

Example:

Learning at a distance

The idea of distance learning has been in (**0**)...B.. for a long time. In recent years, due to the rapid (**1**)........ in computer technology, an extremely adaptable method of study has evolved around this idea. Distance learning is becoming increasingly popular with students, and the (**2**)........ of today's university population is changing as a result. For students whose chosen university is beyond daily travelling distance, studying online using what is known as e-learning is an attractive (**3**)........ because it enables them to complete a degree without the expense of paying for accommodation in the (**4**)........ of their place of study. Similarly, parents at home bringing up young children can take advantage of this flexible method of study because web-based support materials can (**5**)........ with any individual time schedule.

Initially, as e-learning (**6**)........ in popularity, there was a certain amount of (**7**)........ amongst university tutors, who feared that students studying in the isolation of their own home might be (**8**)........ of daily contact with their fellow students, something they regarded as an important aspect of a university education. It soon became (**9**)........ , however, that e-learning can actually improve communication, through the creation of so-called 'discussion boards', where the students submit their questions online, making them readily (**10**)........ to all. This system encourages a lively exchange of opinions between students, and it also means that the tutor's response to each query is immediately available to a wide (**11**)........ . Nevertheless, it is recognised that human support is still a key factor in the learning experience, and on most distance-learning courses, students are (**12**)........ with face-to-face contact at some point.

0	**A** actually	**B** existence	**C** continuity	**D** duration
1	**A** alterations	**B** movements	**C** openings	**D** advances
2	**A** proportion	**B** composition	**C** arrangement	**D** alignment
3	**A** option	**B** selection	**C** preference	**D** favorite
4	**A** whereabouts	**B** situation	**C** vicinity	**D** precincts
5	**A** stay in	**B** put in	**C** fit in	**D** go in
6	**A** grew	**B** emerged	**C** leapt	**D** enlarged
7	**A** attention	**B** trouble	**C** worry	**D** concern
8	**A** deducted	**B** deprived	**C** denied	**D** deleted
9	**A** evident	**B** conspicuous	**C** distinct	**D** straightforward
10	**A** allowable	**B** accessible	**C** achievable	**D** applicable
11	**A** following	**B** assembly	**C** reception	**D** audience
12	**A** offered	**B** provided	**C** delivered	**D** permitted

Paper 3 Part 2

For questions **13–27**, read the text below and think of the word that best fits each gap. Use only **one** word in each gap. There is an example at the beginning (**0**).

Example: | 0 | | I | N | | | | | | | | | | | | | | | | |

The first lady of space

In June 1963, a 26-year-old Russian woman took a giant step for womankind (**0**) _in_ the male-dominated world of space exploration. Valentina Tereshkova (**13**)........ 71 hours to complete 48 orbits of the earth in her spacecraft. Not (**14**)........ was she the first woman to travel in space, but she stayed up there longer than any of the men who had gone before her. It required a very special woman to complete (**15**)........ a task successfully, yet Valentina came from a small town on the Volga river, where she (**16**)........ up in a harsh farming environment. What's more, (**17**)........ her mother was a widow, Valentina was ten years old before she first went to school.

Eventually, the family moved to the city, and Valentina (**18**)........ herself working alongside her mother in a textile factory. She also joined a local aviation club where she took (**19**)........ parachuting as a hobby, making (**20**)........ total of 126 jumps. In 1961, when news of Yuri Gagarin's first manned space flight reached the factory, everyone was filled (**21**)........ excitement and national pride. Valentina's mother said that the next person in space (**22**)........ to be a woman. Inspired by her mother's words, Valentina found out that actually anyone (**23**)........ volunteer for the space programme if they wanted to, so that is (**24**)........ Valentina did. Much (**25**)........ her astonishment, she was chosen. One explanation for her selection was the (**26**)........ that cosmonauts were required to jump from their spacecraft after re-entry to the earth's atmosphere and parachute to safety – a task at (**27**)........ Valentina had excelled in trials.

Paper 3 Part 3

For questions **28–37**, read the text below. Use the word given in capitals at the end of some of the lines to form a word that fits in the gap **in the same line**. There is an example at the beginning **(0)**.

Example: | 0 | E | N | T | E | R | T | A | I | N | M | E | N | T | | | | | |

Handset Blues

In the average living room, you'll find as many as half a dozen remote-control handsets, each operating a different element of the audio-visual

(0)...................... system. The one for my DVD player, for example, has an   ENTERTAIN

(28)...................... thirty-nine buttons, only six of which I use with any degree of   CREDIBLE

(29)...................... . What's more, some of these buttons perform functions   REGULAR

which I only **(30)**...................... understand and clearly don't really need as I   VAGUE

never use them. In all **(31)**...................... , when I bought the player I lacked the   HONEST

foresight and **(32)**...................... to read the exhaustive explanations provided in   PATIENT

the user's manual, and now the opportunity has past since that document has

long been **(33)**...................... . Although clearly at fault, I'm sure I'm not alone in   LAY

this.

Meanwhile, my mobile phone seems to have an almost **(34)**......................   LIMIT

number of complex operations in its menu structure, most of which appear

totally **(35)**...................... to the business of making or receiving phone calls.   RELEVANT

I know I should try harder to understand the full potential of these gadgets, but

as long as they perform their primary functions, I'm afraid I can't be bothered.

But isn't it time the manufacturers put a bit more **(36)**...................... into the   THINK

layout of these buttons? The design is hardly user-friendly to say the least, and

I can't be the only one to find them such a source of **(37)**...................... .   IRRITATE

Paper 3 Part 4

For questions **38–42**, think of **one** word only which can be used appropriately in all three sentences. Here is an example **(0)**.

Example:

0   I was on the .... of booking my foreign holiday when I heard that my cousins from Australia were coming to England, so I changed my plans.

The issue of the work canteen was seen by many employees as the most important .... on the agenda for the meeting with the management.

Naomi couldn't see the .... of double-checking her spelling in a dictionary when she had a spell-checker on her computer.

Example: **0**

---

38   Most of the roads on the island were built by the Ancient Romans and so tend to proceed in a straight .... rather than following the contours.

Although she usually liked the poet's work, Cerise found the final .... of that particular poem rather disturbing.

Please call me on my mobile, as the .... to the house is being repaired after the recent storm damage.

39   If you're interested in doing voluntary work, it's best to go and .... in person rather than just send a form by email.

In the case of cuts, the first aider should .... pressure to the injured area to stop the bleeding until medical help can be sought.

The charges for hiring the club's equipment do not .... in the case of young people under 18, who may use it free as part of their membership fee.

40   The local football .... is the only one in the area still without floodlights for evening matches.

Professor Twain's research is recognised as having broken new .... in the field of medical engineering.

We were thrilled to discover that the .... on which our house is built had once been the location of a 12th-century castle.

41   If the examiner asks you something, don't spend too long thinking about what to say – just give a .... answer to the question using everyday language.

Ginny was delighted to receive .... fives from the judges, the highest possible marks anyone could get in the competition.

Melanie had always dreamed of having long .... hair like the other girls in her class.

42   She doesn't live next door to me, but a bit .... down the road, opposite the chemist's.

If you need any .... information, please don't hesitate to call me.

.... to our phone conversation of this morning, I am pleased to inform you that your goods have now been dispatched.

Paper 3 Part 5

For questions **43–50**, complete the second sentence so that it has a similar meaning to the first sentence, using the word given. **Do not change the word given.** You must use between **three** and **six** words, including the word given. Here is an example **(0)**.

Example:

0   Fiona's computer was affected by a virus once before.
     TIME
     This is .... Fiona's computer has been affected by a virus.

Example: | 0 | N O T | T H E | F I R S T | T I M E | T H A T |

43   The phone rang, so I never found out what happened at the end of the programme.
     NOT
     If the phone .... found out what happened at the end of the programme.

44   Cindy's parents are not happy about her spending so much time at the gym.
     APPROVE
     Cindy's parents .... that she spends so much time at the gym.

45   It's ages since the lift in the library last worked.
     ORDER
     The lift in the library .... ages.

46   As far as I'm concerned, having that old car repaired is pointless.
     POINT
     I can .... that old car repaired.

47   I don't think many local people will support the campaign.
     UNLIKELY
     In my .... get much support locally.

48   The firefighters acted quickly and prevented the blaze from spreading.
     PART
     Quick .... the firefighters prevented the blaze from spreading.

49   Do you mind if I ask you one or two questions about your spending habits?
     OBJECTION
     Would you .... answering one or two questions about your spending habits?

50   We will need to consider everyone's views before making our final choice.
     TAKEN
     Everyone's views will need .... before we make our final decision.

Listening

Paper 4 Part 1

You will hear three different extracts. For questions **1–6**, choose the answer (**A**, **B** or **C**) which fits best according to what you hear. There are two questions for each extract.

Extract One

You overhear two friends discussing a rock-music concert they have just been to.

1   **What do they agree about the concert?**
    A   The band's music was too loud.
    B   The band's choice of material was inappropriate.
    C   The band created a great atmosphere for the audience.

2   **What does the man appreciate about the band?**
    A   They play material he's familiar with.
    B   They play songs that their loyal fans like.
    C   They play music which reflects current trends.

Extract Two

You hear part of a travel programme about a city break destination In Europe.

3   **The woman is telling us about**
    A   the achievements of the city's local government.
    B   international recognition for the city's policies.
    C   the work of local environmental groups.

4   **What is the man doing?**
    A   listing the alternatives for a day out in the city
    B   suggesting an itinerary for a longer visit to the city
    C   stressing the small-scale nature of the city's attractions

Extract Three

You overhear two athletes at a sports ground talking about training.

5   **Why does the man now use power weights in training?**
    A   It's more fun than using the multi-gym by itself.
    B   The risk of injury is less than with other types of equipment.
    C   He's changed to an event that demands a different training programme.

6   **When the woman runs at big events, she feels**
    A   unsure of her ability to do her best in front of spectators.
    B   confident in her ability to stay calm under pressure.
    C   aware that other athletes share her excitement.

Listening

Paper 4 Part 2

You will hear part of a radio programme in which the presenter, Hilary Barrington, is talking about the experience of swimming with dolphins. For questions **7–14**, complete the sentences.

Dolphin quest

Dolphin Quest is located in the **7** [_____] once used by the navy in Bermuda.

All visitors to Dolphin Quest are required to wear a **8** [_____]

Non-swimmers sit on a **9** [_____] just below the surface of the water.

Before approaching the dolphins, visitors make a signal with their **10** [_____]

The dolphins' skin is described as **11** [_____] to the touch.

Visitors are told that **12** [_____ and _____] are regarded as a sign of appreciation by the dolphins.

Hilary says that, for the dolphins, meeting humans seemed to be an **13** [_____] experience.

Hilary says that experts regard contact with dolphins as a good way of relieving **14** [_____]

Paper 4 Part 3

You will hear part of an interview with the artist Jocelyn Burton, who makes jewellery and other objects out of precious metal. For questions **15–20**, choose the answer (**A**, **B**, **C** or **D**) which fits best according to what you hear.

15   Why did Jocelyn first start making things out of silver at art college?

    A   She failed to make the grade as a painter.
    B   She was advised to learn a practical skill.
    C   She had to do it as part of her course.
    D   She realised it would allow her to develop artistically.

16   How did Jocelyn feel during her fine art classes?

    A   aware that she wasn't wholly committed
    B   intimidated by her classmates
    C   unappreciated by her tutors
    D   lacking in original ideas

17   In her first job, Jocelyn felt

    A   proud that her work was sold in fashionable shops.
    B   frustrated to be working only with jewellery.
    C   determined to become recognised as an artist.
    D   unsure of the value of the experience she gained.

18   How did the work of Jocelyn's own studio contrast with that of other silversmiths?

    A   It was more affordable for ordinary people.
    B   It was aimed at a totally different market.
    C   It was slightly heavier in weight.
    D   It was designed to be amusing.

19   When describing her current work, Jocelyn says that

    A   she remains open to new ideas.
    B   she has established a recognisable style.
    C   she prefers to work with one particular metal.
    D   she now aims to make more functional objects.

20   Jocelyn gives the example of the teapot to illustrate her point that some objects

    A   are only intended to be decorative.
    B   reveal the real ambitions of their designers.
    C   are only valuable because they are made of silver.
    D   reflect the style of the period in which they were made.

Paper 4 Part 4

You will hear **five** short extracts in which various people are talking about a school teacher who influenced them.

TASK ONE

For questions **21–25**, choose from the list **A–H** what each speaker remembers about their teacher.

TASK TWO

For questions **26–30**, choose from the list **A–H** what has happened to each speaker as a result of their teacher's influence.

You will hear the recording twice. While you listen you must complete both tasks.

A	He put pressure on me to achieve high academic standards.
B	He encouraged me to take risks.
C	He punished me in a way that was unfair.
D	He showed me that I had become self-centred.
E	He made me take responsibility for my own actions.
F	He taught me the importance of being honest.
G	He inspired me through his enthusiasm for his subject.
H	He believed in me when others didn't.

Speaker 1 ☐ 21
Speaker 2 ☐ 22
Speaker 3 ☐ 23
Speaker 4 ☐ 24
Speaker 5 ☐ 25

A	I've been able to motivate my colleagues.
B	I've acquired friends with a shared interest.
C	I've decided to follow a career in education.
D	I've got qualifications which will help my career.
E	I've realised a long-held ambition.
F	I've been able to get on better with my family.
G	I've had the opportunity to go self-employed.
H	I've started to earn a high salary.

Speaker 1 ☐ 26
Speaker 2 ☐ 27
Speaker 3 ☐ 28
Speaker 4 ☐ 29
Speaker 5 ☐ 30

Speaking (15 minutes)

Paper 5 Part 1 (3 minutes)

The examiner will ask you a few questions about yourself.

Interlocutor   Good morning (afternoon/evening).

My name is .... and this is my colleague ....

And your names are?

Can I have your mark sheets, please?

Thank you.

First of all, we'd like to know a little about you.

> • Where do you come from?
>
> • How long have you been studying English?
>
> • What other languages do you speak?

(Ask candidates further questions in turn.)

> • How do you think you will use English in your future life?
>
> • What has been the hardest thing for you in learning English? Why?
>
> • Do you hope to travel in the future? Where would you like to go?
>
> • How do you think travel is going to change in the future?

Thank you.

Paper 5 Part 2 (4 minutes)

People and pictures (Compare, contrast and speculate)

Interlocutor   In this part of the test, I'm going to give you three pictures. I'd like you to talk about them on your own for about a minute, and also to answer a question briefly about your partner's pictures.

(*Candidate A*) It's your turn first. Here are your pictures. They show people and visual images. I'd like you to compare the pictures and say what feelings the people might have about the visual images they are looking at.

(*Candidate A speaks for about one minute*)

(*Candidate B*) Which person do you think feels most attached to their visual image?

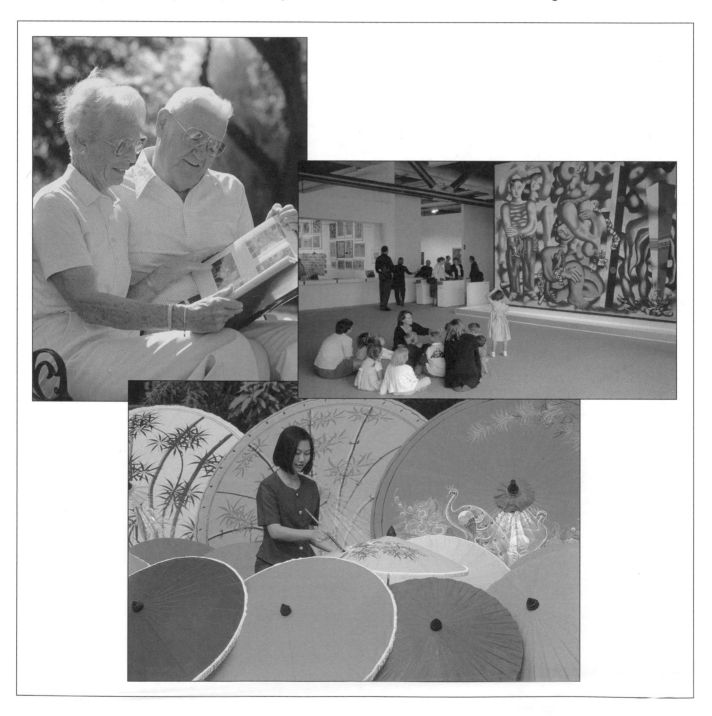

Crowds (Compare, contrast and speculate)

Interlocutor   Now (*Candidate B*), here are your pictures. They show people in crowds. I'd like you to compare the pictures and say why the people might be in the crowds and how they might be feeling.

(*Candidate B speaks for about one minute*)

(*Candidate A*) Which crowd do you think would be the most enjoyable to be in?

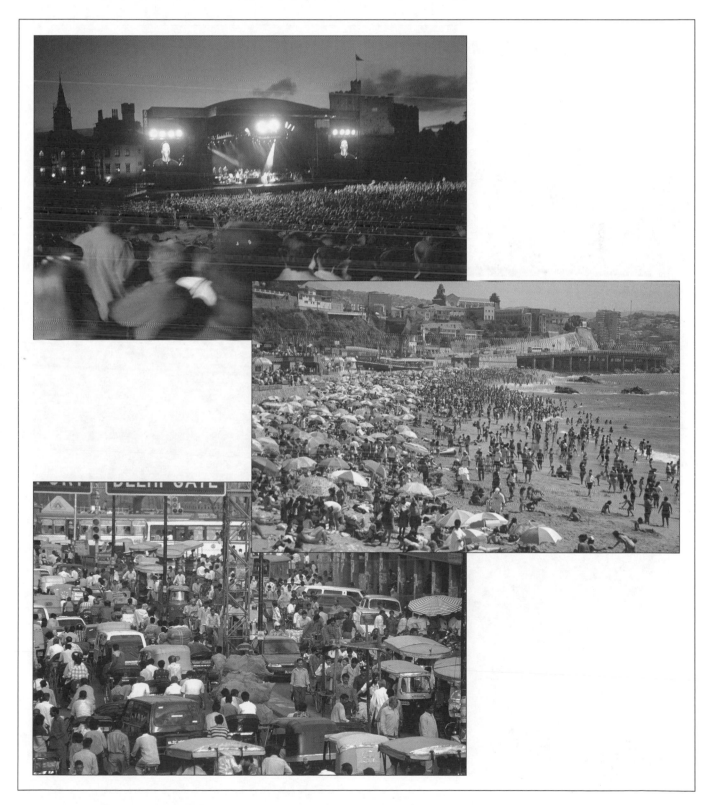

Paper 5 Part 3 (3 minutes)

Interlocutor   Now I'd like you to talk about something together for about three minutes.

A secondary school is organising a work-experience programme for its 16-year-old students. Each student will spend a week doing a job and finding out about working life.

First, talk to each other about what the students might learn by doing each of these jobs. Then decide which three jobs you think would be would be most suitable for inclusion in the scheme.

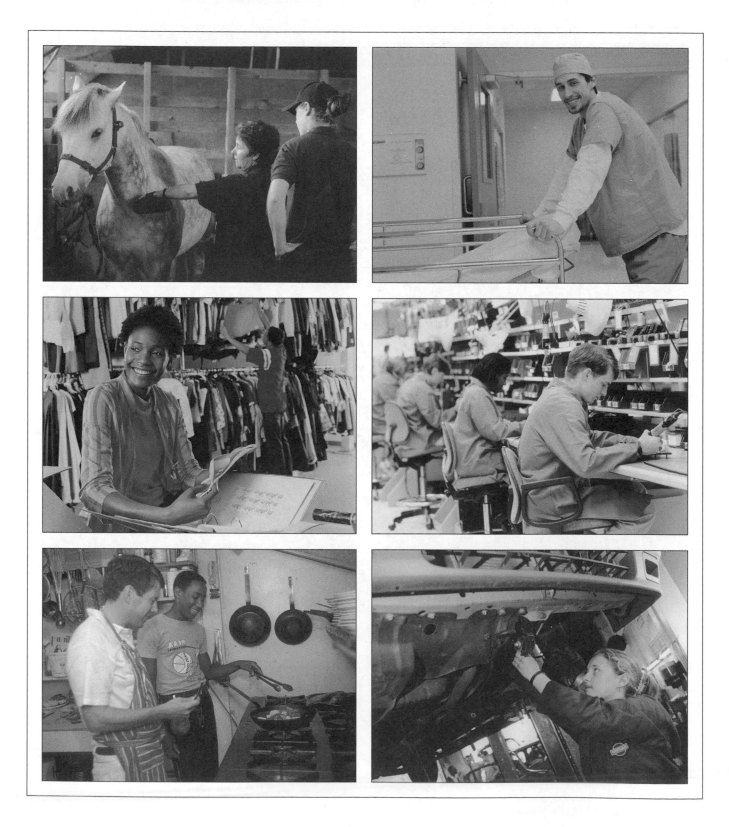

Paper 5 Part 4 (4–5 minutes)

Discuss these questions.

- How useful do you think a scheme like this would be for the students?

- Is it important to try a range of jobs before finally choosing a career?

- In what other ways can young people find out about the range of jobs available to them?

- When young people have to choose which subjects to study, should they be thinking of a future career or following their interests?

- Do you think the education system should prepare young people for the world of work, or does it have another purpose?

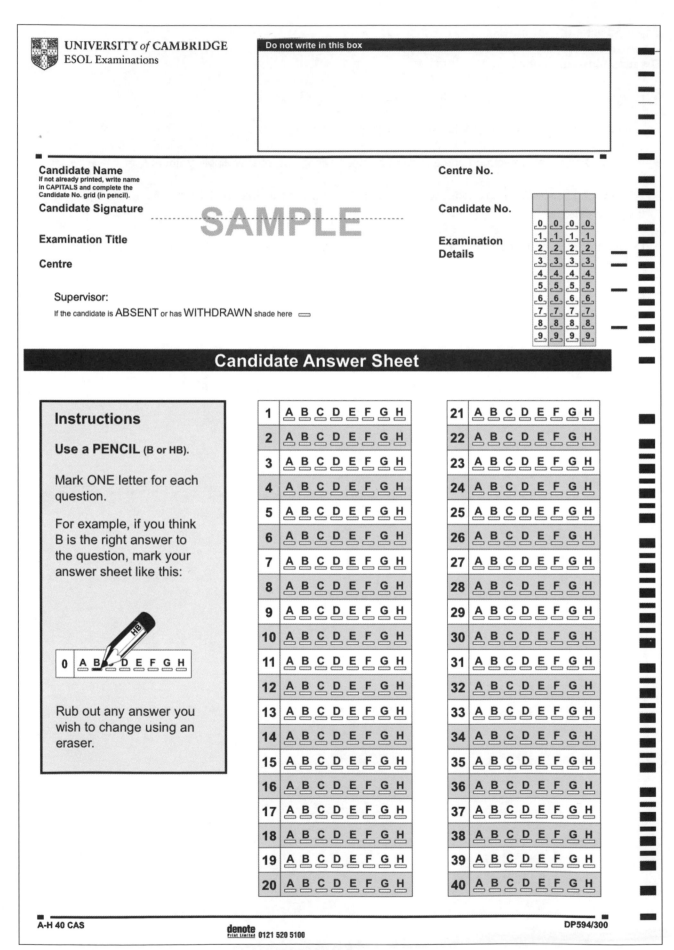

SAMPLE

Part 3

28 29 30 31 32 33 34 35 36 37

Part 4

38 39 40 41 42

Part 5

43 44 45 46 47 48 49 50

© Cambridge ESOL

UNIVERSITY *of* CAMBRIDGE
ESOL Examinations

Do not write in this box

SAMPLE

PHOTOCOPIABLE

Centre No.

Candidate No.

Examination Details

Candidate Name
If not already printed, write name in CAPITALS and complete the Candidate No. grid (in pencil).

Candidate Signature

Examination Title

Centre

Supervisor:
If the candidate is ABSENT or has WITHDRAWN shade here ☐

Instructions

Use a PENCIL (B or HB).
Rub out any answer you wish to change.

Part 1: Mark ONE letter for each question.

For example, if you think B is the right answer to the question, mark your answer sheet like this:

0 | A ▢ B ▇ C ▢ D ▢

Parts 2, 3, 4 and 5: Write your answer clearly in CAPITAL LETTERS.

For Parts 2, 3 and 4, write one letter in each box.

0 | EXAMPLE

Candidate Answer Sheet

Part 2

13 14 15 16 17 18 19 20 21 22 23 24 25 26 27

Part 1

	A	B	C	D
1	A	B	C	D
2	A	B	C	D
3	A	B	C	D
4	A	B	C	D
5	A	B	C	D
6	A	B	C	D
7	A	B	C	D
8	A	B	C	D
9	A	B	C	D
10	A	B	C	D
11	A	B	C	D
12	A	B	C	D

CAE UoE

Continues over →

DP597/30*

© Cambridge ESOL

143

KEY

Module 1

Use of English p.6

2b 1 C (*a lasting impression* = collocation)
2 D (to provide a contrast, not a reason or time marker)
3 D (*to put something on record*)
4 B (*deeply affected* = collocation)
5 A (*leaves* + *-ing*)
6 A (non-financial context)
7 C (*to accept an offer*)
8 B (= *to remember*)
9 D (*a worldwide scale* = collocation)
10 C (*with* not part of phrasal verb)
11 B (*by chance* = collocation)
12 C (*to tire of something/somebody*)

Language development pp.7–8

1 1 a have told   b has been telling
2 a has been wearing   b has worn
3 a have eaten   b have been eating
4 a have been taking   b have taken
5 a have (always) lived b have (only) been living
6 a have been hearing   b have heard
7 a have cooked   b have been cooking
8 a has stolen   b has been stealing

2a 1 was 2 moved 3 started 4 was 5 has been playing 6 studied 7 graduated 8 have influenced 9 has learnt 10 moved 11 has been living / has lived 12 became 13 released 14 has sold 15 has released

3 1 I **was living** at home when I passed my driving test, but after that I moved out.
2 When the accident happened, John **was driving,** but it wasn't his fault.
3 He said he was feeling sick and he **apologised** for not coming.
4 My tooth was hurting again, so I **decided** to visit the dentist that afternoon.
5 I had already **heard** the news when the director told me.
6 When I arrived, I saw that 20 people **were waiting**; some **had already been waiting** for over three hours.
7 When my exam results **came**, I got exactly the grades that I **had been hoping / had hoped** for.
8 I think my boss **had slept** badly the night before, as he was being very critical that day.

4 1 were 2 had given up 3 worked 4 (had) agreed 5 had been working / had worked 6 felt 7 wanted 8 had been planning / had planned 9 ended up 10 celebrated 11 was working 12 was / used to be 13 (had) quit 14 had bought 15 gave in 16 had never travelled 17 was

5 1 we'll have been living 2 we're moving 3 We're buying 4 we plan 5 is going to take 6 have finished 7 is 8 I'll be starting 9 will take

6 1 about 2 unlikely 3 verge 4 expect 5 are 6 not 7 bound 8 due

7 1 was going to / was about to 2 were due to be 3 were going to be 4 was due to have 5 was due to

6 about to

8 1 will have finished 2 am going to spend 3 will probably stay 4 are starting 5 due to open 6 will be serving 7 will be 8 were going to work 9 was/is planning 10 'll need 11 starts

Use of English p.9

2 1 He finds it strange that people should want to visit it.
2 Fewer people are doing/seeing carpentry these days.

3 1 where 2 who 3 out 4 should 5 are 6 if 7 being 8 not 9 so 10 into 11 is 12 used 13 as 14 enough 15 What

Listening p.10

1a 1 3
2 Extract One is about a course of seminars; Extract Two is about a student doing work experience; Extract Three is about a lecture two students have just attended.

1c 3 How does Dora <u>feel</u> about <u>her choice</u> of work experience <u>placement</u>?
A She's <u>pleased</u> that she <u>followed</u> her <u>tutors' advice</u>.
B She's <u>grateful</u> for the wide <u>range of experience</u> she's getting.
C She <u>appreciates</u> the fact that her <u>suggestions are valued</u>.
4 What possible <u>disadvantage</u> of the work concerns her most?
A becoming <u>too focussed</u> on what she does
B <u>losing interest</u> in <u>cooking</u> as a <u>hobby</u>
C having to <u>work unsociable hours</u>
5 What do they <u>agree</u> about?
A The <u>lecturer wasn't</u> very <u>good</u>.
B It was <u>difficult to follow</u>.
C It was on a <u>boring topic</u>.
6 <u>Why</u> did the <u>male student choose</u> this course?
A the <u>flexibility</u> it offered
B the <u>reputation</u> it enjoyed
C the <u>challenge</u> it would provide

2 1 B 2 B 3 C 4 A 5 B 6 A

Audio script

Extract One

M: And next on the programme, we have news of a series of seminars to be held in the city later in the year. The course title *Dawn of Opportunity* has been given to the series of five day-long events which are being organised by the city's Commercial Institute in collaboration with <u>the local development agency, which is providing the funding</u>. Stephanie has the details.

F: The <u>aim is to give young people under the age of 25 affordably priced help in setting up their own business ventures</u>, under the guidance of some of the city's leading strategists. Vimmi Singh, a trained accountant who ran her own highly successful Internet sales company before joining the Institute, will be leading the workshops. She is confident that the seminars will provide enterprising young →

people with what it takes to get a business off the ground. I've got the programme for the five sessions here in front of me, and each has a suitably inspiring title. For example, the first one is called 'Envisioning your Business'. This first session will help …

Extract Two

Int = Interviewer, D = Dora

Int: Now Dora, as part of your course you're doing a stint as a pastry chef in quite a well-known London restaurant – how did that come about?

D: Well, my college tutors advised me to find a place in a hotel because I'd get a greater range of experience. But I fancied being a pastry chef and so applied to do my work experience placement here. I think it was the right move because <u>it's exciting to be able to put forward your own ideas,</u> and be encouraged to experiment as I am here. I think I'm really going to enjoy working in a restaurant.

Int: Any drawbacks so far?

D: Well, I'm not too worried about the long hours. If you love what you do, it's less important – and I certainly couldn't justify doing anything else. My friends keep asking me all about my work here and I get really enthusiastic about it. <u>My only fear is that I'm going to become a bore and talk about nothing else.</u> Although I'm sure I'll still cook if I have friends round, I'm already making less effort at home as the number of desserts I produce at work increases!

Extract Three

M: So did you enjoy that lecture?

F: <u>What I understood of it</u> – I think I'm going to have to do some more reading before lectures in future – I guess you're expected to really, aren't you?

M: I don't know about that. You're meant to have done the general pre-course reading as background, but I thought the lectures were meant to, like, give you the introduction to the specific topic so that then you could go away and read up about it. Anyway, <u>most of it went over my head too</u> – so maybe he's just not much good as a lecturer.

F: Oh I like him – it's just his subject that's so impenetrable. Perhaps I should change course.

M: Well, at least we have that possibility. <u>That's why I went for this course actually – the fact that you could change options pretty easily if you needed to.</u> I had no idea at the time that it had a good reputation, or that it would be so challenging – though for me that's a positive thing, because I'm not looking for an easy ride.

F: Really?

Language development pp.11–12

1a 1 A new training manager is required (by the company).
2 The post has been advertised in all national newspapers (by the Human Resources Department).

3 A highly motivated individual is being sought (by the company).
4 Someone was being trained for the role, but she left.
5 Forty-five applications have been received so far (by the company).
6 Unsuccessful candidates will not be contacted.
7 Only the five best candidates are going to be interviewed.
8 The interviews will have been completed (by the Director) by the end of next week.

1b 1 An aptitude test must be completed by each candidate.
2 I should have been warned that the interview room was unavailable.
3 The interviews will have to be rearranged.
4 I must be told about any changes to the schedule.
5 Something has to be done about the lack of space.
6 The company's interview procedure could have been improved.

2 1 The police officer was told a lie (by Jenny).
2 Louis hates being told what to do.
3 ✗ – *intransitive verb*
4 I don't like being checked up on.
5 Our customers are encouraged to give us their opinions.
6 ✗ – *intransitive verb*
7 I think his arm is / has been broken.
8 The cause of the accident is being looked into (by the police).

3 1 being   2 being   3 to be   4 to be   5 being   6 to be   7 being   8 to be

4 1 I wanted to be offered the opportunity to travel.
2 She could remember being carried out of the burning building.
3 He didn't expect to be made redundant.
4 She is hoping to be elected as mayor.
5 My father insisted on being called 'Sir'.
6 I hate being let down at the last minute.

5 1 to have/get; altered   2 having/getting; cut   3 to have/get; laundered   4 had/got; enlarged   5 have/get; redecorated   6 have/get; checked

6 1 had   2 get   3 have/get   4 having/getting   5 needs   6 having/getting   7 to   8 had   9 was   10 to   11 get   12 need

Use of English pp.12–13

1a 1 three   2 one   3 it's the same word in the same form
1b It's an adjective
kind = fits grammatically, but doesn't make sense in the context
simple = fits grammatically and makes sense
problem = doesn't fit grammatically because it's a noun
easy = fits grammatically and makes sense
nicely = doesn't fit grammatically because it's an adverb
hard = fits grammatically, and makes some sense, but seems to be contradicted by the word 'lively' in the context.
1c Yes, they both fit.
1d Only 'easy' fits because the word before the gap is 'an',

which means that 'simple' does not fit grammatically.

6 carry

7 2 fair   3 work   4 slow   5 charge

Language development

… *we were advised …* – past simple

… *Keira was asked to …* – past simple

… *serious mistakes were uncovered …* – past simple

Reading pp. 14–15

3b 1 *a huge number of people are involved …it's important that we're all pulling in the same direction* (line 33)

2 *My age does count against me at times …I've learned to be diplomatic* (line 29)

3c B (*the most satisfying part of the job is helping my clients to relax* (line 49))

4 1 A (*a huge number of people are involved …it's important that we're all pulling in the same direction* (line 33))

2 B (*I left school at 16 to begin my training* (line 39))

3 C (*he refuses to be told what to say and likes to do his own research* (line 79))

4 A (*My age does count against me at times* (line 29))

5 C (*… travelled extensively with his family, equipped him very well …* (line 65))

6 B (*I enjoy … helping my team to develop skills that will help them when it comes to thinking about promotion* (line 57))

7 A (*I let their temper tantrums just bounce off me* (line 31))

8 C (*There was no explanation for what the programme was* (line 70))

9 B (*the most satisfying part of the job is helping my clients to relax* (line 49))

10 C (*I've had fantastic opportunities to go places I've always wanted to see* (line 86))

11 B (*My parents would've liked me to stay close to home where they could keep an eye on me* (line 41))

12 A (*'I plucked up the courage to ask him for a job' …Kieran's cheek paid off, and he began working amongst some of the best production teams* (line 21))

13 C (*'It was a totally new environment for me' …viewers perceived his chatty presentation as a fresh, irreverant style of journalism* (line 73))

14 A (*I'd always wanted to act, but …I realised I'd never make the big time* (line 15))

15 B (*you have to concentrate totally on your personal objectives* (line 45))

Writing p.16

1 1 international student readers

2 b

3 *why you are nominating your friend, how your friend would benefit from the holiday*

2a Reason for nomination: paragraph 2

Final recommendation: paragraph 5

Name of nominee: paragraph 1

Benefits of winning: paragraph 4

Specific example: paragraph 3

3 1 rely on   2 a little depressed   3 He is always willing to help.   4 Allow me to   5 with an excellent mark   6 a valuable benefit   7 Moreover   8 benefit greatly from

4 *Complete model answer with corrected mistakes underlined*

My best friend

The moment I saw the advert for the 'Best friend' award, I knew who I wanted to nominate – my oldest and best friend, Julio.

I <u>have known</u> Julio since we were four years old, when we started school together. The teacher put us next to each other in class, and we've been inseparable ever since. I can always turn to him in a crisis, or when I'm feeling a bit down. Nothing is ever too much trouble for him.

Let me give you an example. Last summer I was working for an important exam, but it was very difficult. Julio gave up all his evenings to help me study, and never <u>complained about</u> the time he could have been spending on something else. I managed to pass with flying colours – and it was <u>entirely</u> due to him. Having his help was a real plus.

This holiday would be perfect for Julio for two reasons. First, he has given up so much time for me, I wish I could find a way to repay him. Second, <u>he has never</u> been abroad, but he would love to see new things and <u>experience</u> different cultures at the same time. The Caribbean would be the perfect destination for him to do this. Plus, he is a fantastic photographer, so we could send in some pictures from our trip to the magazine.

So, for being the best friend anyone could ask for and a person who would get so much out of this holiday, I nominate Julio.

Module 2

Use of English p.17

1b c)

2b 1 C (= *found by chance*)

2 D (*to run a course*)

3 B (*signed up for (enlisted on, enrolled on, joined)*)

4 A (= *soon*)

5 A (*to illustrate a point* = collocation)

6 B (*rose + from*)

7 A (contrast to what was expected)

8 D (*dared + to*)

9 C (it is *deep breathing* that helps you relax)

10 B (*to overcome an obstacle*)

11 A (*a wave of optimism* = collocation)

12 C (*credit-card limit* = collocation)

Language development p.18

1a 1 which   2 who   3 where   4 whose   5 when   6 whom   7 that   8 why

1b sentence 7

2 1 those   2 which   3 both   4 whom   5 which   6 why   7 at   8 on

3 1 A, C, D   2 B, C   3 C, D   4 A, C   5 A, D   6 A, B
7 A, B   8 B, C
4 1 a locket containing a lucky charm
2 People wishing to learn
3 Jeremy is the person to talk to
4 People asked to choose

Use of English p.19

2 1 never known a more hardworking person
2 since Robin last went back
3 delays to all flights because
4 took it for granted that
5 has to/must be pierced before
6 expected to hand in her resignation
7 had started by the time
8 used to find the idea

Vocabulary p.20

1a 1 epic   2 scene   3 location   4 plot   5 score
6 soundtrack   7 screenplay   8 adaptation
9 background   10 close-up
1b 1 epic   2 plot   3 background   4 location
5 screenplay   6 adaptation   7 soundtrack   8 scenes
9 close-up
2 1 on a shoestring   2 was a runaway success   3 cult
classic
4 on the edge of your seat   5 a dramatic finale
6 lavish production   7 sequel to   8 blockbuster /
box-office hit/smash   9 remake

Listening p. 21

1a 1 five   2 superstitions that they have   3 two   4 twice
2 1 C (*don't have the hassle of getting valuable gear to the
venue … Once I'm in the water … my breathing and
rhythm … competitors in the other lanes*)
2 H (*training on the roads … at the track … I've no
equipment to blame*)
3 G (*road races … going downhill at speed … get a
puncture*)
4 B (*the actual sport involves a lot of sitting in one
position … before I get behind the wheel … first past
that flag*)
5 D (*weeks on end alone … on deck … on shore*)
6 G (*my father gave me a lucky coin … My brother's got
one, too*)
7 E (*I can't think what makes me do it, actually*)
8 D (*I get so wound up at the top races, I need all the help
I can get!*)
9 B (*it gives me the time and space to empty my head of
other rubbish*)
10 H (*he's a comfort to me … he's there to keep my spirits
up in the darker moments*)

Audio script
Speaker 1
I have to travel a lot to international competitions, which
I don't much enjoy, but at least I <u>don't have the hassle of
getting valuable gear to the venue</u>. A few years ago, <u>my</u>

<u>father gave me a lucky coin</u> – he was a sailor and said it'd
always brought him good fortune when travelling. <u>My
brother's got one, too.</u> I always get really excited before a
race. I know it's silly, but in the changing rooms I touch
the coin before going out, just for luck. <u>Once I'm in the
water</u>, though, I think of nothing but <u>my breathing and
rhythm</u>. I never look at the <u>competitors in the other lanes</u>
– that'd just put
me off.

Speaker 2
It was when I started winning races that the sport really
took over my life. I'm fortunate that, where I live, <u>training
on the roads</u> is no problem, and I go out in all weathers.
But it's all about preparation, not luck. I never shave
before an important event, though – that's my only
superstition – <u>I can't think what makes me do it, actually</u>,
because there are much more important things to focus
on – it's just become a tradition. My mum says it saves
your strength, not shaving – but she's only joking! She
knows that <u>at the track</u>, it's all down to me. <u>I've no
equipment to blame</u> if I fail, so I concentrate on giving
my best.

Speaker 3
My parents have always supported me and come to all my
<u>road races</u>. It was at my first big event that my boyfriend
gave me this silver necklace to wear. I won that time, so
I've worn it ever since. I suppose that's a superstition,
although it can't really make a difference, can it? But if I
took it off now, it'd seem like tempting fate. I have to
admit, though, that when I'm waiting at the start, I touch
it. <u>I get so wound up at the top races, I need all the help I
can get!</u> Especially when I'm <u>going downhill at speed</u>! I
just hope I don't <u>get a puncture</u> – that'd be a disaster!

Speaker 4
I don't like the monotony of gym work, so I do things like
going to the pool, or out on my bike to keep fit, because
<u>the actual sport involves a lot of sitting in one position</u>.
The nearest I get to a superstition is always getting up
early and going for a run on the day of a big race. Apart
from the physical benefits, <u>it gives me the time and space
to empty my head of other rubbish</u> before I get behind
the wheel. I don't actively think about the dangers when
I'm racing, otherwise I'd be on edge all the time, but I
need to have 100% concentration if I want to be <u>first past
that flag</u>.

Speaker 5
I couldn't imagine not having a mascot – I've had my
teddy bear since I was little. Of course, I don't believe that
he helps me win, but <u>he's a comfort to me</u>. I spend <u>weeks
on end alone</u>, away from my family, so <u>he's there to keep
my spirits up in the darker moments</u>. I like the idea of
upholding traditions, but I don't take these things too
seriously. You know, like, for the celebrations at the end of
my last race when I dressed him up in a pirate costume
and paraded him up and down <u>on deck</u>. I don't carry him
round everywhere <u>on shore</u>, though – that would be
taking it a bit far!

Language development p.22

1 1 C (A is too short, B turns the student into the questioner)
   2 A (neither B nor C talks about the student's family)
   3 B (A doesn't say what the student likes, C answers a slightly different question, about the student being happy)
   4 B (A is too abrupt, and C lists the student's preferred sports rather than directly answering the question)
   5 C (both A and B talk about why English is important in general, rather than how the students themselves will use it)

Language development p.23

1 1 a; the; the; the   2 the; the; ø   3 an; a; ø; the   4 ø; the; the; ø; a   5 the; ø; the; the   6 ø; ø; the   7 a; ø; ø
2 1 Some of the girl's clothing **was** torn.
   2 He gave us some very useful **advice**.
   3 None of the information he gave me **was** correct.
   4 A number of students **have** complained …
   5 A lot of people **enjoy** watching sport.
   6 The number of people interested in the job **has** surprised us.
3 1 little   2 some   3 much   4 many   5 any   6 a lot of   7 less   8 enough
4 1 both   2 both   3 Neither   4 both   5 both   6 neither   7 each   8 either   9 Neither   10 both
5 1 shred   2 pinch   3 drop   4 piece   5 slice   6 bit   7 hint   8 heap

Use of English p. 24

1b 1 Because he seems to be an unusually lucky person.
   2 three
2b 1 not   2 a   3 into   4 it   5 from   6 with   7 which   8 before   9 time   10 as   11 either   12 the   13 looking   14 would   15 his
4 articles in Q2 and Q12
   pronouns in Q4 and Q15
   Q9 completes the fixed phrase *just in time*
   Q13 completes the phrasal verb *looking forward to*
   prepositions in   Q3 *plunged into*
                  Q5 *suffering from*
                  Q6 *escaped with*

Writing p.25

1 1 to promote the leisure complex
   2 give <u>a brief description of the complex</u>, outlining <u>why it is important to the town</u>, <u>describe its main facilities</u> and <u>plans for the future</u>
   3 informal
2 a 4   b 2   c 1   d –   e 3   f –
3 1 C   2 A   3 D   4 B
4/5 *Complete model answer*
THE NEW METRO COMPLEX
It's here at last! Are you bored? Are your evenings dull and uninteresting? Help is at hand!
Whether you are 14, 40 or 80, the New Metro Complex has something for you.

When will the New Metro Complex open?
Opening Day is September 15th, and for the first week there's a spectacular offer of BUY ONE GET ONE FREE on all available facilities. Don't miss out! Come to the old converted Cattle Market on September 15th!
Why is the New Metro Complex important for this town?
The Complex offers a ONE-STOP SHOP for everyone in the town, a place where you can meet friends, relax and socialise, get fit or go shopping – all under one roof! As well as this, it will attract more people from the outlying towns and villages. This can only be good for local businesses!
What can you expect to find in the New Metro Complex?
In the welcoming atmosphere of the complex, you will find:
- three restaurants catering for a wide variety of tastes
- five cafés for a quick bite to eat
- an indoor sports arena which will host tournaments and provide facilities for local clubs
- a five-screen cinema showing the latest films
- specialist boutiques
- a multi-storey car park ensuring easy access to the complex

There's more to come
Doesn't that sound excellent? Well, that's not all! No leisure complex would be complete without a bowling alley, and there are plans to add this within two years, with a small theatre being completed a year after that.
Come along!
Why not come along on September 15th and give it a try? There will be special competitions and offers on the day, and even a special appearance by a mystery celebrity. Don't miss it!

Reading pp.26–27

1 creating or doing something false in order to mislead people
2 1 He wants to find out why people react in particular ways in buildings that are believed to be haunted.
   2 They recorded people's reactions in old buildings that are believed to be haunted.
   3 People often felt the most scared in the exact places that are believed to be haunted.
   4 He thinks that changes in the temperature and magnetic field in the atmosphere cause the experiences.
   5 He plans to build a fake haunted house where he can make these changes to temperature and magnetic fields artificially.
3 1 D (*such an unusal idea* links to *evidence to support this explanation* (line 15))
   2 F (*the precise spots reputed to be haunted* (line 24) links to *One was Hampton Court … Another was the South Bridge*)
   3 C (*This provided Wiseman …* links to *As a result …* (line 28))
   4 G (*to prepare people psychologically* (line 33) links to *Wiseman insists that he should be able to tell the volunteers*)

5 E (*people found the special effects less believable as they became more obvious* (line 42) links to *It's the same in everyday life, we are sensitive to very slight alterations*)

6 A (*historic venues already full of ghostly folklore* links to *So, at present, he is searching for disused buildings …* (line 58))

Module 3

Use of English p.28

1b They usually choose other famous people as their friends.

2 1 relationships   2 tendency   3 unexpected
4 attractions   5 supposedly   6 tension   7 rivalry
8 considerable   9 admiration   10 existence

Language development p.29

1 1 The planet **V**enus is warmer than **M**ars because it is closer to the sun/**S**un.
2 This winter, I'll be working every **S**aturday in **D**ecember in the run up to **C**hristmas and **N**ew **Y**ear.
3 **M**y friend **F**abio's father has a house near **L**ake **C**omo in the north of **I**taly.
4 I'd like to study **S**panish in **S**outh **A**merica in either **A**rgentina or **C**hile.
5 She's the new doctor; she's taken over from **D**octor **D**igby.
6 For more information, please contact **B**arclays **B**ank at 42 **H**igh **S**treet, **B**iggleswade.
7 The sacred **R**iver **G**anges starts high in the **H**imalayan mountains and eventually flows through **B**angladesh into the **B**ay of **B**engal.
8 **A**re you fascinated by fame? **D**o you seek out celebrities? If so, read *Stalkers Weekly*, the new magazine for star spotters.

2 1 If **you're** going out for coffee, **I'd** love a cappuccino!
2 Please ask the maintenance man if **he's** fixed the tap in the kitchen. Apparently **there's** been a leak in there.
3 I need a laptop. **Mine's** broken so **I'm** using yours. OK?
4 **How's** the report coming on? **I'll** need it in the morning.
5 **Who'll** be locking up tonight? I **won't** be here.
6 Janine says you **can't** call her at home because **she's not / she isn't** going to be there tonight.
7 Daniel called to say he **won't** be coming in today as **he's** got a headache.
8 Melanie says **she's** booked the Victoria Hotel. She says **it's** a great place and has its own pool.
9 Melissa says if **she'd** known there was going to be a strike, **she'd have / she would've** set off earlier.
10 Dave and Mike said **they're not / they aren't** going to be more than ten minutes late.

3 1 It was the American journalist Henry Louis Mencken who said, 'A celebrity is one who is known to many persons he is glad he does not know.'
2 'Fame and tranquility can never be bedfellows,' said Michel de Montaigne, the 16th-century French writer.
3 'I may be a living legend,' said singer Roy Orbison, 'but that doesn't help when I've got to change a flat tyre.'
4 The actor Alan Alda once joked, '**It** isn't necessary to be rich and famous to be happy. It's only necessary to be rich.'
5 It was the actor and film director Woody Allen who remarked, 'I don't want to achieve immortality through my work. I want to achieve it through not dying.'

4 Robert Garside is nothing if not dedicated. For the last six years, the 36-year-old Briton has had just one goal: to be the first person to run around the world. Since starting out in New Delhi in October 1997, Robert has dodged bullets in Russia, outrun thieves in Mexico and found true love in Venezuela. Garside, who often feels homesick, says, 'I miss a really good pot of tea!'
In June 2004, he plans to set off on his next venture: to become the first person to swim around the world, covering a distance of approximately 25,000 miles. He says that, as with the run, the greatest problems will be, 'isolation, politics and the weather.'

Use of English p.30

2e show
3 1 gained 2 pick 3 affect 4 point 5 fall

Writing p.31

1 1 <u>It is hard to say why the marriages of well-known actors seldom last.</u> <u>Some</u> have said it is because of the pressure of being in the public eye. <u>Others</u> have suggested it is because actors spend a lot of time away from their partners as they are touring or filming. ~~Many films take months to shoot and there are often delays.~~ <u>Another possible reason</u> is that the opportunities for being unfaithful are so much greater, especially if you are in constant contact with adoring fans. ~~Some actors are gorgeous and have huge fan clubs.~~ <u>The final reason</u> could be that actors are people who crave constant attention and need to be loved, and it is hard to maintain that level of devotion in a long-term relationship.

2 I'm not that interested in fame. ~~Some famous people have far more money than they need.~~ <u>For me, the most important thing in life is to know that I have used my time and energy well.</u> <u>So</u> I'd rather have a lower paid job where I was helping others than earn a fortune making money from those around me. <u>Some people</u> judge their success by how much they have gained for themselves, <u>whereas</u> I'd like to be judged on what I have given back, not on what I have taken from life. ~~My mum has always gone out of her way to help people.~~ The more people give, the more everyone has. When I'm old, I'd like to be able to look back on my life with a clear conscience.

2 1 A – too specific, not just about magazines
B – correct
C – too vague

2   A – correct
    B – too specific – not just about young people
    C – too specific – not about TV

3a Paragraph 1: 3
    Paragraph 2: 1
    Paragraph 3: 4
    Paragraph 4: 2

3b *Suggested answer*

A paparazzo's days are often long and boring. A typical day would start early in the morning and not finish until late at night, and a large part of that time would be spent standing around, waiting for something to happen. The job can be depressing at times, as we know that if we can't produce a picture worth selling, we won't get paid. So why do we do it? Because we are all waiting for that one piece of luck that will bring us the picture worth a million.

Other paparazzi are friends as well as rivals. After all, we're all in the same boat. So while we're waiting, we chat and compare the stories we're working on, sharing ideas and experiences. This comradeship makes the job more bearable and a lot less lonely.

The paparazzo is nothing without his camera. It goes everywhere with you, as you never know when that big story is going to happen right in front of your eyes. Regular practice is important, as being able to use your camera quickly and accurately is one of the paparazzo's most important skills. It is also vital to keep it in good working order and update it regularly to keep up with new technology. You really can't afford to be let down by your equipment.

To be successful, the paparazzo needs a network of contacts. We rely on these contacts to give us information and tip-offs, so we have to get on well with all kinds of people, from hotel porters and barmen to taxi drivers and even hairdressers. These people are all in contact with the rich and famous, and they could all one day phone with the one big story that all paparazzi are waiting for.

Listening p.32

1a 1 Anita Roddick, a well-known businesswoman
     2 a TV programme in which she pretended to be an old woman

1c 1 Q2   2 Q3   3 Q5 and Q7

2 1 undercover research   2 make-up artist   3 invisible
    4 tinned food / tins of food   5 anger; impatience
    6 senior citizen   7 wisdom   8 employment

4 2 This student has got the wrong person – it was the make-up that made Anita look older than her mother – their clothes were very similar.
    5 This student has only written part of the answer – the word *and* in the box indicates that two words are needed.
    6 This student has included information (*such as*) which is already in the sentence stem (*like*) and only included part of the answer. With these words in the gap, the sentence doesn't make sense.
    8 This student has got the right answer – but hasn't spelled it correctly.

Audio script

Hello, I'm Anita Roddick. Many of you will recognise me as the founder of The Body Shop. Well, I'm now 62 and have no plans to retire from my business, having become a non-executive director and consultant to The Body Shop. I've also set up a new venture, Anita Roddick Publications Ltd. But it suddenly occurred to me that I still have no idea what being old is going to be like, how people will perceive me, so I decided to do a bit of what I call 'undercover research'.

So Discovery Europe, a TV company, arranged a make-up artist and costume designer, and for four days I was transformed into an old lady. Actually, the make-up artist went a bit overboard and gave me so many wrinkles that when my mother – who's now 87 – appeared on the programme with me, she looked ten years my junior! We were dressed similarly, however, and that certainly was a first for us!

Anyway, the idea was that I'd go out onto the streets to find out how the elderly are treated. Predictably, I suppose, in modern Britain, the answer is often 'badly' – although there are some notable exceptions. What struck me most was how I seemed to become invisible. I guess I'm used to being recognised in the street, but when I was dressed as an old person, people seemed to look through me as if I wasn't there.

For example, I was carrying two shopping bags, and not just little ones with a loaf of bread in – big ones bulging with tinned food, which anyone could see I was struggling with – but no one offered to help me. And when it came to crossing a busy road, I deliberately acted as if I were confused by the traffic and the noise. Now you'd think people would be sympathetic, or at least understanding in that situation, but all I could sense was people's anger and impatience. Drivers were banging their hands on their steering wheels because they had to wait until I got out of the way. In our modern world of fast communications and busy urban lifestyles, I concluded, we seem to have lost the art of kindness. There is a debate about what to call older people in Britain. Terms such as 'old-age pensioner' and 'senior citizen' now sound patronising, whereas trendy terms like 'silver surfer' just seem silly. I personally favour 'elder'. Native Americans call their old people 'elders', and it denotes wisdom. It illustrates their approach, which is much more one of respect.

In modern society, people seem to be judged on the basis of their economic productivity – and perhaps that's why in countries with the highest participation rates of older people in employment, such as Sweden, older people are treated with more respect. There are more than ten million people in Britain over the age of retirement, and I really think it's time they made their voice heard.

Language development pp.33–34

1 1 must / have (got) to / need to   2 needs to / has to
    3 must not   4 will have to / (will) need to   5 needn't / doesn't have to   6 must have   7 needn't / don't have to
    8 needn't have

2 1 must / should / ought to   2 Should/Must   3 shouldn't
4 should have   5 should / ought to / must
6 should / ought to

3 1 couldn't / wasn't able to   2 were able to   3 could have
4 will be able to   5 haven't been able to / can't
6 won't be able to / can't   7 could / was able to   8 can

4 1 could   2 might   3 might have   4 can   5 should
6 shouldn't

5 1 This can't be the building we're looking for.
2 I suppose that he might/could have phoned while I was out.
3 Someone must have broken into the house while we were out.
4 Michael was in New York all last week, so it can't have been him that you saw.
5 He can't/couldn't have crashed the car.

6 1 could   2 would   3 will   4 shall

7 1 A   2 C   3 B   4 C   5 A   6 B   7 A   8 B   9 A   10 B
11 C   12 A   13 B   14 C   15 C   16 A   17 B   18 B

Use of English p.35

1 1 likely is it that the film
2 2 have been set out
3 have gained access
4 Silin must be away because/since/as
5 not worth applying for this post
6 as it may seem
7 must have left
8 not been a great deal of

Reading pp.36–37

1 *Suggested answers*
1 An 'ethical employer' is one that is socially aware and formulates its policies to put environmental and social principles before profit.
2 It is aimed at students and new graduates looking for a job.

2 **Rachel Hare** is a student at **London University** whose views are reported.
Lauren Steadman works for *Ethical Consumer Magazine*, which advises people on this issue.
Helen Wallis works for *People and Planet*, which is an ethical careers service.
Tom Chance is a student at **Reading University** whose views are reported.
The Industrial Society is an organisation which does research in this area.
Axiom Software is a graduate careers publisher. It carried out a survey.

6 1 A   (*we should be slightly sceptical when …companies say they are committed to 'socially responsible behaviour'* (line 1))
2 C   (*over half of UK graduates said they would choose a job … rather than one with a more lucrative salary* (line 25))
3 A   (*companies have sophisticated PR … without much substance to try to look good* (line 44))
4 B   (*workshops … on how to … the chance to talk through the issues … arrive at their own particular priorities* (line 51))

5 C   (*Helen helps them investigate whether the company … is living up to those standards* (line 65))
6 D   (This is a global question. You get the answer by understanding the writer's attitude throughout the text.)

Writing p.38

2 Introduction: c   Overview: a   Evaluation of events: b
3 1 In addition   2 On the other hand   3 This was in spite of the fact that   4 Finally
4 More money was raised than on the same day last year.
The event was organised by about 50 people.
People felt obliged to give money when they were approached directly by collectors.
The jumble sale was enjoyed by everyone attending it.
5 *Complete model answer*
Introduction
The purpose of this report is to describe the fundraising day held on June 16th. It was an extremely enjoyable day. I will evaluate its success and make recommendations for future events.
Overview
On the whole, the day was a great success. Events organised included house-to-house collection and a jumble sale. More money was raised than on the same day last year, and more people attended. The event was organised by about 50 people, mostly students from the university.
Evaluation of events
Some events were more successful than others. It was clear that one event raised a lot more money than the others, and this was the house-to-house collection. This raised 40% of the overall total. This may be because people felt obliged to give money when they were approached directly by collectors. In addition, the street collection was successful financially, probably for the same reason. On the other hand, the jumble sale was enjoyed by everyone attending it, but it only raised 20% of the money. This was in spite of the fact that the sale was the only interactive event of the day. Finally, the last 10% came from various activities including an appeal in the local newspaper.
Recommendations
There are several recommendations that can be made. Firstly, in view of the success of events with the personal touch, I would suggest that a greater range of interactive activities should be provided, so that everyone can get involved. These should include a sponsored run and street parties.
In addition, all officials should be given a badge when they are collecting money so that they can prove that they are genuine collectors.
Conclusion
To sum up, this year's event was extremely successful, and with planning, even more money could be raised next year.

Module 4

Use of English p.39

1 1 architect
2 the Nobel Peace Centre in Oslo
3 She is the managing director of his business.
2 1 C (*cast* = film/play, *side/team* = sport, *team* + *of*, *crew* = boat/film)
2 A (*responsible* + *for*)
3 D (*to single out* a special person)
4 B (a *figure* is a person)
5 C (*late thirties* = collocation)
6 A (*in addition to* is a fixed expression)
7 D (*to house* is a transitive verb)
8 B (*to gain recognition*)
9 A (*to be in great demand* = collocation)
10 D (*public appearances* = collocation)
11 B (*to take the load off* someone's *shoulders*)
12 A (*practised at, skilful in, experienced at*)

Language development p.40

1 1 difference 2 persistence 3 confidence
4 appearance 5 performance 6 correspondence
7 dependence 8 assistance 9 existence
10 preference
2 1 responsible 2 believable 3 collapsible
4 defensible 5 adaptable 6 suitable 7 reversible
8 breakable 9 flexible 10 adjustable
3 1 insecure (unsafe, unpredictable, unwell)
2 unable (incapable, informal, inadequate)
3 unrealistic (irresponsible, irrelevant, irrational)
4 unpleasant (impatient, improbable, immature)
5 unlucky (illegal, illogical, illiterate)
4 1 a generalise b generalisations c generally
d generalities
2 a intended b intentions c unintentional
d intentionally
3 a dependable b independent c dependence
d independence
4 a powerful b powerless c empower d powerfully
5 a original b origin(s) c originality d originally
e unoriginal
6 a pleasure b pleasant c displeased d pleasing
e pleasurable
7 a various b varied c variable d variance e varying
f variety g variously

Use of English p.41

1 1 Team-building courses have become popular because
employers have realised that good working
relationships can help a company's long-term
performance.
2 The benefits of these courses include employees
getting to know and understand each other better,
and being able to demonstrate skills that they might
not be able to reveal at work.
2 1 acknowledge 2 disruptive 3 effectively
4 fashionable 5 residential 6 strengths

7 adventurous 8 creative 9 hidden 10 beneficial

Listening p.42

1a 1 5 2 Life-changing decisions 3 2 4 2
2 1 F (*I was made redundant ... I was desperate*)
2 D (*I was so frustrated!*)
3 C (*realised it was time to do my own thing*)
4 E (*Anna didn't want to be a full-time mum*)
5 G (*I took early retirement*)
6 E (*I can't believe I ever had the nerve*)
7 D (*it took me a year to get the diploma ... really worthwhile*)
8 H (*If something goes wrong, I just think, 'So what? ...*)
9 A (*Male friends say ... which is irritating because ...*)
10 C (*I've discovered that I have a real affinity with the young, which is really exciting*)

Audio script

Speaker 1
<u>I was made redundant</u>. It happened overnight, and even though I'd been in a well-paid post, I'd <u>got hardly any savings</u>. Jobs in my line of work are few and far between, so <u>I was desperate</u>. When a friend said he was selling his health-food shop, I just said I'd buy it – the words just popped out of my mouth. I had to take out a huge loan to do it, and initially it was really touch and go, because I'd never set up a business before. I'm sure my friends thought I'd go under, and looking back, <u>I can't believe I ever had the nerve to take such a risk</u>. But I turned the corner eventually and now the sky's the limit!

Speaker 2
I started working as an architect in London, building new cinemas. That's where I first encountered visual impairment issues – planting a seed for the future! Later, I realised the higher you go in architecture, the less actual designing you do: soon I was taking a managerial role, with three people under me. <u>I was so frustrated</u>! I'd been working voluntarily with blind people and decided to give up my job and train as a rehabilitation worker. <u>It took a year to get the diploma I needed, but it was really worthwhile</u> and I've hardly noticed the drop in salary. Although it's anything but nine-to-five, helping people rebuild their lives is a real inspiration.

Speaker 3
I was feeling lonely after my children left home. Then one day I thought, 'You're in a rut – be brave, do something different.' The first step was buying a motorbike – I'd always wanted one. The family all teased me at first. But I soon loved the freedom it gave me, and <u>realised it was time to do my own thing</u>. I'd been saving up for a new kitchen, but instead I sold the house and went to India to work for a charity. I've had to get on with so many new people and I've learned to trust my own instincts. <u>If something goes wrong, I just think, 'So what? I'll just do something else instead'</u>.

Speaker 4
When our second child was born, <u>Anna didn't want to be a full-time mum</u>. She's a lawyer, and her work brought in more money than mine, so it made sense for me to →

stay at home to look after the children. Some men would feel awkward in my position, but I appreciate being around to see my kids grow up. <u>Male friends say they'd change places with me any day given half the chance – which is irritating because they think it's an easy option – but they haven't a clue what I actually do.</u> The children just never stop – it sucks the energy out of you. No two days are the same and it's all go!

Speaker 5

When <u>I took early retirement</u>, Pete and I took the chance to change our lives dramatically. He already had a generous pension, so we decided to go to Africa. We knew it was right for us, having seen the beauty of the African bush, and experienced the wonderful climate on previous holidays. The brilliant thing is, I've started teaching local children. Although I was really nervous at first, being unqualified, <u>I've discovered that I have a real affinity with the young which is really exciting</u>. Pete has surprised himself, too – he's started doing DIY, which he hated before. Our nearest neighbours are six kilometres away, so our social life is a bit limited – but we keep busy.

Vocabulary p. 43

1 1 c get on with   5 a look up to
2 f fell for   6 d relies on
3 g takes after   7 e let down
4 b fell out over

2 1 the black sheep of the family   2 seen eye to eye
3 get their own way   4 hit it off   5 run in the family
6 've lost touch

3 1 close family   2 siblings   3 extended family
4 confidant/mate   5 circle of friends   6 acquaintances
7 friend of a friend   8 colleagues   9 partners
10 companion   11 flatmate   12 associate   13 ex

Language development pp. 44–45

1 1 It came as no surprise to me that my brother passed his exam with flying colours.
2 I'm horrified that you could accuse me of such a thing.
3 It is likely that the deal will be finalised tomorrow.
4 I'm delighted that I can bring you this good news.
5 It is ridiculous that funding for the project has been cut.
6 There is no proof that he is/was involved in this fraud.
7 I really regret that I didn't go to university when I was young.
8 It was obvious to the jury that she was guilty.

2 1 G 2 C 3 A 4 F 5 I 6 E 7 B 8 H

3 1 how 2 when 3 why 4 where 5 which 6 what
7 who

4 1 What 2 Why 3 Who 4 How 5 Who; What
(*either order*)

5 1 Whether 2 if/whether 3 if/whether 4 whether
5 if/whether 6 whether 7 if/whether 8 whether

6 1 Growing up 2 keeping 3 to assert 4 to criticise / criticising 5 to say 6 Going 7 to be 8 having

7 1 It can be helpful to discuss problems with a friend.
2 His aim is to become a top chef by the age of 30.

3 Tom's really keen for us to meet Mary.
4 The only way the company can survive is to cut costs.
5 The ability of human beings to solve problems is one of the definitions of intelligence.
6 The tendency is for the oldest child in a family to be the most ambitious.
7 The main priority of younger siblings is to establish their own identity.
8 The most valuable contribution therapists can make is to help people recognise patterns of behaviour they need to change.

8 1 a It would be a great honour to meet the Dalai Lama.
b Meeting the Dalai Lama would be a great honour.
2 a It is very important to spend time on your own.
b Spending time on your own is very important.
3 a It would be very hard to find out his true identity.
b Finding out his true identity would be very hard.
4 a It is ridiculous to say that the company is not interested in making money.
b Saying that the company is not interested in making money is ridiculous.

Use of English p.46

1 1 They do special physical exercises to help them concentrate and learn better.
2 The children settle down more quickly and concentrate better.

2 1 do 2 is 3 other 4 are 5 what 6 which 7 same
8 and 9 as 10 sure 11 one 12 into 13 through
14 addition 15 go

Writing p.47

1 1 an article
2 why you think the family is still the most influential part of a young person's life
3 c

2 Plan B

3 1 Blood is thicker than water.   2 incredible demands
3 bombarded on all sides   4 a vast array   5 the going gets tough   6 play a part   7 through thick and thin
8 bedrock

4a 1 c   2 d   3 b   4 a

4b 1 c   2 d   3 b   4 a

4c … probably have problems of their own!
… no one is a better friend than a parent!
Where do young people get their role models from?
Is it the exotic media stars admired by so many?

5 Title a) is the most suitable.

Reading pp.48–49

1 1 They are all twins.
2 high-achieving, well-respected in their particular field
3 competition between brothers and sisters

2 1 Bryony and Kathryn: athletics/sport
Neil and Adrian: acting
Louise and Jane: art

Anita and Carole: music

2 They are all very close, although they don't always agree on everything.

3b 1 *feel left out* means that someone felt excluded.

2 *they do row about … petty things* means that they fall out over unimportant matters.

3c *people's indifference to our distinct personalities* suggests that people assume they are identical

we … forced to accept / we tolerate it suggests that they resent this

4 1 B (*there's this unexplained synchronicity … the producers appreciate it* (line 51))

2 A (*their brother … did feel left out* (line 17))

3 A (*what they do row about … invariable over petty things* (line 20))

4 D (*We feel we take more risks precisely because there's two of us. We spur each other on* (line 110))

5 C (*they wanted to give us just one fee for our exhibitions!' 'That's taking sisterly love a bit far!'* (line 85))

6 B (*These two films represent the … twins' big break … they have been avid film fanatics for years* (line 34))

7 C (*The former found the separation 'a bit traumatic'; the latter viewed it as 'a terrific challenge'* (line 61))

8 B (*he doesn't see them following the same path … I'm sure we'll head in different directions* (line 40))

9 D (*we take after our mother, who's very musical* (line 94))

10 A (*they don't seem to be competitive … It's not something we get worked up about* (line 10))

11 B (*people's indifference to our distinct personalities … We tolerate it* (line 56))

12 C (*They ended up producing all but identical photographic displays … They are not identical; in fact, you might not even think they were sisters* (line 64))

13 D (*there's a danger of living up to that label after a while* (line 113))

14 C (*they never had any irreconcilable differences … there's an enormous element of trust … there's no need to define who's responsible for what* (line 79))

15 A (*have to face up to building separate lives … but neither relishes the prospect … it's scary* (line 25))

Module 5

Use of English p.50

2 1 undeniably 2 response 3 preparation 4 celebration 5 emergence 6 movement 7 influential 8 prestigious 9 prominently 10 inspiration

Language development pp.51–52

1a 1 angry–irate 2 bad–disastrous 3 pleased–delighted 4 interesting–fascinating 5 large–huge 6 hungry–ravenous 7 similar– identical 8 small–minute 9 valuable–priceless 10 rare–unique

1b *Suggested answers*

1 slightly – 2 fairly – 3 quite + 4 absolutely + 5 completely + 6 rather – 7 utterly + 8 a bit –

2 1 most 2 dead 3 somewhat 4 a bit 5 incredibly 6 rather

3a 1 sensitive 2 ashamed 3 useless 4 unacceptable 5 useless 6 educated 7 disturbed 8 healthy

3b 1 highly sensitive 2 highly critical 3 utterly useless 4 totally unacceptable 5 utterly useless 6 highly educated 7 deeply disturbed 8 perfectly healthy

3c 1 heavily armed 2 perfectly understandable 3 highly critical 4 heavily dependent 5 bitterly cold 6 totally unacceptable 7 painfully aware 8 deeply moving 9 highly respected 10 totally incompetent

4 1 tight/tightly 2 right 3 mostly 4 late 5 hard 6 hardly 7 hard 8 cheap (*informal*)/cheaply 9 deadly 10 dead 11 wide 12 widely 13 free 14 freely

Use of English pp.52–53

2e close

3 1 set 2 rare 3 widely 4 part 5 taken

Listening p.54

2 1 C (*I reckoned that the idea of organised walking tours could easily catch on with people of all ages*)

2 B (*I really want to think carefully about what we do with the money we make*)

3 D (*they soon find something in common with each other*)

4 C (*judging by our clients' response, I believe the sentiment is appreciated*)

5 A (*All those recruited need to embrace the company's objectives … reinforced through ongoing training*)

6 A (*there's even a danger that certain travel journalists are getting bored with it, portraying it as wishy-washy idealism*)

Audio script

Int. = Interviewer, CW = Christopher Winney

Int.: Welcome to the Holiday programme. Today I'm talking to Christopher Winney, who runs a holiday company with a difference. He organises walking tours for holiday makers all over the world, but says his main aim is to support the environment. Christopher, you've just won an award for actively promoting responsible tourism via your company, ATG Oxford. Tell me, what inspired you to set up the company?

CW: I used to be a not-terribly-successful travel writer and when I was asked to do a book on long-distance walking, I jumped at the chance in the knowledge that it might lead to other commissions. So, I walked from London to Rome, and it was the most enjoyable thing I've ever done. I thought, 'Why isn't everybody walking across Europe?' Well, of course, people have been doing it for centuries! But nobody seemed to be tapping into the business potential. <u>I reckoned that the idea of organised walking tours could easily catch on with people</u> →

of all ages, especially if it was linked to the principles of conservation and sustainable tourism, because people who like walking generally like to give something back.

Int.: So, how exactly does ATG give something back? Is it financial?

CW: We give away ten per cent of our pre-tax profits to environmental charities. We also try to source only locally produced food and support local industries on our walking tours. You can't get away from the fact that there's an additional cost involved, but it's easily justified. I'm not a do-gooder with a mad gleam in my eye, but if the objective of my business was just for me to enjoy a better lifestyle, it'd be a very limiting exercise. I really want to think carefully about what we do with the money we make, and if the choice is paying off my bank loan or restoring a unique piece of landscape, then there's no contest.

Int.: So, what sort of people do your holidays appeal to?

CW: Nice ones. Walking is a great leveller. We have all sorts, from the rich and famous, to people who have really saved hard to afford one of our holidays. But people who are attracted to what we offer tend to be like-minded. We cater for all levels of walkers – you don't have to be superbly fit! There are some clients who hardly get any exercise normally, but they still end the holiday smiling! Our clients come from all backgrounds, but they soon find something in common with each other; people who go walking tend not to be elitist.

Int.: Running a business without advertising is quite a risk. What made you decide to stop?

CW: If what we're offering isn't good enough to make people come back year after year, and recommend our products to their friends, then we're failing in our task. I had no argument with the advertising we did, we just realised we could do without it. Deciding to cut it out, and to put revenue into conservation projects instead, was a nervous moment, but we've survived. For a company founded on principles of conservation, it wasn't a hard choice to make, and judging by our clients' response, I believe the sentiment is appreciated.

Int.: And what's the key to ensuring that what you offer really represents responsible tourism?

CW: Travel and tourism is a tough industry, but good environmental practice is just a question of awareness. Of course, it's about maintaining high standards in terms of providing the right kind of activities, and also making sure that the accommodation available meets the needs and expectations of clients. But above all, it's down to the people you employ. All those recruited need to embrace the company's objectives, and this has to be reinforced through ongoing training. For instance, we like to use exclusively organic produce on our trips, which requires someone on the ground locally to keep a close watch on participating hotels and restaurants. It's important to have confidence in all aspects of the service you provide. It's a question of going the extra mile.

Int.: How do you see the future of environmentally friendly tourism?

CW: When we started, many people were ignorant of the whole concept. Now, though, it's something everyone's at least heard of – and there's even a danger that certain travel journalists are getting bored with it, portraying it as wishy-washy idealism, which couldn't be further from the truth. Personally, I'd like to see more of the large companies becoming voluntarily involved in conservation, and playing their part in convincing the tourists. If this doesn't happen, tourism will have an increasingly destructive effect in many areas of the world; careful investment in local communities, on the other hand, creates a wealth of common understanding and goodwill, which is of immense long-term value.

Int.: Thank you, Christopher. We'll have to leave it there. I wish you every success.

Vocabulary p.55

1 1 d   2 c   3 a   4 f   5 h   6 g   7 b   8 e
2 1 renewable energy   2 sustainable   3 biosphere
   4 hydroelectric   5 Solar   6 Tidal   7 environmentally
   friendly   8 biodiversity
3 1 increased/risen   2 rise/increase   3 inefficient
   4 consumes   5 exhaust   6 destruction   7 contribute
   8 tackled   9 means   10 fuels   11 renewable

Language development p.56

1 1 were walking; was; would you know
     or are walking; is; do you know
   2 can see; are
   3 (will) have; crouch
   4 hadn't been standing; would have survived
   5 would not have been injured; had not been carrying
2 1 If I knew how to light a fire, I would have lit one.
   2 If I hadn't studied economics at university, I wouldn't understand how the economy works.
   3 If she had told us where she was going, we would know where to look for her.
   4 If we had taken sensible safety precautions, we would not be in danger now.
   5 If I didn't work in a zoo, I wouldn't have been bitten by a snake.
   6 If I hadn't handed my essay in this morning, I would be able to show it to you.
   7 If it had snowed last night, it would be freezing on the mountain today.
   8 If he had (got) his phone with him, he would have called me to say he was going to be late.
3 1 A   2 B   3 C   4 A   5 B   6 A   7 D
4 1 …you **should** eat organic food.
   2 If the company **hadn't dumped** / didn't dump

chemical waste in the river, the fish **wouldn't** have been killed off.

3 Unless we ~~don't~~ stop burning oil, we'll destroy the ozone layer.

4 ✔

5 If the government **changes** the law, companies **will** have to stop dumping waste. / If the government **changed** the law, companies would have to stop dumping waste.

6 If it **makes** you happy, I'll recycle all these magazines. / ✔

7 I'd be grateful if you **could/would** investigate the issue of water quality soon.

Use of English p.57

1b 2

2b 1 C 2 D 3 C 4 A 5 A 6 C 7 C 8 B 9 C
  10 C 11 A 12 B

> **Language development**
>
> if we can invent ingenious things like the mobile phone and the MP3 player, someone should have come up with a gadget to replace the umbrella by now

Reading pp.58–59

1 1 a society where things that are unwanted or unused are just thrown away

2 He doesn't like the fact that things are just thrown away.

3 c

5 1 C (*devising new ways to use art and humour to get us thinking about the environment … what our attitudes to rubbish … say about society* (line 5))

2 D (*to get them thinking about the value of things … the material you throw away … paid for and consumed!'* (line 23))

3 B (*they were … wary that I might give people the impression that our National Parks are filthy* (line 31))

4 C (*it's really rather creative behaviour* (line 49))

5 A (*Steve's in his element as his adopts the role of lively, gesticulating artiste* (line 60))

6 C (*this is my first venture into the world of modern art* (line 75))

7 D (*until now I've always kept my dislike of detritus quiet … he'd summed up the essence of ecology; that everything matters* (line 81))

Writing p.60

1 1 Chiara 2 the President of the Student Union

2 *Points to include*
- What happened at Chiara's college: litter-picking day, free meal for volunteers, introduction of fines for dropping litter, no-smoking policy
- Why it would be a good thing: raise awareness among students
- What it would involve: organising publicity (leaflets), providing cleaning materials and rubber gloves, providing a reward for helpers

3 *Missing parts*
- introduction of a no-smoking policy
- explain why it would be a good thing – to raise awareness among students at this college
- provision of cleaning materials and rubber gloves

4 *Complete model answer (missing information in bold)*

Dear Cris

I am writing to tell you about a special event that was organised at East College and was extremely successful. It was a clean-up day, aimed at solving problems of litter in the college. The day started with volunteers meeting up outside the Union building – they picked up litter around the grounds and gave out leaflets to other students, encouraging them to be tidier. They all had a free meal afterwards, and what was so good about the day was the impact it seems to have had on the college afterwards. Students have become a lot more aware of the importance of keeping the campus clean. They also tried imposing fines for dropping litter, which was not very successful, **and introduced a no-smoking policy on campus, which, on the other hand, has been extremely popular and successful.**

I think we should do the same thing here, **to raise awareness of this important issue among our students.** We would need to organise some publicity (posters and leaflets) and some sort of reward for volunteers. At East College, they provided a free meal, but I think that would be really difficult to organise. We could give volunteers a free ticket to the next disco instead. **We would also need to provide cleaning materials and rubber gloves for the volunteers. The rubber gloves, it seems, were especially popular!**

Can we meet to talk about it? What about next Saturday?

Best wishes

Sam

Module 6

Use of English p.61

2 1 extraordinary 2 development 3 lawyers 4 disqualify 5 competitors 6 hypothetical 7 reportedly 8 horizontally 9 treatment 10 modification(s)

Language development p.62

1 1 The person who 2 What / The thing that 3 The reason 4 What 5 The place where

2 1 The place where all the teenagers usually hang out is the park.

2 The reason I was so angry with her was that she had promised to be home by nine o'clock.

3 The thing that is so impressive is his ability to score goals from outside the penalty area.

4 What drives me mad is her habit of leaving her things all over the house.

5 The time they're due to arrive is six o'clock.

6 The person you need to talk to about this is your tutor.

3 1 The reason she dialled 999 is that she panicked.
  2 The place where we usually meet is the café on the High Street.
  3 The people the aid agencies are trying to help are the refugees.
  4 The country that has the best health service in Europe is France.
  5 What / The thing that I would really like to do is train as a doctor.
  6 The month when our sales are highest is August.
4 1 No, it was Louis Pasteur who discovered the process of fermentation.
  2 No, it was the science of microbiology that Pasteur founded.
  3 No, it is pasteurisation that is now routinely used to treat milk for domestic consumption.
  4 No, it was the germ theory of disease which/that was Pasteur's most important medical discovery.
  5 No, it was in 1885 that he created a vaccine for rabies.
5 1 It was last Wednesday when/that I developed a bad allergic reaction.
  2 It was on the way home that I first felt ill.
  3 It was because I felt so lousy that I went back to bed the following morning.
  4 The cough was bad, but it was the headache that was the real problem.
  5 It was only when I saw the doctor that I discovered the cause.
  6 It was on Monday that I felt well enough to go back to work.
  7 It was someone at work who suggested what might have caused the problem.
  8 It was breathing in paint fumes that caused the problem.

Use of English p.63

1 1 who put forward the
2 2 greatest ambition was
  3 as long as you take
  4 came as no (great) surprise to
  5 unless I get/have/receive
  6 hardly likely to take off
  7 (very) highly recommended (to me) by
  8 we would have been able to

Writing pp.64–65

1 1 These 2 or 3 Instead 4 and 5 rather than
  6 Whereas 7 others 8 too 9 although
2 1 B 2 A 3 A 4 C 5 B 6 A 7 C 8 B 9 B 10 B
  11 A 12 B
3 1 one 2 to 3 that 4 does 5 did 6 so 7 both
  8 yours 9 there/then 10 such
4 *Suggested answer*
  Aromatherapy uses fragrant oils, which are rubbed into the body. It is good for both physical and emotional disorders, as it works on both a physical and an emotional level. You can have a whole course of treatments, but you don't have to. Just one is enough to feel some benefit. If relaxation is the aim try aromatherapy, if not try something else.

5 1 A, C 2 B, D 3 B, C 4 A, C 5 A, B 6 C, D
  7 B, D 8 C, D
6 1 d 2 f 3 h 4 a 5 e 6 b 7 c 8 g

Listening p.66

1 1 b) 2 a word or expression 3 c) 4 a bank/friend/family member, etc.
2 1 stones 2 (a) couch potato 3 cycling 4 parents
  5 personal trainer 6 handbags 7 clinic 8 *Fun and Fitness*
4 1 Judy does say she uses oils, but not at varying temperatures. The words *heated and chilled* are the cue for the correct answer, which is *stones*.
  2 The student has written the words *health fanatic*, but this is a distractor. Judy says she hated exercise in her 20s. The correct answer is introduced by the cue *what people call*.
  7 The student has written *perfume*, but this is a distractor. You have to listen carefully to the verb tenses. She says that last year, she set up a website selling handbags (the correct answer) and next time she is going to try selling pefume.
  8 The student has written *The Easy Way to Health*. These words occur immediately after the word *book*, but you have to wait until the next sentence for the actual title of the book, introduced by the cue *it's called*.
5a 1 c 2 d 3 b 4 a
5b 1 redundancy payout 2 health fanatic 3 energy levels
  4 lifestyle

Audio script

Hello, my name's Judy Simpson, and I work as a complementary therapist – helping people to feel better by using a range of holistic body treatments. I've been a therapist for five years now, doing a range of treatments including aromatherapy, using essential oils, and acupuncture – but the newest is a healing therapy which uses heated and chilled <u>stones</u>, which everybody seems to love.

Funnily enough, I haven't always been a health fanatic, in my 20s I'd never heard of complementary therapy – I was what people call a '<u>couch potato</u>' because I actually hated exercise in any form. I had a good job in catering, but I was working long, irregular hours, eating badly and not getting enough exercise. It wasn't until I went on holiday with some friends that I realised just how unfit I was – it was a <u>cycling</u> trip, and I just couldn't keep up with the others. I decided there and then to take control of my life, I'd always wanted to be self-employed and run my own business – it was just a matter of deciding what to do.

That's when I saw a training course for complementary therapists advertised in a magazine. The idea of doing this sort of work on a freelance basis appealed to me. But, the course was fairly expensive – beyond my means, anyway. It was at that point that I was unexpectedly made redundant, so I had to do something. I'd only been in the job a couple of years, so there wasn't a big redundancy payout, but fortunately my <u>parents</u> stepped in with a timely loan, which allowed me to sign up for the course. And it really changed my life, making me think about my own diet and lifestyle. I learned being totally obsessive about these things isn't a good idea, but we all need to find the right balance in our lives. Much to the amazement of my friends, I even got myself a <u>personal trainer</u> – mainly because I couldn't stand the thought of spending hours at the gym. As a result, my energy levels increased tremendously and I realised that complementary health has an effect on every area of your life.

My new lifestyle has given me confidence to try lots of new things. For instance, I love <u>handbags</u>, and last year I set up my own website selling them. It was a disaster – I hardly sold any – but at least I'd tried it and I've no regrets. I'm going to try selling perfume next time. At the moment, though, I'm very involved in the designs for my own <u>clinic</u>, which is due to open in about six months – so I don't have a second to spare.

If you think a healthy lifestyle is for you, but you're confused by all the stuff you read in the media, I've just written a book about finding the easy way to health, it's called *Fun and Fitness* – and I've got a copy here if anybody would like to look at it. Believe me if I can do it – anyone can!

Now if anyone's got any questions, I'll be …

Language development p.67

1 1 working   2 to be   3 (to) clear   4 digging / to dig
5 to remove   6 scratching   7 using   8 saying
9 to think   10 dig   11 to be   12 to be

2 1 The teacher asked me to wait outside.
2 My friends warned me not to trust her.
3 I arranged for some friends to help me move house.
4 My parents refused to let me stay out late.
5 We all had to wait for Jane to finish her meal.
6 He wanted her to go with him.

3 1 a eating   b to take
2 a swimming   b to swim
3 a to start   b travelling
4 a him buying   b to buy him
5 a to say   b getting

4 1 reading   2 to iron   3 to inform   4 studying   5 to tell   6 giving up   7 to pick up   8 to ask   9 arriving   10 showing

Use of English p.68

2e happy

3 1 take 2 grown 3 deal 4 apply 5 strength

Writing p.69

1 1 a A b B
2 a both b both c A d A e B f both
3 a B b A

2/4   *Complete model answer for Text A*
Come to sunny Compton!
There are many reasons why Compton should feature on your list of places to visit in this region, and not the least of **these** is its family orientation. ~~It's a great place for families to spend time together.~~ Families will have a good time here, and there are some really interesting places for **them** to visit.

Known locally as the jewel of the coast, its golden sandy beaches are delightful and are also extremely safe for small children. ~~The beaches are beautiful and not dangerous.~~ Compton also has a lifeguard station within easy reach.

The town has something for everyone. For the best view of the picturesque old buildings, it's a good idea to take the sightseeing bus tour – **this** takes two hours and is well worth it.

Places to visit include the museum, with its fascinating exhibition showing the history of Compton, and the zoo, which boasts many rare and beautiful species of animal. The castle is also well worth a visit, and has beautiful gardens and a specially designed play area for children.

A range of accommodation is available, with plenty of small friendly hotels that are ideal for families.

If you want to visit somewhere all the family will love, look no further than Compton!

3/4   *Complete model answer for Text B*
Compton is a ~~nice~~ **lively** place to have fun with friends – it's a ~~nice~~ **thriving** town with lots going on.
<u>What's the town like?</u> The town itself is interesting, with good shops – these include not only extremely ~~nice~~ **exclusive** boutiques selling expensive designer clothes, but also cheaper chain stores. You won't have any trouble finding what you want in Compton, and you can be sure of finding the most up-to-date merchandise there.
<u>So what is there to do in the evenings?</u> Compton has a good nightlife, too, including ~~nice~~ **trendy** clubs and a cinema complex which shows the latest films.
There are dozens of cafés and restaurants serving delicious food at very reasonable prices, and loads of friendly pubs and nightclubs where you can meet people and have fun. There are also plenty of buses, which continue running late into the night, so getting home won't be a problem. Come to Compton for the time of your life!

Reading pp.70–71

1 1 a
2 Because he argues that the Tyrannosaurus Rex was a scavenger, contrary to popular belief.
3 Tyrannosaurus Rex had blunt teeth, not the sharp teeth needed for tearing meat; it had legs designed for walking, not running; the numbers of Tyrannosaurus Rex were in similar to proportion to scavengers of today, such as vultures.

3 1 D (*you come up with a supposition … You can't just overturn a hypothesis …* links to *the controversial theory he's been working on* (line 9))
2 F (*It has now reached the point where … inviting people to make up their minds* links to *an idea … met with … scepticism … but … recently been gathering momentum* (line 13))

3 B (*... so left without a degree* (line 26) links to *Ironically, Horner has now become one of the world's foremost dinosaur experts*)

4 G (*By calculating this biomass ... it's possible to work out how many of each type existed* links to *If you look at how many meat eaters there were ... compared with the scarcity of the herbivorous dinosaurs* (line 45))

5 A (*where the flocks of vultures wait to feed on animals killed by hyenas* (line 52) links to *Horner frequently likens Tyrannosaurus Rex to these scavenging birds*)

6 E (*somebody else could study this and find out that there's something weird going on. But nobody has done it yet* (line 56) links to *it could be more rigorous, but in the absence of a more wide-reaching study, it's going to stand*)

Module 7

Use of English p.72

1 1 The family sailed to Australia.
2 Jonathan continued to work.

2 1 B (*described + as*)
2 D (*to get something out of your system*)
3 A (*at all costs* is a fixed expression)
4 B (= *enthusiastic*)
5 A (*leave* is *granted* by an employer)
6 C (*omission* and *default* refer to things; *truancy* implies lack of permission)
7 D (= *provided that*)
8 B (*up to speed* is a fixed expression)
9 C (*to fulfil* a *duty*)
10 B (*to set foot* in a place)
11 C (*fit + out*)
12 A (*to enable someone to do something*)

Language development p.73

1 1 enquiries   2 satisfying   3 likeable   4 volcanoes
5 shelves   6 hesitation   7 occurrence   8 advise
9 dying   10 preferred; preference

2 1 impossible   2 remarkable   3 embarrassed   4 exceed
5 acceptance   6 unbelievable   7 incredible
8 volunteered

3 1 receipt   2 guarantee of success   3 occupation
4 achievement   5 immediate   6 separated
7 approximately   8 decision   9 necessarily
10 leisurely

4 Dear (1) Sir/Mad~~d~~am
I am (2) ~~writting~~ **writing** to (3) complain**e** about the service I (4) ~~recieved~~ **received** in your restaurant last night. (5) General**l**y the food was poor and the service was (6) awful~~l~~.
The (7) potato**es** were nearly raw, and the (8) ~~source~~ **sauce** that the chicken was cooked in was much (9) ~~saltyier~~ **saltier** than was (10) nec~~e~~essary.
The (11) ~~waitor~~ **waiter** kept (12) dropping (13) ~~thinks~~ **things,** including two (14) ~~knifes~~ **knives**, which he then put back on the table for us to use.

In (15) ~~addittion~~ **addition** we were forced to wait nearly an hour between the main course and the (16) ~~desert~~ **dessert**. When we pointed this out to your staff, they became rude and (17) ~~aggresive~~ **aggressive.**
I don't think you realise how much (18) distres**s** this causes to a person like myself who (19) a~~l~~lways (20) ~~trys~~ **tries** to maintain the highest (21) ~~standads~~ **standards** in all aspects of my (22) ~~live~~ **life**.
I look forward to hearing your (23) ~~explainations~~ **explanations** and how you propose to compensate us.
Yours (24) ~~sincerly~~ **sincerely**

Use of English p.74

2 1 overcome   2 physically   3 participants   4 enthusiast
5 jokingly   6 governing   7 unlikely   8 grudging
9 outdoor   10 satisfaction

Writing 1 p.75

1 1 D   2 B   3 C   4 A   5 C   6 B   7 A   8 C   9 A
10 C   11 B   12 C   13 D   14 A   15 B
2 1 cost   2 prepared   3 accept   4 made
5 happy/content   6 secret   7 laughing   8 surprise
3 1 surprise   2 sale   3 apologies   4 suit   5 generosity
6 assistance   7 trustworthy   8 insistent

Listening p.76

1a 1 3
2 Extract One is about a round-the-world sailor; Extract Two is about motivation; Extract Three is about a new book
1c 1 What do they agree about the sailor?
A She's a good role model for young people.
B She should pay more attention to safety.
C She's not as innocent as she appears.
2 What is the man's opinion of the sailor?
A He admires her determination.
B He distrusts her motives.
C He doubts her sincerity.
3 What is tonight's programme going to focus on?
A the findings of economists
B the work of one researcher
C the views of philosophers
4 Dr Senik's theory suggests that people
A tend to set themselves false goals.
B are happier if they do set themselves goals in life.
C become frustrated if they fail to set themselves realistic goals.
5 They agree that the main strength of the book is the fact that
A it gets off to a very good start.
B it will be a useful guide for travellers in the area.
C it deals equally well with both history and the landscape.
6 They feel that the description of the modern-day journey
A contains unnecessary detail.
B captures the essence of the region.
C could have explored some issues more deeply.
2 1 C   2 B   3 A   4 B   5 C   6 B

Audio script

Extract One

F: Did you see that programme about Ally Stone on television last night? It's incredible what she's achieved, and she's such a sweet person, so young and innocent in many ways.

M: Well, I'm not taken in by that. Innocents do not drive themselves, day after day, night after night with minimal sleep. Apparently, she was always adjusting the sails on that boat – not to make it safer, but to make it faster! <u>She's an extremely tough individual</u>.

F: <u>OK, I take your point on that</u> – but you must admit that she's an incredible person – inspirational really.

M: Well, she's pushed herself beyond what ordinary people are capable of, which is an impressive thing to do alright, but let's not kid ourselves that she's normal – that she represents a good role model. <u>Basically, she's an obsessive, hooked on ambition and achievement and living in extreme danger.</u> She has huge determination, OK, but it comes from her ability to convince other people, hard-nosed business people included, to come up with the cash to fund her obsessions. I'm not sure how admirable that is really.

F: Gosh – I'd never thought of it like that.

Extract Two

M: One of the great puzzles of human nature is why people strive for more material things and greater achievements in life – when these things don't seem to make them any happier in the long run. Philosophers have pondered this conundrum for centuries, and <u>modern economists have been examining it over several decades in a multitude of cultures, and we'll be looking into the detailed conclusions of those studies in tonight's programme</u>. But first of all, let's hear from Mandy, who's been doing a bit of research of her own.

F: Thanks, Bob. Yes, I spoke to economist Dr Claudia Senik and she put forward the theory that for the basic person there is pleasure in progress. <u>We are proud to aim for something and so in striving for that, we're already making ourselves happy today.</u> Once we've achieved our aims, however, they quickly lose their lustre; we find things aren't as satisfying as we'd hoped, and we'll want something else. So, in other words, people are at the mercy of their needs and greeds. But Dr Senik offers a more positive view – forget about achieving your goals, she says, just enjoy working towards them. Bob …

M: Thanks, Mandy, and now …

Extract Three

F: Books that are worth reading often have outstanding first paragraphs – a category into which Justin Marozzi's excellent *South from Barbary* fits with ease, don't you think?

M: Possibly, but then in many ways this is the perfect travel book: an exhilarating journey – one-thousand five-hundred miles by camel in the wake of early nineteenth-century explorers and campaigners against the slave trade, across some of the most inhospitable terrain on earth. <u>But what made it for me was the way it's all described with panache that does justice both to the beauty of the Sahara and to the cause that he recounts.</u>

F: <u>I'd certainly go along with that</u>. It's a measure of Marozzi's skill that he handles the big themes of history and the small irritations of twenty-first century camel travel – waiting for his tea, doing the washing up, bickering with Ned, his travelling companion – with equal charm.

M: Yes, <u>it takes a talented journalist to get modern-day Libya just right</u>, and Marozzi has all the qualities: observant, patient and extremely well-attuned to the wackiness and eccentricity that lurk just below the surface.

F: Exactly.

Vocabulary p.77

1a 1 d 2 g 3 a 4 c 5 f 6 b 7 h 8 e

1b 1 I used to buy shoes in the sales for the sake of it.
2 The exhibition was excellent, so I couldn't tear myself away and get the train home.
3 I keep telling myself there was nothing I could have done to help.
4 You can never get served, even though the shop is not short of staff.
5 Although Alice was pregnant, she concealed it from her friends.
6 She pretended that she was in control of the situation, but she was fooling herself.
7 I'd feel nervous without my address book.
8 I spent so much time playing and thinking about chess that it took over my life.

2 1 bug 2 hooked 3 freak 4 mood 5 break
6 collapse 7 choice 8 throwing 9 leads 10 sucked

3 1 got 2 tear 3 in 4 another 5 given 6 sake
7 short 8 told 9 myself 10 over

Language development p.78

1 1 didn't 2 could 3 would 4 would 5 hadn't

2 1 I wish that chocolate **didn't** bring me out in a rash.
2 I wish I **could** remember where I've put my keys.
3 He talks as though he **earned/earns** a huge salary, but I know he doesn't.
4 I'd sooner **spend** my money on clothes than food.
5 If only travel ~~would~~ cost less, I'd travel a lot more.
6 It's time we **stopped** messing around and **started** work.
7 I'd rather you **spoke** to James because you know him better than I do.
8 I wish I **hadn't spent** all my money yesterday, then I would still have some in my bank account.√

3 1 I wish I was fitter.
2 If only I had my phone with me.

3 I wish I could find a job that I really enjoyed.

4 If only I had studied French at school.

5 If only my daughter told me where she was going.

6 I wish I hadn't left my sunglasses on the beach.

7 If only someone would invent decent clothes that didn't need ironing.

8 I wish I hadn't called the shop assistant dishonest.

9 I wish these aeroplane seats were wider.

10 If only my parents could have come to the wedding.

4 1 He talks to his dog as though he was talking to a human being.

2 I'd rather you didn't wear your shoes in the house.

3 Suppose/Supposing you moved house, where would you go?

4 He'd sooner stay where he is than move house.

5 It's time I settled down and got a place of my own.

6 I've lived here six months, but it feels as if it's longer.

7 It's high time we had this room redecorated.

8 Supposing/Suppose the rent went up, could you afford to stay?

5 1 She talks to me as though she was my mother.

2 I'd sooner you drove, if that's OK.

3 It's time we went to bed.

4 I'd rather you didn't tell me how the film ends.

5 Supposing the information turns out to be wrong, what will you do?

6 She looked as if she had been crying.

7 Suppose she had drowned? How would you have felt?

8 It's high time you got a job and became independent.

Use of English p.79

1 1 wish I had not upset my

2 2 had any intention of inviting

3 ever having set

4 to keep in touch with her

5 looked as if

6 rather you didn't/did not tell

7 wish Ian wouldn't/would not

8 a great deal of enthusiasm

Reading pp.80–81

3b *professionally I had bitten off far more than I could chew*

3c *we hit it off with the locals*

4 1 B *(from the moment we set foot on the island … we hit it off with the locals in no time (line 37))*

2/3 B *(We wasted no time in abandoning … much to the horror of my parents (line 39))*

   D *(If we'd listened to the pessimistic predictions of our relations, we'd never have carried on (line 87))*

4 B *(I used to think I wasn't cut out to be a full-time mother. But here I can combine work and childcare … (line 51))*

5 A *(had to draw on the experience of people I knew from the world of art and design (line 15))*

6 D *(Even though the odds were stacked against us – given our cottage-sized budget … crumbling ruin … neither of us ever questioned what we'd taken on (line 82))*

7 D *(I can't see us ever giving it up because we get so much out of it (line 93))*

8 C *(it wouldn't tie me down to working shop hours (line 62))*

9 A *(professionally I had bitten off far more than I could chew (line 20))*

10 A *(I invested in a comprehensive business course … (line 25))*

11 D *(Peter and I have always shared the same dream … I couldn't have managed it without him (line 90))*

12 C *(to my amazement, several took me up on my offer (line 69))*

13 B *(in order to succeed … we had to muck in with the others …we all shared the responsibility (line 43))*

14 A *(The rent I was paying was astronomical and I began to feel very exposed (line 22))*

15 C *(I didn't go into this to make a fortune (line 73))*

5 1 g 2 c 3 d 4 a 5 h 6 e 7 f 8 b

Writing p.82

1b 1 without any warning   5 It was unsuccessful

6 reverse their decision   7 In the first place

9 opposed the idea

1c *Suggested answers*

2 to come to terms with the proposal   3 it is not sensible   4 impossible to implement   8 followed the rules   10 they lost the majority of their customers immediately   11 I might find myself unemployed   12 it might be an idea to encourage managers

2 1 concerned   2 implemented   3 explain   4 attempted   5 introduce   6 appear

3 I am writing to complain about the proposed ban on smoking in public places. I work in Café Noir, a well-known restaurant popular with visitors in the centre of town.

I am very concerned about this proposal, for a number of reasons. Firstly, I don't understand why this is being implemented without any warning, and why there has been no discussion – there is no time for anyone to come to terms with the proposal. And secondly, it is not sensible to suggest it in outdoor bars and restaurants – such an idea is impossible to implement.

To support my argument against the proposed ban, I would like to explain what happened when the authorities tried to enforce a ban on smoking in my home town. It was unsuccessful, and the politicians had to reverse their decision. In the first place, few people followed the rules. Of course, most businesses opposed the idea. A small number of restaurants tried to implement a no-smoking policy, but they lost the majority of their customers immediately. If the same thing happened here, I might find myself unemployed. As a suggestion, it might be an idea to encourage managers to introduce specific non-smoking areas instead. This would appear to be a better solution.

Module 8

Use of English p.83

2 1 reliable 2 research 3 tendency 4 easily
5 response 6 unpredictable 7 luxurious
8 impression 9 portrait/portrayal 10 nostalgic

Language development p.84

1 1 I will 2 will I 3 do I 4 I get 5 I have 6 have I
7 could I 8 I could 9 had she 10 She had

2 1 Under no circumstances will the company give a
refund without a receipt.
2 Not only is the new computer system safer, it is also
more reliable.
3 Not since we visited Nepal some years ago had we
been anywhere so interesting.
4 Rarely do we come across such a hard-working
student these days.
5 Hardly had we started dinner when/than she
suddenly said she had to leave
6 Only now do I realise how dishonest she is.
7 Not a penny did we spend on food all the time we
were there.
8 No way will I work on the afternoon of the Cup Final.

3 1 Years it took to complete the building of the tunnel.
2 This I'm going to enjoy!
3 Weeks we waited with no news from them.
4 Jerry's going to run a marathon? That I'd like to see!
5 They say the health service is improving? That I find
very difficult to believe.

4 1 The door opened and in came Stella.
2 …and off he ran as fast as his legs would carry him.
3 …and out sprang a black dog.
4 …and up flew the balloon into the treetops.
5 There was an outhouse behind the main building; in
front, there was an old well.

5 1 So tired was he that he could hardly walk.
2 Such danger was there in the streets that we dared not
go out.
3 Such was their anxiety that they did not sleep at all
for three days.
4 So confident were they of victory that they planned
the celebrations before the election had taken place.
5 Such was his ability on the football field that no one
could stop him scoring goals.

Use of English p.85

1 1 a website
2 You make a bid, and the highest bidder is able to buy
the goods.

2 1 B (*goes + by the name*)
2 D (*widely regarded* = collocation)
3 A (*alter the course* = collocation)
4 B (*= in fact*)
5 A (*to turn out to be*)
6 A (*the proud owner* = collocation)
7 D (*on + offer*)
8 C (*lies in the fact that* is a fixed expression)

9 D (*word-of-mouth recommendations* = collocation)
10 A (*sense* = non-personal)
11 D (*appeals + to*)
12 B (summarises the argument)

Language development
Not only has the company gone …
Rarely do you find people …

Language development p.86

1 1 actually, 2 Not surprisingly, 3 honestly,
4 Annoyingly, 5 Obviously 6 Naturally, 7 arguably
8 presumably

2 1 funnily 2 Indeed 3 Worryingly 4 surely
5 frankly 6 understandably 7 of course 8 Granted

3 1 Generally 2 considered 3 whole 4 large 5 rule
6 main

4 1 speaking 2 Believe 3 honest 4 far 5 truth
6 Judging 7 afraid 8 turned

5 Suggested answers
1 Generally speaking / By and large 2 as far as I know
3 Obviously / Of course / Granted / Admittedly 4 As a
matter of fact / Indeed 5 Strictly speaking 6 As it
turned out 7 surprisingly/funnily enough
8 Worryingly 9 Surely

Listening p.87

2 1 D (*I now have to leave home at six to avoid the jams
… it's nose-to-tail all the way back*)
2 G (*sitting in front of a screen … I use it for … keeping
in touch with the children*)
3 A (*dinnertime, when I like to catch up with the news
on the satellite channel … she says … mealtimes
should be a time for conversation*)
4 C (*usually pick up a snack on the way home … that
stuff's getting so popular*)
5 E (*I was making calls … I'd be popping out to see if I
had a message*)
6 F (*I'm feeling run-down*)
7 B (*it's a lot cheaper than calling them on their mobiles*)
8 E (*Mum objects, though … she's not convinced*)
9 C (*otherwise people would never fit in everything they
wanted to do*)
10 H (*the bill came … I started to plan my expenditure*)

Audio script

Speaker 1
I used to get out for a run at least three mornings a week
– cheaper than the gym and it kept me fit and set me up
for the day. But those days are over, I'm afraid, because
I now have to leave home at six to avoid the jams, and I
still get held up – it's worse each year. Thank goodness
my office hours are flexible – that's one advantage of
doing everything on screen. Then it's nose-to-tail all the
way back. It's no wonder I'm feeling run down because
when I get in, there's no chance to do anything except eat
whatever my wife's left for me to pop in the microwave,
then collapse in front of the TV.   →

Speaker 2

I used to think it was a strange thing to do – <u>sitting in front of a screen</u> when you could actually be talking to someone. But my husband's away a lot, works irregular hours, so it comes in terribly handy – you can see why it's caught on the way it has. The main thing <u>I use it for is keeping in touch with the children</u> now they're away at university. They'd never normally put pen to paper, but this way they reply within hours sometimes, and <u>it's a lot cheaper than calling them on their mobiles</u>. They were never much into computer games as kids – though all their friends had them, of course – but that hasn't held them back, really.

Speaker 3

I can't wait to get to university – I'll have my own study-bedroom, with a link to the computer network, so it'll be much easier to plan my work schedule, and no more arguments. At the moment, at home, I spend three hours a night studying, and the only time I have to relax is <u>dinnertime, when I like to catch up with the news on the satellite channel.</u> <u>Mum objects, though</u> – <u>she says</u> it's unhealthy because <u>mealtimes should be a time for conversation</u>, but I've no idea what she wants me to talk about! I keep telling her we need to keep up-to-date with current affairs, and everyone does it, so I can't miss out – but <u>she's not convinced</u>.

Speaker 4

My boyfriend goes jogging every lunchtime, but in my job I can never manage to get away for long enough. My hours are so unpredictable, it makes planning anything difficult. I do yoga two evenings a week – which is much more relaxing. Those nights, I <u>usually pick up a snack on the way home</u>, eat it quickly, then dash out again. He says that kind of diet isn't good for me, but you can see why <u>that stuff's getting so popular</u>, because <u>otherwise people would never fit in everything they wanted to do.</u> I'm always careful to pick something that's low in fat, though, like they tell you to on TV – and I keep fairly fit.

Speaker 5

When they put up the rent on my flat, I thought if I gave up my gym membership, I'd manage it. But the gym wasn't the problem. I drive a lot in my job, so like everyone these days, <u>I was making calls</u> whenever I was held up in traffic – I mean, you've got to keep tabs on your friends, haven't you? Even in the office where they're prohibited, <u>I'd be popping out to see if I had a message</u>. Then <u>the bill came</u> – talk about a shock! Luckily my father bailed me out – on condition that <u>I started to plan my expenditure</u>. He was OK about it, but reminded me how email's much more cost-effective, so I've gone over to that.

Vocabulary p.88

1 1 joyriding 2 armed robbery 3 drunk driving
4 drug dealing 5 computer hacking 6 shoplifting
2 1 slander 2 arson 3 burglary 4 shoplifting
5 manslaughter 6 joyriding 7 hacking 8 forgery
3 1 mugging 2 mugger 3 burgle 4 burglar
5 murder 6 murderer 7 arsonist 8 stealing/theft

9 thief 10 forge 11 forger 12 robbery 13 robber
14 joyride 15 joyrider
4a 1 search 2 fight 3 maintain 4 scene 5 acting
6 commit 7 detect 8 catch 9 liaise
4b 1 amnesty 2 schemes 3 tackle 4 anonymity
5 arrest 6 come forward 7 penalty 8 clamp down

Language development p.89

1 1 Nirvana are still my ~~most~~ favourite band of all time.
2 James is slightly taller ~~as~~ **than** his brother.
3 Life is ~~a great much~~ **much / a great deal** noisier nowadays.
4 This is easily the ~~worse~~ **worst** murder we have ever had to deal with in this city.
5 The job now is nothing like **as** dangerous as it was.
6 Some people think that shoplifting is not such **a** serious crime as burglary.
7 Murder is by far ~~a~~ **the** most serious crime anyone can commit.
8 He is one of the most experienced **officers** in the police force.
2 1 The trial was so complex that it went on for weeks. / It was such a complex trial that it went on for weeks.
2 The cost of legal proceedings can be so high that some people cannot afford it.
3 Lawyers earn such a lot of money / so much money that many people want to become one.
4 Some laws are so outdated (that) they need to be rewritten.
5 The evidence was so strong / Such was the strength of the evidence / The strength of the evidence was such that the jury reached a decision very quickly.
6 After the trial, there were so many people outside the court (that) we couldn't see anything.
3 1 The police arrived too late to catch the criminals.
2 There were not enough officers on duty to control the crowd.
3 The crime was too serious to ignore.
4 There was enough evidence against him for the police to charge him.
5 Too many crimes are committed for the police to solve (all of them).
6 The joyrider drove too fast for the police cars to catch him. / The police cars couldn't go fast enough to catch the joyrider.
4 1 The sooner they change the law, the better it will be.
2 Prisons are becoming more and more overcrowded.
3 The more police officers we have on the street, the safer we will feel.
4 More and more police officers would like to carry a gun.
5 The more serious the crime, the tougher the penalty.
6 In some places, criminal gangs are becoming more and more violent.
5 1 As 2 like 3 like 4 as 5 like 6 as

Use of English p.90

2e stand
3 1 appearance 2 manage 3 fit 4 wild 5 dull

Writing p.91

2 The student has used approach A. The problems he writes about are: modern emphasis on material success; families living in different communities from each other; people using the Internet too much. The solutions he suggests are: people should not think of money so much; councils should provide more social opportunities; we should have more Internet cafés.

3 1 It is often said that   2 as a result   3 if so   4 Finally   5 So   6 although   7 Obviously   8 In this way   9 In spite of   10 To sum up

Reading pp.92–93

1 Suggested answers
1 A 'young offender' is a criminal in Britain who is not yet an adult in the eyes of the law.
2 Some may see them as a waste of time, while others may welcome them as a distraction from their everyday routine.

2 1 Nathan – a young offender
2 Sally Brookes – the theatre company's Programme Director
3 Lou Heywood – the theatre company's Touring Director

5 1 A   (*depending on a 'front' … I felt I had to be the "tough" guy or the "cool" guy to survive … you just carry on pretending that you're a particular kind of person* (line 2))
2 D   (*his willingness to admit this … the result of an innovative drama course … extended to young offenders to help them examine their reactions to things* (line 16))
3 D   (*the audience … calls out for the character to lift the mask and explain … how he might find ways to act on that feeling, rather than according to the front* (line 34))
4 A   (*we work from the premise that each person can nonetheless make active choices and has a responsibility for their actions* (line 52))
5 C   (*they get to explore behaviour patterns one step removed … they themselves don't end up feeling judged or interrogated* (line 60))
6 B   (*Like all the trainers at Geese, Lou Heywood … comes from a background of drama training* (line 69))
7 B   (*Lou believes that each workshop must be tailor-made to the needs of a particular group* (line 75))

6 1 c   2 g   3 i   4 h   5 a   6 f   7 e   8 d   9 b

Module 9

Use of English p.94

1 Repeats what people say to him, invents his own sentences and own words, remembers things he has done, asks for things.

2 1 B (*describe + as*)
2 D (*close companions* = collocation)
3 C (*repeat + back*)

4 A (adverb of contrast)
5 B (*to run to a total*)
6 C (*in + context*)
7 A (*particularly impressive* = collocation)
8 D (*comment + on*)
9 B (= *remembers*, transitive verb)
10 A (*life expectancy* = collocation)
11 B (logical follow-on from previous sentence)
12 C (*high hopes* = collocation)

> **Language development**
>
> *So successful has she been that N'Kisi is now the world's most talked-about talking bird.* (The verb is inverted.)

Language development pp.95–96

1 1 John reported that sales had increased by 20 per cent.
2 Dave announced that the new campaign started / would start three days later.
3 Adam told them that they were getting a lot of positive feedback from consumers.
4 Jenny said that she had met the clients the day before and she was sure they didn't have any worries.
5 Adam confessed that he hadn't seen the new posters yet.
6 Dave admitted that unfortunately he didn't have them with him, but he promised that he would get everyone a copy the next day.
7 Jenny encouraged everyone to keep up the good work and reminded everyone that she would see them all there again at the same time the following week.

2 The interviewer asked me:
1 where I had worked before.
2 why I wanted to work for this/that company.
3 if I had ever worked in marketing before.
4 what my favourite advertising slogan is/was.
5 if I am/was a good communicator.
6 where I thought I would be in ten years' time.
7 if/whether I worked better on my own or as part of a team.
8 what I least liked about my old job.
9 what impression I had when I went in there this/that morning.
10 if/whether I could start next/the following Monday.

3 1 Harvey explained that he might not be here/there tomorrow/the next day.
2 Amanda said that she shouldn't have said what she did.
3 The shop assistant promised that he/they could get it for me by the following Tuesday.
4 My neighbour said that he/she could help if I needed a hand.
5 I told the class they didn't need to do any more; they had done enough.
6 The teacher explained that he/she wouldn't be there next / the following week because he/she would be on holiday.
7 Rachel asked if she should put the lights on, as it was getting dark.
8 The critic admitted that it is/was a great film.

4 1 A   2 B   3 B   4 A   5 C   6 B   7 A   8 C

5 1 My classmate advised me to ask him to speak more slowly.

2 Dad promised that he would get a film on the way home.

3 My colleague refused to help me tonight.

4 My brother denied reading my private diary.

5 My secretary reminded me that I had an appointment at 4 p.m.

6 Anne's friend begged her to tell her where she got that shirt.

7 The driver thanked me for helping him/her change the wheel.

8 Julie blamed Gerald for getting lost.

6 1 Fake CDs are known to be widely available.
It is well known that fake CDs are widely available.

2 It has been announced that the police have made a major arrest.

3 It is reported that 100,000 CDs have been confiscated.
A hundred thousand CDs are reported to have been confiscated.

4 It is believed that the fake CDs were made abroad.
The fake CDs are believed to have been made abroad.

5 It is thought that the CDs were smuggled into the country in boats
The CDs are thought to have been smuggled into the country in boats.

6 The man arrested is suspected of being the ringleader of an international gang.

7 He is reputed to have made millions of dollars from crime.
It is reputed that he has made millions of dollars from crime.

8 He is rumoured to have homes on five continents.
It is rumoured that he has homes on five continents.

9 It has been suggested that fewer people would buy fake CDs if genuine ones were not so expensive.

10 The industry is said to be looking at new ways to prevent illegal copying.

Use of English p.97

1 1 is (widely) thought to be

2 2 rumoured to be about to

3 reminded him that he

4 turned down Roy's

5 advised the tourists not to

6 is Gus a brilliant

7 the interests of security

8 no circumstances should this door be

Listening p.98

2 1 A (*I just wished she'd put on a pair of jeans like the other mums, rather than showing us up all the time*)

2 D (*I never knew what Mum thought … she was so bound up in her own career that she didn't make much of it*)

3 A (*as a student, you're always struggling to make ends meet*)

4 C (*I'm determined to give them the confidence to go off and lead their own lives*)

5 A (*reflect on my own upbringing … All that will inform my writing*)

6 B (*I was never keen on the whole celebrity thing, but I'll have to see how I feel as all that fades away*)

3a 1 make 2 take 3 catch 4 attract
3b 1 c 2 d 3 a 4 b

Audio script

Int. = Interviewer, JH = Jessica Hanson

Int.: Jessica Hanson's been a top model in the fashion industry for over ten years. But she's recently retired from the catwalk, and is here in the studio with me today. I suppose it's every little girl's dream, Jessica, to be a fashion model. Was this something you always wanted to do?

JH: When I was a child, my mother was the editor of a fashion magazine, so I was surrounded by that world from an early age – but it somehow just failed to catch my imagination at that stage. My mother had dealings with all the top designers so, you know, she'd come to meet us from school wearing all sorts of outrageous outfits – attracting a lot of attention at the school gate. <u>I just wished she'd put on a pair of jeans like the other mums, rather than showing us up all the time.</u> My sister, always the confident, sociable one, just used to laugh it off – but I used to take it to heart if I thought we were being giggled about.

Int.: But your mother had a strong influence on you, though?

JH: When I was going through school, she was very tough, very strict with us – we didn't get much praise – though I wouldn't call her critical or unkind. But, like, if I won a prize at school, my father would be thrilled – but <u>I never knew what Mum thought</u>. I was the first person in the family to get to university, but <u>she was so bound up in her own career that she didn't make much of it</u>. I think I must've inherited my drive from her – and in the fashion industry, that certainly comes in useful.

Int.: So how was it that you ending up in modelling?

JH: I did English literature at university – I wasn't doing that badly, but it wasn't really my scene exactly either. Then I met someone at a party who turned out to be an agent. He had no idea I was my mother's daughter, but offered me the chance to do some modelling. I jumped at it, not least because, <u>as a student, you're always struggling to make ends meet</u>. And things took off from there – I wasn't trying to make a point or anything, but after that, I was offered several more modelling jobs. At the end of the course, much to my parents' amazement, I decided to take it up professionally.

Int.: And now you're retiring. Why's that?

JH: It's mainly because of the children. I've got twin girls, and I was given the opportunity to write a book – which, as an occupation, is more conducive to family life. I want my children to know I'm there for them if they want to talk to me – being on the end of a telephone line's not enough. <u>I'm</u>

determined to give them the confidence to go off and lead their own lives, as I did – I want them to feel supported, but not pushed – so it's up to them exactly what they end up doing. I'm not going to be breathing down their necks.

Int.: Tell us about the book.

JH: While I was at university, I wrote short stories, though I never managed to get anything published – and at the back of my mind was the idea that I'd like to be a novelist one day. And that's stayed with me – although it's something I've kept very much to myself. So much so that my friends don't quite know what to make of it – you know, they assume it's some kind of publishing gimmick. But I think I do have something to say – I'm not just jumping on the bandwagon. I've seen a bit of the world since I wrote those rather naive short stories and, of course, had time to reflect on my own upbringing and the ups and downs of family life. All that will inform my writing, but it's not going to be a novel about a model.

Int.: So, will this book be the first of many?

JH: I'll need to see how well it does before deciding, I think. But I don't regret closing the door on the superficiality of the fashion world. My life will be less stressful now, and I can't see myself going back. I hope people don't forget me, but I don't crave publicity either – I was never keen on the whole celebrity thing, but I'll have to see how I feel as all that fades away. Actually, I'm not doing the writing for the money, but I do need to have a career because I don't want the girls to be the only thing in my life – that would be no good for them. I suppose I am rather like my mother in some ways.

Int.: Well, we wish you every success with it.

JH: Thank you.

Vocabulary p.99

1a cloth – U – neutral
clothes – C (plural) – neutral
clothing – U – formal
dress/attire – U – formal
garment – C – formal
kit – C/U – informal
outfit – C – formal
wardrobe – C (usually singular) – neutral
wear – U – formal

1b 1 wardrobe   2 cloth   3 garments   4 clothes
5 clothing   6 kit   7 wear   8 dress   9 outfit

2 1 style   2 label   3 design   4 brand   5 logo   6 pattern

3a 1 let out / take in   2 let down / take up   3 dress up / dress down   4 change into / out of   5 wrap up
6 slip on / off   7 do/zip up   8 grow into / out of

3b 1 change out of; (slip) into   2 dress up   3 grew out of
4 wrap up   5 slipped on   6 let out   7 turn; up   8 Do; up

4 1 in   2 height   3 style   4 catch   5 comeback
6 statement   7 victim

Language development p.100

1

noun [C/U]	desire
verb [T]	desire
adjective (describing something you desire)	desirable
negative adjective	undesirable
adverb (from adjective)	desirably
noun [U] (from adjective)	desirability
negative noun [C] (someone/something that isn't wanted)	undesirable
adjective (from past participle)	desired

1 desirable   2 undesirable   3 undesirables   4 desired
5 desirability

2

noun [C]	origin
plural noun	origins
adjective	original
negative adjective	unoriginal
adverb	originally
verb [I, T]	originate
noun [C] (thing or person)	original
noun [U] (from adjective)	originality

1 origin   2 original   3 unoriginal   4 original
5 originally   6 origins   7 originality   8 originates

3

adjective	secure
negative adjective	insecure
adverb	securely
negative adverb	insecurely
noun [U]	security
negative noun [C, U]	insecurity
verb [T]	secure

1 security   2 insecure   3 securely   4 secure   5 secure
6 insecurities   7 secure   8 insecurely

4

adjective	popular
negative adjective	unpopular
noun [U]	popularity
negative noun [U]	unpopularity
adverb	popularly
verb [T]	popularise
noun [U] (from verb)	popularisation

1 popular   2 popularity   3 popularise   4 unpopular
5 unpopularity   6 popularly   7 popularisation

Use of English p.101

1 b) and c)

2 1 all   2 out   3 or/otherwise   4 What   5 which   6 by
7 on   8 Take   9 as   10 unless   11 make   12 In
13 up   14 got   15 instead

Language development

family – families, strategy – strategies, toy – toys,
holiday – holidays

Reading pp.102–103

1 a Hamish Pringle is the author of a book on the subject.
b David Graham is an expert in TV audience data.
c Michael Winner is a celebrity who appears in an advertisement.
d £100 = cost of attending the function
e 200,000 years ago = these attitudes were formed
f 150 = size of groups in which humans lived then

3 1 D (*new book* (line 6) links to *the author*; *the effectiveness … shrewdness of the casting* (line 9) links to *the most successful celebrity … the actress Prunella Scales*)

2 B (*So eliminating … a well-known name … is not easy* (line 14) links to *Nonetheless, if we all agree …*; *Can we bottle it?* links to the response *And here another expert thinks he may be on to something* (line 17))

3 G (*He thinks …* links with *According to Graham, academic evolutionary psychologists believe we may be …* (line 23))

4 F (*foraging bands of 150 or so …* (line 29) links with *To be successful in such a social grouping …*)

5 E (*What intrigues Graham … finding practical applications …* (line 39) links with *He proposes, if he can find partners or clients willing to sponsor a study …*; *… whether they connect up with the theory of evolutionary psychology* links with *… in due course, the same theoretical framework …* (line 43))

6 A (*soap operas are 'fast food for the brain' …* links with *The analogy here is with our taste for sweet and fattening treats* (line 51))

5a 1 d   2 f   3 e   4 a   5 c   6 b
5b 1 c   2 d   3 e   4 f   5 a   6 b

Writing p.104

1b–e Proposal suggesting ways of raising the profile of the Adventure Centre to increase bookings
Introduction
The aim of this Proposal ~~are~~ **is** to suggest ways of promoting the Adventure Centre to increase bookings, and make recommendations for ~~action~~ ~~it is~~ **action. It is** based on information **gathered** from customer feedback.
Feedback
The Centre is ~~generaly~~ **generally** popular with those who come, but there is a problem with publicity. Some said that they ~~have not~~ **had not** heard of the Centre until a friend told them about ~~them,~~ **it,** and others complained that they could not find the website.

Suggestions and recommendations
In order to deal with the problems ~~identefied~~ **identified** in the feedback and to increase ~~bookings; we~~ **bookings, we** recommend the following measures.
1 To address the problem of publicity:
  • journalists should be invited to special Open Days
  • a specialist should be <u>employed</u> to redesign the website, to make it more ~~accesible~~ **accessible**
2 To attract more bookings:
  • introduce a series of special ~~offer's,~~ **offers,** including offering reduced prices in the low season, and special packages for school parties.
Conclusion
Implementing the measures above should lead to ~~the~~ **a** general increase in awareness of the Centre and a subsequent increase in bookings. If the Centre is to <u>thrive</u>, we urge the directors to put them in place immediately.

2 *Suggested answers*
Task A
Proposal suggesting ways in which publicity for the Adventure Centre could be improved
Introduction
The aim of this proposal is to suggest ways in which publicity for the Adventure Centre could be improved. It is based on information from feedback provided by visitors to the Centre and observations made by staff.
Results of feedback
Clearly, many people find it difficult to navigate round the website and are often directed to the wrong part of the site. Some claim that brochures ordered via the website have taken a long time to arrive, partly because a second-class stamp has been used. The brochures themselves have also been criticised for being unclear and containing incorrect information – the telephone number is an old one. Many said that they only found out about the Centre from friends.
Suggestions and recommendations
In order to improve publicity, we recommend taking the following measures.
• it is vital to take on a computer specialist to deal with the website problems; it must be redesigned to be faster, more user-friendly and more accessible to Internet browsers
• brochures should be updated regularly so that information is current; they should also be redesigned to be clearer and more eye-catching
• publicity should always be sent out by first-class post, so that it arrives the next day
• the Centre needs a higher media profile; there should be Open Days with organised events and specially invited journalists who would run follow-up features on the Centre
• the budget for publicity should be increased.
Conclusion
The suggestions above should result in a great improvement in publicity for the Centre.
Task B
Report on problems with publicity for the Adventure Centre with recommendations for change
Introduction
The aim of this report is to explain problems associated

with current publicity for the Centre, and suggest ways in which it could be improved. It is based on complaints made by visitors to the Centre, and observations made by staff.

Background information

There have been a lot of complaints about the difficulty of finding out information about the Centre. It seems as though word of mouth is the only way that some people hear of it. The Internet should be an effective way of advertising, but many people find the Centre website very complicated and hard to navigate. This puts many people off, and they go elsewhere for their holiday. Some claim that brochures ordered via the website have taken a long time to arrive, partly because a second-class stamp has been used. The brochures themselves have also been criticised for being unclear and containing incorrect information – the telephone number is an old one, and the pictures are old and uninspiring.

Suggestions and recommendations

In order to improve publicity, we recommend making the following changes.

• take on a computer specialist to redesign the website so that it is faster, more user-friendly and more accessible to Internet browsers

• update brochures regularly so that information is current and presented more effectively

• use first-class post at all times.

Conclusion

The publicity must be improved, as it is the first point of contact for our visitors and will result in a loss of custom if the recommendations are not implemented.

Module 10

Use of English p.105

2 1 initially   2 suspicious   3 charmingly   4 involuntary
5 analysis   6 necessarily   7 amusing   8 depressing
9 helpless   10 responsibility

Language development

unnecessary, unnecessarily, necessitate, necessity

Language development pp.106–107

1 1 I kept calling the box office because I was trying to get tickets.
2 When I had bought my popcorn, I settled down to enjoy the film.
3 We stood at the back of the concert hall and tried to see what was happening.
4 Just as I arrived at the theatre, I realised that I had left the tickets behind.
5 The lights went out, and as a result, the audience was left in total darkness.

2 1 Growing up in Los Angeles, she dreams of becoming an actress.
2 Brad has had a busy year, starring in three films.
3 Living in London, it is easy for me to get to the theatre.

4 Reading the review, I realised that I had seen the film before.
5 Holding a top hat in one hand and a cane in the other, he performed an amazing tap dance routine.
6 Not being able to swim, he had to rely on other actors to do all his swimming stunts for him.

3 1 Being an art lover, she was very keen to go and see the exhibition.
2 Having packed / After packing the car up, we set off.
3 Never having been to Italy before, I was feeling slightly nervous.
4 Despite being pleased to be in New York, I missed my old friends.
5 Putting the phone down / Having put the phone down, I grabbed my suitcase and ran.
6 Not having performed on the stage before, I didn't know quite what to expect.

4 1 Once the cast had been chosen, they could start the rehearsals.
2 Because the show is booked solid for weeks, it is hard to get into.
3 If the chase scenes are carefully edited, they could look spectacular.

5 1 Bored, I fell asleep in the second act.
2 Given the right coaching, Claudia could become a great soprano one day.
3 Rated by the critics as a 'must see' show, it should be pretty good.
4 Poorly constructed, the set was starting to collapse.
5 Better publicised, the show would have been more successful.
6 Once properly advertised, the show started to do better.

6 1 I bought a programme so that I could see who else was in the show.
2 I sat down and started watching, and then realised I had seen the film before.
3 I've seen the Rocky Horror show a lot of times, and as a result I have learnt most of the words.
4 If you heard her sing, you'd never believe she was totally untrained.

7 1 We got seats at the front to have a better view.
2 They sold enough tickets for the production to be a financial success.
3 To hear her talk, you'd think she was a great actress herself.
4 We arrived at the theatre only to discover that the lead actor was sick.
5 I had had enough rehearsals to be confident in the role.
6 To be successful, a new musical needs to have at least three great tunes.

8 1 The plan was for the show **to be** transferred to Broadway after a few months in London.
2 The children jumped up, ~~to shout~~ **shouting** 'He's behind you!' when the villain appeared.
3 Not ~~to have~~ **having** a ticket, I couldn't get into the concert.
4 Unsuccessfully, I searched the Internet ~~finding~~ **to find** the soundtrack.
5 I enjoyed the show, ~~laughed~~ **laughing** all the way through.

6 Julie was the first person ~~playing~~ **to play** the role in the theatre.

7 ~~Walking on stage the audience greeted the singer with a loud cheer.~~ **As the singer walked on stage, the audience greeted him/her with a loud cheer.** *(subject of both clauses must be the same)*

8 I'm very disappointed not **to** have seen Elvis perform live.

9 She walked on stage only ~~realising~~ **to realise** she had forgotten her words.

10 ~~Rising to their feet, the soloist bowed to the ecstatic audience.~~ **The soloist bowed to the ecstatic audience, who rose to their feet.** *(subject of both clauses must be the same)*

9 1 having (been) closed down   2 being   3 Having persuaded   4 to renovate   5 restore   6 Helped   7 welcoming   8 staging

Use of English p.108

2e flat

3 1 call   2 engage   3 fair   4 split   5 bear

Listening p.109

1a 1 3

2 Extract One is about a singer-songwriter; Extract Two is about the environmental impact of rock concerts; Extract Three is about a concert.

1c 1 What does he say about the <u>process of writing</u> songs?
  A He <u>likes</u> to work to a <u>formula</u>.
  B He's <u>always thinking</u> about his <u>work</u>.
  C He finds it <u>hard</u> to <u>settle down</u> to <u>work</u>.

2 When answering the <u>interviewer's second question</u>, he is
  A describing the <u>songwriter's craft</u>.
  B <u>denying</u> that his later <u>songs lack originality</u>.
  C explaining what he <u>finds hard</u> about <u>songwriting</u>.

3 What point does the <u>male speaker</u> make about <u>concerts</u>?
  A They are becoming <u>more financially important</u> to bands.
  B They provide a <u>chance</u> for a <u>band</u> to show <u>environmental awareness</u>.
  C It's <u>not easy</u> to <u>calculate</u> how much <u>damage</u> they do to the <u>environment</u>.

4 The woman feels that some of the <u>data</u> relating to <u>carbon emissions</u> at <u>rock concerts</u>
  A has <u>underestimated</u> the problem.
  B has been based on <u>questionable assumptions</u>.
  C has <u>failed</u> to <u>make people</u> sufficiently <u>aware</u> of the issue.

5 How does the <u>woman feel</u> about going to the <u>concert</u>?
  A <u>unsure</u> if she can <u>afford</u> it
  B <u>reluctant</u> to <u>commit</u> herself
  C <u>doubtful</u> about the <u>sound</u> in the <u>venue</u>

6 How does <u>she react</u> to the <u>man's second suggestion</u>?
  A She <u>doesn't like</u> the <u>word</u> he uses.
  B She <u>doesn't agree</u> with his <u>reasoning</u>.
  C She <u>doesn't like</u> the idea of <u>eating out</u> in London.

2 1 A   2 C   3 C   4 B   5 C   6 A

Audio script

Extract One

Int = Interviewer, S = Singer

Int: Is there a set way in which you go about writing a song?

S: For me, no. If anyone does have a formula, then that's the way they do it. For me it comes from anywhere and everywhere, all sorts of different places. I don't think I could do it if there were set rules. <u>You see I've got all this stuff running through my head all the time</u>, and sometimes I just want to turn it off, you know? It can be annoying to have to go and get a pen and paper and write it all down – all these thoughts, these half-dreams, these bits and pieces of what people might have said – sometimes you just want it to go away.

Int: But doesn't it get easier?

S: The craft can get easier, but <u>you've got to invent more ways of saying what it is you want to say</u> because you don't want to repeat yourself, even though what you're saying might be repetitive – life is repetitive – but you can't afford to give people the impression that they've heard it all before – you have to keep thinking: 'How can I say this in new ways?'

Extract 2

M: What we hear these days is that because of the demise of the recorded music market, <u>the only way for a band to make money is to go out and tour</u>. But for a rock star hoping to cut down their carbon footprint, that's going to be a headache.

F: You mean that figure everyone quotes, that Madonna's last tour produced 440 tonnes of CO2?

M: And that figure didn't include the half of it. I mean, the hotels, the PA, the lights, the meals – all that gets counted in these days.

F: Yeah, concerts are by their nature ecologically disastrous, sure, but <u>I think you have to take some of the hype with a pinch of salt</u>. Like the idea that there are 80,000 people out there and they've all been sitting in traffic jams for five hours with the engine running – well, no, in the UK, it's reckoned that 60% of fans go to concerts by public transport – so it depends. You can't say that what goes for the USA is going to be true everywhere.

Extract Three

M: Did you see that Rufus Wainwright's doing a concert here, on a Sunday night in October? I bet it'd be good, shall we go and see it?

F: I'm in two minds actually. <u>You know the acoustics in the concert hall are not brilliant</u> and we did say we wouldn't go again after the last time. Given how much it costs, it might be better to spend a bit more and go to the show in London. Only thing is that's on a Tuesday, so it would mean missing work.

M: Listen, why don't you see how much the tickets are

actually going to be and do a costing for the whole trip – a meal as well if it's in London.

F: A costing? Is that an idea you've picked up on your management course? If we want to go to the concert, why don't we just go – if we book early, we'll probably get better seats. They'll all be gone by the time you've done all your costings!

M: OK. It's getting tricky missing work anyway, so the Sunday night option's probably better. Let's see if I've got the number on my phone …

Vocabulary p.110

1 D   2 B   3 B   4 A   5 C   6 B   7 A   8 D   9 A   10 D
11 C   12 B   13 A   14 C

Language development p.111

1   1 A, B   2 B, C   3 B, C   4 B   5 A, B   6 C   7 A
8 B, C
2a 1 for   2 over   3 about   4 in   5 of   6 against
2b 1 rude   2 annoyed   3 perfect   4 deficient   5 pleased
6 scared
3   1 of   2 from   3 for   4 for   5 with   6 from   7 for
8 for   9 for   10 at   11 from   12 with   13 at   14 of
15 of   16 for   17 about   18 about

Use of English p.112

1   Some people do not approve of singers like Hayley because they believe that classical music should not be made popular in this way.

2   1 some/every   2 what   3 which   4 such   5 as   6 of
7 that   8 taken   9 would   10 been/become/got   11 if
12 may/could/might   13 had   14 for   15 unless

Language development

dismissive of   interested in

Writing p.113

2   1 Having recently tried out two games, I had mixed reactions.
2 Although I enjoy playing computer games, I want to be challenged by them.
3 In my opinion, this game was not challenging enough.
4 In spite of the (excellent) graphics, they did not make up for the rather boring game.

3   1 The second game, called *Demons on the Loose*, was considerably more interesting.
2 The game involved attacking villains and demons which are hidden among the very realistic graphics.
3 In my opinion, this game is better than *Castle Raider*, not only because it is much more difficult to find the demons but also because the levels are difficult to get through.

4 Number 1 is the best conclusion.

5   *Complete model answer*
I appreciate it when new games come on the market, but unfortunately not all of them are equally good. Having recently tried out two new games, I had mixed reactions to them.
The first game is called *Castle Raider*, and is a 'search and rescue' game. Although I enjoy playing computer games, I want to be challenged by them. In my opinion, this game was not challenging enough. There are 16 levels, **and the idea is to find a person who is trapped in the castle and rescue them from dangerous situations.** Each level is more complex than the last, but I found they were easy to get through and took very little time. In spite of the excellent graphics, **which include colourful settings within the castle,** they did not make up for the rather boring game. **Children might enjoy it, but it is not very sophisticated.**
The second game, called *Demons on the Loose*, was considerably more interesting. The game involved **finding hidden treasure by** attacking villains and demons which are hidden among the very realistic graphics. In my opinion, this game is better than *Castle Raider*, not only because it is much more difficult to find the demons, but also because the levels are difficult to get through. Imagine a game which takes four hours to complete a level! The game gives you value for money, **and anyone who likes a challenge will really enjoy it.**
All in all, if you're looking for fast fun, challenge and value for money, then *Demons on the Loose* fits the bill.

Reading p.114–115

4   1 D   (*the raw intensity of the music here makes up for the lack of studio polish* (line 50))
2/3/4 A (*and their own compositions* (line 10))
C (*eight self-composed tracks* (line 34))
E (*Manu's melodic tunes* (line 63))
5 F   (*he is in fact owner of, and inspiration behind, popular restaurants in London and Paris* (line 72))
6 B   (*singers less well-known outside the Arab-speaking world* (line 26))
7 F   (*While most compilations sound … is an entity in its own right* (line 74))
8 E   (*reflecting his mixed ethnic background* (line 56))
9 B   (*backed up by intelligent sleeve notes* (line 19))
10 A   (*was praised in the British music press* (line 3))
11 D   (*formidable reputation as a live act … goes some way to showing why* (line 38))
12 C   (*trained as a teacher in Havana* (line 29))
13 D   (*a non-stop musical maelstrom* (line 41))
14 A   (*the unlikely but successful addition of accordion, trumpet and slide guitar* (line 12))
15 C   (*a fast-developing talent; someone to keep a close eye on* (line 36))
5   1 e   2 d   3 a   4 g   5 c   6 b   7 f

Practice exam

Reading
Paper 1 Parts 1–4

1 C (*if you live ... as Leo Hickman does* (line 3))

2 D (*Snow is on the wane* (line 12))

3 C (*In reference to Tony Burton's letter ...* (line 1))

4 B (*the enormous hype ... is raising lots of money ... for the charity* (line 16))

5 A (*I had to concede that the Aborigines had lived in harmony with their environment* (line 6))

6 B (*Unlike urban Aborigines ... without being seduced by mod cons* (line 10))

7 F (*catching fish on four different channels* (line 10) links with *On each of these ...*)

8 C (*a whole range of products ... financial services* (line 18) links with *you can acquire celebrity status through frequent appearances on the back of biscuit cartons*)

9 A (*due to its tendency to fly out of the water* (line 28) links with *As a result, ... you can buy leaping fish T-shirts*)

10 G (*they swing them into the boat with as little ado as possible* (line 42) links with *To compensate for these visual shortcomings, ...*; *such a well-orchestrated spectacle* (line 45) also links back to paragraph G)

11 B (*the fishermen use the very latest techonology to assist them* links with *Despite all this* (line 53))

12 D (*the 175 entrants have been gradually whittled down to just ten finalists* (line 59) links with *I watch the anglers standing apprehensively on the central stage*; the story of a *keen amateur fisherman* contrasts with a more recent fishing story about Darren Nixon (line 62))

13 C (The word 'unsmiling' shows that the question he asked the class was not a joke – he is being serious about the course.)

14 D (*I hadn't thought about who would want to be led by me, but it was a perplexing and humbling question.* (line 12))

15 A (*the course was going to force me to ask questions of myself that I wasn't sure I wanted the answers to ... my fear of exploring my own weaknesses* (line 22))

16 B (*the quiet leaders are often overlooked and underdeveloped ... the most competent leaders are not always the ones that are obvious to us* (line 40))

17 A (*Leadership is all around us ... the leaders all around us contribute to our everyday lives* (line 54))

18 B (*there was no skill he could teach me that I didn't innately know* (line 70))

19 C (*Evaluate the leadership skills that you demonstrate and concentrate on building them* (line 80))

20 C (*Yet no portrait ... is candid, and none of its documentary aims to reveal the truth* (line 43))

21 A (*this retrospective tribute* (line 8))

22 F (*We all know that he's been one of the best of our travel writers* (line 86))

23 B (*100 photographs, one for each year of the 20th century* (line 30))

24 E (*a real curiosity ... classical musicians and writers* (line 78))

25 C (*They are posed, hi-tech and ingeniously constructed* (line 42))

26 D (*mistitled The Art of Seeing ... the most dramatic of them looks staged* (line 49))

27 F (*photographic autobiography ... his skills with a camera lens complement his personal journeys* (line 85))

28 E (*The use of black and white ... 1960s photography ... turn their backs on the colour technology to remind us of the swinging days* (line 66))

29 B (*the book's commentary makes a connection between the examination of the body and wider cultural issues* (line 32))

30 D (*photographers ... heroes of the profession* (line 58))

31 B (*useful introductions aimed at novices and students of photography* (line 26))

32 E (*surely he was at the peak of his professional career during his 14-year association with* Queen magazine (line 73))

33 D (*favourite shots by two dozen staff photographers ... the long-established news agency* (line 50))

34 A (*his camera lens transformed ... composition* (line 18))

Paper 2 Writing

Part 1
Suggested answer

Report on the visit to the UK

This report is based on personal experiences during last year's UK trip, plus information gathered from fellow students.

Programme

The trip involved a considerable amount of travelling, and some people found this excessive. For instance, the train journey from London to Edinburgh was felt to take too long. Another unpopular aspect of the programme was the early start time for the language classes, although these were successful in all other respects.

Accommodation

The London hotel, with its busy staff, provided little opportunity for students to practise their English. In contrast, staying with the very welcoming families in Scotland gave us ample opportunity to do so.

Sightseeing

The bus tour around London was very informative, but should have been in English rather than our own language. Younger students found the museum visits a little dull, and older students mentioned a lack of organised evening entertainment in London. In Scotland, there was an excellent tour around Edinburgh, and everyone enjoyed the wonderful dancing display in the evening.

Recommendations

Overall, this trip was a success, but we have some improvements to suggest. A longer stay with local families would give more scope for language improvement and rethinking the travel arrangements could make the trip less tiring.

Part 2

Suggested answers

2 Speaking around the world

I wonder how many people reading this article are trying to learn another language? Probably most of you! Whether you are studying alone or in a class, language learning has never been so easy.

Twenty years ago, in the country where I was brought up, language teaching was done using very traditional methods; students had only textbooks, a cassette player and a teacher to help them make progress. There was nothing wrong with these methods, but we have many more resources available to us today.

Indeed, we can choose from a huge range of language-learning methods, and each student can select the method and timescale that suits him or her best. For example, switch on the TV and you can get access to programmes in a variety of languages, or you might choose to follow a language course on video. You can also use your home computer to study languages on the Internet according to your own personal timetable.

Even if you find it easier to learn with a group of other students, you can take a classroom-based course which makes use of all this language-learning technology.

But what will advances in technology have to offer us in the future? Will we be practising our speaking in the virtual reality of a foreign country? What about the boredom of learning endless vocabulary? Maybe this will become a thing of the past?

But whatever the future holds, I know I'm glad to be a language student now, rather than 20 years ago!

3 Reference for Alexandre Henderson

To whom it may concern

I have known Alexandre for the last ten years and worked with her on several occasions. She is a cheerful, optimistic person, and her warm and sensitive personality, makes her an ideal person to work with young people. She is used to caring for children, as she comes from a large family and she has frequently been a reliable babysitter for me, looking after my two children aged seven and ten.

Alexandre has always been an enthusiastic sportswoman and is one of the leading members of our local tennis club. She has also recently competed in a national athletics event, winning trophies in both long-distance running races and the high jump. She shows great determination and follows a regular personal training programme to maintain a good all-round fitness level.

Alexandre has been a colleague of mine, working on a part-time basis as a personal trainer at our local gym for the last two years. I have watched her working with clients of all ages, encouraging them to achieve their personal goals. She shows great patience and kindness towards those who are not used to exercise, and she is able to motivate the best athletes to excel at their particular sport. She has recently completed a six-month course on sports technology in order to bring her technical knowledge up to date.

Alexandre is a person who is extremely honest and also totally trustworthy. I have no hesitation in recommending her for this position.

4 A proposal for the International Cultural Exhibition

France is a country of endless variety. Each city and department has its own character and history. As you travel through the country, you can see the ever-changing scenery, from the wide flowing rivers in the Loire to the beauty of the high Alps in the Savoie. I suggest that an exhibition featuring France should illustrate the full range of its geography and culture through the medium of colour photography and video film.

Historical cities

The beauty of the capital city, Paris, is well known worldwide, but there are historical towns and cities throughout France which should be included in the display. The history of France goes back centuries, and this is reflected in the style of the architecture as you visit cities such as Bordeaux in the west, Beaune in the east and Montpellier in the south.

Art and culture

No exhibition of France would be complete without some of the wonderful works of art which have been produced by French artists. There could be a small art exhibition for visitors to see, perhaps with French jazz music playing in the background to help to create a truly French atmosphere.

Food and wine

French cuisine enjoys worldwide renown, and there are fine cheeses and wines produced in all the various regions. A range of these different foods could be made available for visitors to the exhibition to taste.

I consider that all these suggestions would give a good impression of the most important aspects of the French culture.

5

Question 5 is intended for those students who are taking the set-text option and answers are dependent on which novel they have read.

Paper 3 Use of English

Part 1

1 D (*rapid advances in* = collocation)
2 B (*composition of a population*)
3 A (*attractive option* = collocation)
4 C (*in the vicinity of* = set phrase)
5 C (*to fit in with*)
6 A (*to grow in popularity*)
7 D (either *worry* or *concern* would link to *feared that*, but *worry* is too strong here)
8 B (*to be deprived of*)
9 A (*to become evident that*)
10 B (*readily accessible* = collocation)
11 D (*a wide audience* = collocation)
12 B (*to be provided with*)

Part 2

13 took   14 only   15 such   16 grew
17 because/as/since   18 found   19 up   20 a   21 with
22 ought/needed/had   23 could   24 what   25 to
26 fact   27 which

Part 3

28 incredible   29 regularity   30 vaguely   31 honesty
32 patience   33 mislaid   34 limitless/unlimited
35 irrelevant   36 thought   37 irritation

Part 4

38 line   39 apply   40 ground   41 straight   42 further

Part 5

43 had not rung, I would/could have
44 do not approve of the fact
45 has been out of order for
46 see no/little point in having/not see the point in having
47 opinion/view the campaign is unlikely
48 action on the part of
49 have any objection to
50 to be taken into consideration

Paper 4 Listening

Part 1

1 C (*I go to rock concerts for the atmosphere … And yes, the buzz they created was amazing.*)
2 C (*at least this band moves with the times*)
3 A (*the local authorities have consistently pursued sustainable policies …It has won national prizes for the cleanliness of its streets*)
4 C (*…in a single day you could …*)
5 B (*the multi-gym isn't enough to improve balance and get to the muscles that can prevent me getting hurt*)
6 A (*I always feel I've underachieved in front of a crowd.*)

Part 2

7 docks   8 life jacket   9 platform   10 hand(s)
11 smooth   12 clapping; cheering   13 exciting
14 stress

Part 3

15 B (*A friend of mine said that I'd never make a living as a painter and suggested I learnt to do something more useful*)
16 C (*lecturers … putting you down*)
17 C (*I was also very focused and willing to push myself forward*)
18 B (*So I went in the opposite direction*)
19 A (*I have a go at all manner of things*)
20 B (*a desperation on the part of the designers to show how original they are being*)

Part 4

21 G (*he was so passionate about what he was trying to explain*)
22 D (*made me think about things from his point of view*)
23 H (*everyone just wrote me off as a failure. But he found the time to talk to me, to find out what the problem was*)
24 B (*you've got to be prepared to stick your neck out*)
25 E (*that made me realise I was messing up my own life*)
26 D (*I wouldn't have got my degree at all*)
27 B (*I've met loads of people, and we've all got something in common*)
28 G (*I hope to start out in my own business soon*)
29 A (*I say to the people on my team, 'Come on – let's give it a try'*)
30 E (*I dreamed of being in a rock group …We're releasing our first album next week*)

Audio script

PART 1

Extract One

M: Wow it was loud in there, I can hardly hear myself think! Great though, wasn't it?

F: Yeah, it was a great night out, but I wasn't expecting to hear so much new material to be honest – it's rather challenging going to a concert where you've never heard half the songs before.

M: Yes, I can see where you're coming from, but personally <u>I go to rock concerts for the atmosphere</u> – not to sing along with all the old hits. I can't stand the thought of old rockers just going on year after year for their ageing fans – *at least this band moves with the times.*

F: Well, you were chanting and clapping along with the rest of them through that encore, so there's no need to go all purist about it. <u>And yes, the buzz they created was amazing.</u> But I didn't say I only wanted to hear the old songs, I was just saying that I like time to listen to new stuff and get into it before I hear it live.

M: So who's being the purist now?

Extract Two

F: It's not just the parks that make the city so remarkable green – <u>the local authorities have consistently pursued sustainable policies and its environmental credentials are impeccable. It has won national prizes for the cleanliness of its streets</u> and was the first city in the country to sign up to Agenda 21, an international charter for sustainable development.

M: That's right. It's a terrific city loaded with architectural and cultural delights and yet small enough to stroll out from the centre to the open countryside in well under an hour. In fact the manageable size of the city and its sights make it ideal for a short break, because <u>in a single day you could</u> do a unique hard-hat tour of the medieval cathedral while it's actually being restored, prowl amongst the dense atmospheric ways of the historic centre, take in a museum or two, then hop on a bicycle, loaned free by the tourist office and whizz along a cycleway to the parks and nature reserves around the city.

F: Yes, and in the immediate vicinity there are …

Extract Three

F: Hi, Michael, how's the training going?

M: Well, I'm doing a mixture of gym exercises, power weights, work on power, endurance and track technique. It's not really very enjoyable, actually.

F: I'm surprised that a short-distance runner like you needs to do power weights.

M: Well, <u>the multi-gym isn't enough to improve balance and get to the muscles that can prevent me getting hurt</u>. They help me get my natural stabilisers going. I'm actually concentrating on the four-hundred metres now rather than the two hundred, but the same principle applies.

F: For me it's all about the mental preparation, especially for big events.

M: Well, you've certainly got to have your head switched on and you've got to enjoy it. I mean it's not every day you're running in front of a stadium filled to capacity!

F: Yeah, and I know nobody gives you medals for just turning up, but I get the feeling other people get fired up on race days in ways that I just don't. I always feel I've underachieved in front of a crowd.

M: Just knowing the start of the season's coming fast gets me going, actually.

F: Exactly!

PART 2

Hello and welcome to the Travel Programme with me, Hilary Barrington. I'm just back from the island of Bermuda, where I've been visiting an attraction that goes by the name Dolphin Quest, based in Bermuda's disused navy docks. As the name suggests, this is a place where you can find dolphins, those famously endearing sea animals. But at Dolphin Quest, you do more than just watch them swimming around performing tricks – because, if you want, you can get in the water and swim round with them, and as everyone has to wear a life jacket, you don't even have to be a swimmer to join in!

For the less adventurous visitor, though, there is a shallow area where you can sit on a platform which lies just under the water, and you can get close to the dolphins that way, even if you're not a swimmer. Then there's a deeper area for keener swimmers and those who want to go snorkelling.

Not many people know this, but there is a proper protocol for meeting a dolphin. You should introduce yourself gradually – even a little formally – keeping to the edge of the water with your arms by your sides until the animals get used to you. After a while, you give them hand signals to prepare them for the fact that you're about to enter their personal space, and then you can start to come closer. After that, you can feed them fish, swim with them or even touch them. They love to be touched – their skin is smooth – and to play. People hug them, stroke them, even kiss them. It's one of the few opportunities you'll get to be a kid again.

What you do have to do in return, though, is show appreciation – clapping and cheering are welcomed by dolphins, and even the most cynical person would be hard pressed not to appreciate the animals themselves, especially when they are appear to be so pleased to see you. As you arrive, they jump, whistle and click to attract your attention. The dolphins just love the attention, and I got the impression that they find being around people very exciting. So you don't get the feeling that they're being exploited particularly.

And hugging a dolphin, it seems, is good for you, too –

according to experts, it's an excellent activity for lowering your stress levels and increasing your feeling of well-being. Many people end up in tears; others are elated, even euphoric. As one of my fellow visitors remarked, it made her look at life in a different way.

At $135 for 30 minutes, it may seem like a rather expensive hug. Nevertheless, swimming with dolphins was at the top of the wish list when 20,000 Britons took part in a survey call 'Your Top 20 Thrills', saying that swimming with dolphins was the thing that they most wanted to try just once in their lives.

If you'd like to find out more about swimming with dolphins …

PART 3

Int. = Interviewer, JB = Jocelyn Burton

Int.: My guest today is Jocelyn Burton, an artist working in precious metals. She's been creating jewellery and other beautiful objects out of silver and gold for the last 30 years. Jocelyn, was it always your intention to go into this sort of work?

JB: My first love was painting – that's why I went to art college. But in those days, there were really very few first-rate women painters around, and that was a bit discouraging. A friend of mine said that I'd never earn my living as a painter and suggested I learnt to do something more useful by enrolling in a crafts course. He was teaching in the silver and jewellery department, so that was the course I went for – it was pure chance, really. But, once I started, I realised that it was a completely blank canvas and a new world in which few artists had done anything much.

Int.: But did you enjoy the fine art classes?

JB: I always had the feeling that, when we were drawing, the lecturers would bend over backwards to admire the work of certain students; but, if you happened to be a woman, they would say, 'I detect the influence of so-and-so' – putting you down when you'd put so much into your work. It was deeply discouraging. Then, at the end of my second year, I won an international design award for a diamond necklace I'd made on my crafts course. Everybody said I should use the opportunity to start professionally, so I went to the college principal and asked for one day off a week to do it. He refused, so I walked out

Int.: That was a brave move.

JB: I was catapulted into the real world. My first job was with a company in London which was manufacturing really very ordinary engagement rings. Although I never wanted to be a jeweller as such, it did give me a great deal of experience that was very useful when I started on my own as a silversmith. I *was* lucky, but I was also very focused and willing to push myself forward, too. It was through working there that I met the managing director of a smart London shop. I showed him samples of my work. When he commissioned a →

collection of objects in silver from me, that meant I could resign and set up my own studio.

Int.: So, how did you make your mark – what was it in your studio's work that caught people's eye?

JB: When I first started, things made out of silver tended to be extremely heavy and masculine. Silversmiths were mostly busy making objects that wealthy businessmen would want sitting on their desks. So I went in the opposite direction and made pretty objects for the dressing table and romantic pens. I know that a lot of silversmiths didn't take my work very seriously, but, in the end, when I was successful, they had to sit up and take notice. That was very satisfying.

Int.: But you've now moved away from that particular style?

JB: I'm extremely unusual in that I have a go at all manner of things. Nearly everyone else in the trade sticks entirely to one style. I love the diversity – I'm passionately interested in making things, and it doesn't matter what the metal is, although the objects created must be beautiful. They must justify their existence by being either attractive or very usable.

Int.: Or both?

JB: Well, it depends. Sometimes, there's a desperation on the part of designers to show how original they are being. I saw a strange silver teapot in a catalogue the other day which would be virtually unusable given the shape of the handle. Though it was a contemporary piece, it reminded me of 1970s architecture, all heavy and square. I mean, why make that in silver? Make it in stainless steel, perhaps, so that lots of people can buy it. But it beats me why you should use a beautiful precious metal like silver to make something that is ugly.

PART 4

Speaker 1
My parents were both very artistic, so I followed the same path. I really struggled with science subjects – I had a kind of mental block against technology, but he showed me that engineering could be creative. His lessons were fun, he involved the whole class – he was so passionate about what he was trying to explain, he'd even use the classroom furniture to demonstrate his point! If it wasn't for him, I wouldn't have got my degree at all, because I used to think university was a waste of time, but I've just been offered a job with a construction company in South America – how about that!

Speaker 2
My parents lived abroad, and I was lonely at boarding school, so I just kept my head down in class, wrapped up in my own problems. He said, 'Imagine how I feel, putting so much effort into a lesson, and all you do is stare at the floor.' It really brought me out of myself – made me think about things from his point of view. It's through him I'm so into amateur dramatics now – I've met loads of people, and we've all got something in common. He pushed me into it and said, 'Why don't you get into the school play?' On stage, I relax – I become the character I'm playing.

Speaker 3
I was always in trouble at school, and my attendance record was awful. I kept playing truant, because I was being bullied a lot. I didn't dare tell anyone – not even my parents. My results were bad, so everyone just wrote me off as a failure. But he found the time to talk to me, to find out what the problem was. He even gave me extra tuition, so I did pass Maths and Geography. I'm training to be a plumber and I hope to start out in my own business soon, so I'll be making serious money – way ahead of all my friends who are going through university now.

Speaker 4
Most of the teachers were very strict, but he was different, he looked like your conventional middle-aged teacher, but he wasn't at all. I had this really weird idea for a science project, and I never thought I'd get it approved, but he said, 'I hadn't thought of that – go for it.' I ended up getting a science prize! I realised that, if you believe in something, you've got to be prepared to stick your neck out and see it through. I work as a graphic designer now, in advertising, and if we've got a winning idea, I say to the people on my team, 'Come on – let's give it a try!' It's the only way to succeed.

Speaker 5
I was disruptive at school, and my parents never disciplined me. Playing the drums was all I cared about, I dreamed of being in a rock group. I had no interest in other subjects, and took my frustrations out on the teachers. He threatened to expel me from school if I didn't control my anger – that made me realise I was messing up my own life. So I asked him for extra help in Maths and, in return, he encouraged me to practise my drumming. It was through his contacts that I started working in a recording studio, which led to me being the drummer in a band. We're releasing our first album next week.